ANIMAL *Life and Lore*

ANIMAL *Life* *and Lore*

OSMOND P. BRELAND

Drawings by Matthew Kalmenoff

Harper & Row, Publishers
New York, Evanston, and London

Contents

v

Contents

Illustrations

Preface

In this nontechnical book about some of the most interesting and important animals in the world may be found bizarre and almost unbelievable, as well as ordinary and commonplace features of many members of the animal kingdom.

Few people could answer the following questions accurately: What is the largest fish ever caught on rod and reel? What animal lives the longest? What is the largest animal that ever lived? What is the jointed snake? How do opossums mate? Can toads live for years sealed in solid rock? How poisonous are spiders? What made the White Cliffs of Dover, England, white? How dangerous are jellyfish? Can any snail kill a man? What was the manna of biblical times? Yet children and students are constantly asking questions of this kind, and the questions frequently occur to curious adults. These and many similar subjects are considered in this book.

Some years ago I wrote two books—*Animal Facts and Fallacies* (Harper & Row, 1948) and *Animal Friends and Foes* (Harper & Row, 1957). These dealt with unusual features, false beliefs, and the importance of animals in the economy of nature and to man. The extremely kind reception given by the public to these two books has caused me to consider revising them and bringing them up to date. Numerous readers have made suggestions for modifications and additions, and have pointed out that the two books could logically be combined into a single volume. This,

ix

then, is a combined revised version of two former books, incorporating many of the suggestions of the readers of the former volumes, and including new information about animal behavior.

Though this book is written in a popular style, every effort has been made to insure its accuracy. Obviously, no one could possibly check personally all the facts and figures that are included; consequently, authorities in various fields have been consulted in person, by letters, and by reading their scientific publications. Where essential, they are mentioned by name, but care has been taken not to overburden the reader with unnecessary references. When even experts do not agree, I have sometimes given both opinions; in other instances I have selected the opinion which seemed most logical, based upon my own training and experience. In some instances my selections may have differed from those that some readers might have made; in each case, however, evidence on both sides was carefully considered before a conclusion was reached.

In popular usage the word *animal* is often thought of as including only the mammals—that group which includes horses, cows, dogs, deer, elephants, and similar creatures. Actually, the word has a much broader meaning, as reference to any standard dictionary will show. Living things are divided into several groups, two of which are the animal kingdom and the plant kingdom. Any creature included within the animal kingdom— whether it be an elephant, snake, bird, insect, or jellyfish—may be called an animal. This book uses *animal* in this sense.

Occasional reference will be made to *vertebrate* and *invertebrate* animals. Vertebrate animals are those that have backbones such as fishes, birds, reptiles, amphibians, and mammals. The backbone is divided into a number of parts or segments, and each part is called a vertebra. The term *vertebrate* is derived from the name of the divisions of the backbone. Any animal that does not have a backbone is an invertebrate animal; these include insects, worms, clams, jellyfish, and a host of other species.

Neither this nor the two preceding books would have been possible without the wholehearted cooperation of many people. These have included friends who are not biologists, colleagues, and biologists connected with numerous institutions and organizations. I wish it were possible to list everyone by name. I sincerely appreciate all the encouragement and assistance that has been received.

Despite all precautions, errors may occur in a book such as this, and important subject matter may be omitted. I will greatly appreciate having errors or important omissions called to my attention.

OSMOND P. BRELAND

University of Texas
Austin, Texas
March 1963

ANIMAL *Life and Lore*

One MAMMALS

More people are probably aware of the impact of mammals upon their daily lives than that of any other group of animals. Milk, butter, shoes, steaks, fur coats, wallets, and tripe are only a few of the supposed necessities we derive from these animals. Additional benefits are obtained from hunting, keeping mammals as pets and beasts of burden—and sometimes debatably beneficial—attendance at race tracks. Our association with mammals is of course not always beneficial. For example, tigers, leopards, and lions still add an occasional human being to their menus, and rabbits, rats, and mice eat our crops as well as causing other damage.

SOME FACTS AND FANCIES

Aside from economics, mammals are among the most interesting of animals. Among them we find a species that may weigh more than 300,000 pounds, and be more than a hundred feet long; at the opposite end of the scale is a tiny creature that weighs about the same as a penny. The fastest runners are among mammals, as are the best jumpers. And, not to be outdone by other groups, some mammals even lay eggs.

Mammals have many features that are not present in other animals. Two of these are the presence of hair and the presence of structures called *mammary glands*. Mammary glands are not normally functional in the male, but in the female they secrete milk that is relished by the growing youngsters. These two features are fairly obvious in most mammals, especially in the familiar domestic species, such as cows, horses, dogs, and cats. The mammary glands, represented by the teats and udder of the cow, are easily discovered in the females of most other species. So far as is known, the female pig or sow is blessed with the greatest number of mammary glands; some have as many as twenty-eight. At the other extreme—if we forget an occasional supernumerary—are human beings, bats, and elephants, with only two.

The name *mammal* is used for the group because the mammary glands are characteristic of the animals. It is derived from a Latin word meaning "breast," and apparently this designation was used because of the position of the mammary glands in the human species.

The hair is quite apparent in most mammals. Even relatively sleek-skinned mammals, such as whales and porpoises, usually have a few bristles.

Mammals are said to be warm-blooded, a term that is frowned upon by biologists, who prefer the more dignified name *homeothermic*. At any rate, either of these means that the body temperature remains relatively constant in healthy mammals despite the temperature of the air or water in which the animals may be living. But in a few mammals the body temperature fluctuates considerably. For example, in some of the sloths— those upside-down, slothful, and altogether repulsive creatures found in South America—the body temperature may vary from 75 to 91° F.

Birds are also "warm-blooded" and this characteristic of the two groups has allowed them to invade all types of environments—air, land, and sea—from the equator to the poles, a much broader distribution than that attained by their relatives. The body temperature of other vertebrate animals (animals with a backbone or vertebral column: fish, amphibians, and reptiles) varies with that of the environment, and they are thus said to be *cold-blooded* or *poikilothermic*.

The period of pregnancy or gestation varies widely among the different species of mammals, and also among the individuals of the same species. Much more study is needed on this subject, but there have been sufficient numbers of observations of certain species to give tentative figures. So far as is known, the elephant has the longest gestation period of any mammal: it varies from 20 to 23 months. The rhinoceros, with about 18 months, is a close second. The approximate period for some of the other large mammals include: giraffe, 15 months; moose, about 8 months; deer, 7 months; and bears, 6 to 7 months. And whales? Surprisingly, only 11 months to a year or so, even in the largest species.

The shortest gestation periods, as might be expected, occur among the smaller mammals. The opossum actually has the shortest—only 12 to

13 days—but as we shall see later, the youngsters must complete their development in the pouch of the female after birth. The golden Syrian hamster, with a 16-day gestation period, will certainly compete for the shortest period involving fully developed young, whereas certain mice, shrews, and voles require 17 to 21 days.

There are many breeds and varieties of each of our domestic animals, and gestation periods vary with the different kinds. However, average periods for some common domestic mammals are: cat, 55 to 63 days; dog, 62 to 68 days; rabbit, 30 to 32 days; sheep, 146 to 150 days; goat, 146 to 153 days; pig, 113 to 123 days; cattle, 278 to 285 days; horse, 322 to 343 days.

There is a commonly held opinion that the size of a baby mammal at birth is dependent upon the size of the mother, and that the proportionate size of the infant compared with the mother is about the same in all species. Whales, the largest of mammals, certainly have the largest babies, but the "size and proportion" idea "falls on its face" in many cases. The kangaroo, with no close competitors, is certainly the champion in reverse with respect to the size of the female compared to that of the youngster. The adult female kangaroo may weigh more than 60,000 times as much as the baby at birth. However, the kangaroo, like the opossum, is a somewhat special case, since the young kangaroo must also develop further after birth in the pouch of the mother. Comparisons in other mammals are noted below. The first figure represents the weight of the baby at birth; the second figure, the number of times the female may outweigh the youngster. Bear, 1: 625–880; deer, 1: 30; dog, 1: 30; human being, 1: 16; bat, 1: 3.

Despite the fact that the average person is familiar with more kinds of mammals than with any other group of animals, there are actually fewer kinds or species of mammals than in many other divisions of the animal kingdom. Scientists who classify animals are still squabbling over what constitutes species, subspecies, varieties, and various categories of classification, but these debates need not concern us here. Suffice it to say that according to recent estimates, there are approximately 3,500 known species of living mammals, some of which are subdivided into subspecies.

Fights Between Some of the Larger Mammals

It is interesting for persons with sporting blood to speculate on which would win if some of the larger mammals of different species were matched in the arena. One engagement would not be conclusive, particularly if animals that had been in captivity for some time were used.

Animals are at their best in the wild state and, of two contestants, the one that had suffered most in captivity would be at a decided disadvantage. Fortunately from the standpoint of this discussion, a number of fights between different species of animals have been observed, either in a sports arena or in nature. But unfortunately the details of such encounters are hard to find.

Elephant vs. *Rhinoceros*. Apparently a fight between these two animals was staged, or at least an attempt to stage one was made around 1500 by King Manuel of Portugal. I have found two entirely different versions of what was probably the same combat, although it is possible that two different fights were involved.

According to one writer, no fight developed. The two animals were brought in cages into a barricaded street, one at each end. The rhinoceros showed great impatience, apparently, to be released so that it could rush over and trounce the impertinent elephant, whereas the elephant was quite calm. When the rhinoceros was released, it lowered its head and advanced toward the waiting elephant. Doubtless the spectators were watching these movements with bated breaths. Suddenly the rhinoceros must have decided that discretion was better than valor, because it turned tail and ran, bumping into the barricade in an attempt to escape. The elephant, thereupon, turned majestically and went back into its cage.

Another version simply states that the rhino won, but no details were given and I have not confirmed this outcome from other sources.

One writer describes a fight in nature between these two animals in which the rhinoceros came off a decidedly second best. The rhinoceros started the fracas by charging the elephant. The elephant calmly seized the rhinoceros around the neck with its trunk, threw it to the ground and spitted it with the tusks. The narrator did not actually see the fight, but a native who claimed to have witnessed it related the story and said that he had helped eat the carcass of the defeated rhinoceros.

Grizzly Bear vs. *Lion*. These two specimens in prime condition would make an interesting match for spectators who were not squeamish. Some people believe that the grizzly would be the winner without much trouble, but I do not believe that the bear would be bored with the contest. It is said that a fight between these two animals was staged in California many years ago and that the bear won, but no details of the bout could be found.

The bear, as I have pointed out elsewhere in this book, is famous for the terrific blows it can deliver with its front paws, and the chances are that if the bear could land a good solid punch the fight would end then and there. A large grizzly outweighs a lion by a good bit, but the lion's superior agility would compensate to some extent for the difference in weight.

Grizzly Bears vs. *Bulls and Bison*. According to reports, it was the fashion to stage bear and bull fights in California before that state was admitted to the Union, and apparently the bear was usually the victor. As the bull charged, the bear would flick out its paw, frequently breaking the bull's neck at the first stroke, thereby with a single blow ending the fight then and there—no doubt to the disgust of the audience.

Even the great bull bison in the heyday of its existence was not safe from attack by grizzly bears. A grizzly was once seen to attack and kill four bison bulls one after the other. The first three were speedily dispatched with a single stroke for each, but the fourth was made of sterner stuff. There was a flurry of paws and horns and, although the bison was eventually killed, the bear itself was severely wounded in the encounter.

But the grizzly bear did not always emerge the victor in an encounter with a bull. J. Frank Dobie in his well-known book, *The Longhorns,* tells of an instance in which a large grizzly was gored to death by an enraged longhorn. The bull was considerably the worse for wear, but he eventually recovered. No one saw the actual fight, but a short time afterward the lacerated longhorn was discovered close to the dead grizzly, which had obviously been killed by the bloody horns of the bull.

Lion vs. *Tiger.* Because of the ballyhoo attached to the noble title "king of the beasts," many people are of the opinion that the lion is capable of overcoming any animal in the world. Certainly the "king" should be able to rule all members of the cat family. If we are to believe the records of the old Roman arena, however, this is not the case. During those lusty days, a lion and a tiger were frequently matched for the edification of the people of the Roman Empire, and in such a combat the tiger usually won. Most biologists who have dared to express their opinions on the subject also consider the tiger a better fighter than the lion.

A well-known biologist has suggested why the tiger usually wins in such encounters. He states that when a tiger fights it balances itself on its hind legs and strikes with both front paws. He says that he once saw a staged fight between a tiger and a lion, which the tiger won. The tiger used both paws, but the lion used only one at a time, and this situation turned out to be quite disadvantageous to the well-being of the lion.

There is, however, one instance on record where a circus lion killed a tiger in an adjoining cage after the two animals had broken the partition to settle their differences, but there is no record of their relative condition at the time. As I have previously indicated, all animals suffer considerably during confinement, and the one least affected would certainly have an advantage in a fight.

It is commonly believed that lions are larger than tigers, and a heavily maned lion does appear larger than a tiger of similar size. But actually the maximum known lengths and weights of tigers are greater than those of lions. The longest field measurement I have noted for a lion is 10 feet

11 inches (including tail), whereas several tigers have been killed which were longer than this, the longest being 11 feet 5½ inches. A weight of 500 pounds has been listed for a lion, but there is one of 700, one of 570 and another of 525 for tigers. The largest tiger skin known measures 13 feet 6 inches (certainly stretched) as opposed to 11 feet 7 inches for the lion skin. In all fairness to the dethroned king of beasts, it should be mentioned that there are more varieties of tigers than lions, and there is considerable difference in size among the groups. It is quite possible that some lions might average larger than some varieties of tigers.

Buffaloes vs. *Lions and Tigers*. The African and Indian buffaloes are well known for the tenacity with which they hold on to life, and for their ferocity once they are aroused. Either animal would be a formidable antagonist for practically any animal in existence.

According to reports, fights between an Indian buffalo and a tiger have been staged in India, in which the buffalo usually won by impaling the tiger with its horns. But the tiger would also get in a few choice scratches and bites of its own, so that the victor frequently had to be killed to relieve its suffering.

So far as has been determined, no one has ever seen a struggle to the death between a single lion and an African bull buffalo, but skeletons of the two animals have been found in a position that would indicate that such combats occasionally do occur, with death as a reward for both contestants. One author states that an adult bull buffalo was known to object so strenuously to serving as a meal for three lions that it successfully beat off its attackers. It is possible that the story may be true. But more evidence for such an occurrence must be presented before it can be accepted unquestioningly.

Ram vs. *Tiger*. Sheep are usually thought of as docile and somewhat timid animals, but everyone who has had the misfortune to attract the attention of an ill-tempered ram knows that the male sheep can be a formidable antagonist. A solid butt from an angry ram has been known to discourage animals several times its size.

In parts of India rams are bred for their fighting ability and are frequently matched for sport. One biologist tells of a man who had a fighting ram that was especially irascible; so, thinking to rid himself of the troublesome beast, he put it in a tiger's den. According to the story, the ram immediately gave the tiger a resounding butt, which apparently so stunned the cat that the ram was able to kill it.

This instance is related to illustrate how animal fights may sometimes have an unexpected end, and to emphasize the fact that a single match between different species does not allow one to form positive conclusions about their respective abilities.

What Is the Fastest Mammal in the World?

Most authorities are agreed that for short distances the cheetah or hunting leopard is the fastest animal on feet, but its endurance is not very great. Men have used the creature for hunting gazelles and antelopes, and it usually overhauls even these swift runners with remarkable ease. But the endurance of some of the gazelles and antelopes at high speed is remarkable, and it is probable that for distances of over a mile or so either the blackbuck of India, the Mongolian gazelle, or the pronghorn antelope of the United States could outdistance any living mammal. The pronghorn antelope is easily the fastest animal in North America.

Some writers are apparently quite pleased with man's running ability as compared to that of other animals, but I find it difficult to share this complacency. To prove man's superiority they cite cases of trained athletes who have beaten horses for a short distance. Yet what chance would a trained athlete have against a horse without a rider, and how many untrained human beings could outdistance even a draft horse? The claim that man is one of the fastest of animals is, of course, true, but the statement is somewhat misleading. The comparison includes all species that belong to the animal kingdom, and even the slowest of us could probably outdistance a snail or even such a speedy animal as the earthworm. But reference to the table on page 10 will show that man at his fastest is quite slow indeed when compared with the really speedy members of the mammalian clan.

The table lists a few of the fastest mammals for which actual records have been made, or for which we have estimates by competent observers. The species are arranged in order of known possible speeds, but when more information is available the order may well have to be rearranged. Some animals place high in the table because of one or more speed records they have made for short distances. No figures are available for some species, which may be able to run faster for short distances than others that are higher in the table.

Species	Known Possible Speed; Miles per Hour	Remarks
Cheetah or hunting leopard	70	This animal has been timed at this speed with a stop watch.
Blackbuck	65	
Mongolian gazelle	60	These animals can maintain this speed for a mile or so after which they drop to slower speeds.
Pronghorn antelope	60	When chased by a car, these animals have maintained this speed for 2 miles, and have averaged 36 m.p.h. for 27 miles.
Gazelles (several species)	50	
Lion	50	This speed is possible for only short distances in charges after game.
Deer (several species)	45 to 50	A white-tailed buck deer was timed by automobile at 49 m.p.h., but one biologist doubts the accuracy of the speedometer and indicates that he considers about 30 m.p.h. the maximum for deer.
Horse	45 to 50	Average speeds for ¼ mile for famous race horses have been given at from 40.18 to 43 m.p.h. More than 45 seems reasonable without saddle and rider.
Elk	45 to 50	Timed at 45 m.p.h. by car.
Jack rabbits (several species)	40 to 45	Reported 45 m.p.h. for ½ mile.

Species	Known Possible Speed; Miles per Hour	Remarks
Coyote	35 to 45	One was timed at 43 m.p.h. for a short distance. This speed seems somewhat excessive.
Greyhounds and Whippets	35 to 40	Whippets have been clocked with stop watches at 35.5 m.p.h. and greyhounds at 36.
Moose	35 to 40	One reported to have been timed at 35 m.p.h. for ¼ mile.
Bison	32 to 35	One has been timed with a speedometer at 32 m.p.h.
Grizzly bear	30 to 35	One animal chased by car attained 30 m.p.h.
Rhinoceros	30 to 35	One animal pursuing a car attained 35 m.p.h.
Elephant	25	One African elephant was timed with a stop watch at 24 m.p.h. for 120 yards.
Man	22 to 25	The average speed of more than 22 m.p.h. has been reached for the 220 yard dash, the race in which the greatest speed is attained. World's record, 1961: 20.0 seconds.

High Jumpers and Broad Jumpers

Obtaining accurate records for the jumping ability of most animals is quite difficult, since, aside from man, few animals vie with each other in this type of physical labor for the mere pleasure of winning. The figures given in the following table do not necessarily represent the maximum possible jump for the species concerned, but rather the approximate distances which one or more of the species have been known to jump, either by actual measurement, or by estimates of competent observers. It is unfortunate that records of this type are so incomplete.

THE JUMPING ABILITY OF A FEW MAMMALS

| Species | Probable Distance Animal Can Jump in Feet | | Remarks |
	Horizontal	Vertical	
Deer	35 to 40	8 to 10	Deer have been know to jump fences 8 feet high from a standing start.
Elk		8 to 10	The elk can easily clear an 8-foot fence, and could probably do considerably better than this.
Horse	25 to 30	8 to 9	Reported records with riders include a horizontal jump of more than 24 feet and a high jump of 8 feet 6 inches.
Impala or pala (A type of gazelle found in Africa)	30 to 40	8 to 10	Actual measurements of close to 30 feet for a horizontal jump are recorded, and it is believed that the 40-foot mark may be frequently reached.
Jack rabbits (several species)	23 to 25	7 to 8	One antelope jack rabbit made a measured jump of 23 feet 4 inches when shot.
Jerboa pouched mice	6 to 7		An Australian animal resembling rats and mice, but possessing very elongated legs and a pouch for carrying the young.
Jerboas	12 to 15	3 to 4	Ratlike rodents with elongated hind legs, found principally in Africa. The body is 4 to 5 inches long.

Species	Probable Distance Animal Can Jump in Feet		Remarks
	Horizontal	Vertical	
Kangaroos (large species)	25 to 30	9 to 10	Individual kangaroos which were being pursued have been know to jump a fence 9 feet in height.
Kangaroo mice or jumping mice	8 to 10		These rodents possess elongated hind legs, and a body length of about 3 inches. They are found in Canada and the northern United States.
Kangaroo or pocket rats	9 to 12		These rats have a body length of 4 to 5 inches and are found in western and southwestern United States.
Klipspringer		25?	A small antelope found in most mountainous areas of Africa. Stands about 20 inches at the shoulder and weighs some 40 pounds.
Puma or mountain lion	35 to 40	9 to 12	One biologist states that he has seen pumas jump from the ground and land in a tree 12 to 15 feet above the ground.
Leopard		8 to 10	Leopards have been reported as jumping to a rock 10 feet high while carrying prey weighing ¾ as much as themselves.
Lion		8 to 10	Lions are reported to have cleared thorn fences 6 to 7 feet high carrying prey almost as heavy as themselves. This feat has been doubted by some biologists.
Man	26 ft. 11¼ in.	7 ft. 5 in.*	Official World's record as of 1962 for broad jump.
Rat kangaroos		8	These creatures belong to the same group as kangaroos, but are smaller.

* Approved by the International Amateur Athletic Association, September 1962.

The possible 25-foot vertical jump of the klipspringer is the figure in the table most deserving of consideration. Mrs. Carl Akeley and some companions made observations upon two of these animals for several days. A female and a youngster about two-thirds grown were seen to attain the top of a rocky pedestal the sides of which sloped outward from the bottom to the top. The only possible way that the animals could have gained access to the top was from the ground, 25 feet below. The observers were so located that they could see the animals as they landed on top, but they could not see the complete jump. Dr. A. Brazier Howell, of the Johns Hopkins University, has made a study of the running speed and jumping ability of mammals. He regards this performance of the klipspringers as most remarkable, but points out that since the complete jump was not seen, the possibility that the jump was made at a single leap can be accepted only provisionally. Klipspringers are well known for their ability to scramble up almost perpendicular cliffs, using very small projections as footholds. In this case an unnoticed intermediate foothold may have been used. At any rate, I would put my money on the klipspringer against all comers in a high-jumping contest.

It is needless to point out that the world record jumps for man are considerably in excess of those that could be made by the average person. Even many trained athletes would have difficulty in approaching these figures, while the floundering efforts of untrained human beings can well be imagined.

What Animal's Teeth Never Stop Growing?

In man and many other mammals, the roots of the teeth close after the teeth have attained a certain size, so that all growth ceases. But in a number of animals, including rodents, walruses, elephants, and wild boars, some of the teeth remain open at the roots; new material is added and the teeth continue to grow throughout life.

For such animals as rodents, this continuous growth is usually quite advantageous, since it prevents their teeth from being entirely worn away by their ceaseless gnawing activities. Occasionally, however, one of the teeth may grow crooked, or the lower jaw may become slightly displaced so that some of the teeth are not used and thus not worn away. But they still continue to grow. The lower teeth may curve over the snout or head and eventually make it impossible for the animal to open its mouth; or they may actually grow through the upper jaw and penetrate the brain. I once saw the skull of a rodent, probably a groundhog, in which that condition had developed. One of the lower incisor teeth had pierced the upper jaw, grown through it for about half an inch and emerged, continuing to grow for an inch or so before the animal died.

What Mammal Lives Longest?

Aside from man, who will not be considered in this discussion, the elephant has the reputation of being the longest-lived mammal. One frequently sees statements, credited even by some biologists, that it lives for 150 to 200 years.

The question has been investigated recently by several specialists, who have found that there is no positive record of an elephant's having lived to be 100 years old. It has been reasonably well verified that one elephant attained an age of over 60 years, one possibly over 70, and several over 50 years of age are known. Another elephant is said to have lived in the United States for 85 years, but I have not been able to confirm this report. It seems probable that elephants do live about as long as any other mammal, and many authorities believe that an occasional specimen may reach 100 years.

Comparatively little information on the maximum age of whales is yet available, but most biologists are of the opinion that they do not live so long as many other mammals. Whales have been killed whose bodies contained harpoons that were marked with the date when they were made. From this "harpoon evidence," one whale is thought to have been approximately 37 years old at the time of its death.

Both a rhinoceros and a hippopotamus have reached 49 years of age, and not much imagination would be required to believe that an occasional individual passes the half-century mark. Until recently, authorities accepted a possible age of over 50 years for the domestic horse, but in a recent article, one expert would accept only 40 years as a probable maximum for horses.

Known ages for other mammals kept in captivity include a zebra of 38, several kinds of bears of 30 to 34, a chimpanzee of 26, and monkeys of just over 20 years.

Records for longevity in cats and dogs have been obtained from owners, who may have been somewhat prejudiced, but all indications are that cats live longer than dogs. One well supported claim for a cat of 31 years has been advanced, and another was still alive at 28 years. Dogs have not done so well, although there is one very old claim of an ancient pooch of 34 years. One dog of 22 and another of 18 are the maximum verified ages.

The World's Oldest Industry

There is considerable evidence that trading in pelts and furs was one of the first established industries. Prehistoric man, according to crude drawings found in caves, covered his nakedness with furs, and down through the ages fur trading became a valuable industry in ancient Egypt, Babylonia, Assyria, and China. The ancient country of Armenia was one of the principal fur centers of the world, and it is claimed by some that the word *ermine* was derived from Armenia. On a world basis there are few mammals that have not given up their skins or furs for the use of man. One biologist lists 143 different kinds that were considered valuable to North American Indians.

Despite the demand for skins, furs, and other products obtained from mammals, until relatively recent times most species had managed to withstand man's onslaughts. With the appearance of firearms and improved methods of transportation which allowed men to pursue their prey into remote areas, animals rapidly lost ground. The pitiful remnant of the American bison, incorrectly called the buffalo, is an outstanding example of such a situation.

Once 60 million bison roamed the plains of North America. But the huge creatures offered two commodities to man—a desirable skin and edible flesh. They were slaughtered by the millions, sometimes only for their tongues; by 1900 there were only some 300 still alive in the United States. Today, in Yellowstone National Park and a few other preserves, the bison has returned slowly from the verge of extinction, and now the herds number several thousand individuals.

However, many mammals were not as fortunate as the American bison. According to one authority, at least 106 species and subspecies of mammals have become extinct during the past two thousand years. Of this number, more than 70 have passed into oblivion during the past one hundred years—extinct forms that include bears, lions, wolves, asses, deer, and even rats.

Until recently there was little regulation as to the name that could be applied to a fur garment. As a consequence, imagination so ran riot that one writer remarked that few mother animals were sophisticated enough to recognize their own offspring by the name of the fur. For example, rabbit fur sold under such romantic names as cape seal, chinchilla, muskrat, white fox, Baltic leopard, and mendoza leopard. Muskrat furs have been called river mink, Hudson seal, and electric seal, and most other furs have been sold under various aliases. Now the Federal Fur Products Labeling Act of 1952 requires that all fur garments costing more than five dollars carry a label stating the true name of the animal involved, and the country from which the fur came.

What Are the Most Valuable Furs?

Over the years there have been two candidates for the title of most valuable fur producer, from the standpoint of the price paid for a single pelt. These two animals are the red fox and the sea otter.

The red foxes, of which there are several closely related species, are widely distributed in North America, Europe, and Africa. These are the animals primarily responsible for the popularity of fox hunting, and for the well-deserved reputation of the cleverness of foxes in general. They occur in several color phases in addition to the traditional red, and it is these color variations that are most valuable. The best-known colors are black, silver, cross, and platinum, and two or more of these may occur in a single litter.

The sea otter was once common along the shores of the Pacific Ocean, from southern California to the Kurile or Chisma Islands north of Japan. Then someone discovered the excellent quality of their fur, and the slaughter began. By 1910 the animal was virtually extinct, but fortunately an international agreement between Japan, Russia, Great Britain, and the United States has allowed the remnants to survive. These valuable fur producers have slowly increased in numbers, and have even returned in fair numbers to some of their former haunts.

It has been maintained that the sea otter has the most valuable fur in the world. Since at present the pelts cannot be processed legally, this may be true. But according to all statistics I have been able to find, the color variations of the red fox have consistently brought higher prices. From 1880 to 1910, the maximum price paid for a single black fox skin ranged from $632 to $2,800. During the same period, the selling price for sea otter skins ranged from $584 to $1,700.

By 1928, silver fox had replaced black fox in popularity. The maximum price for black fox during the early months of 1928 was a mere $115, whereas one type of silver fox listed for $600. At this time the sea otter was protected, and no legal figures on it are available for comparison.

One of the most recent color phases of the red fox to gain popularity is a domesticated strain of the silver fox known as the platinum. When the first few platinum fox pelts appeared on the market, one particularly fine one is reported to have sold for the fantastic sum of $11,000, the highest price ever paid in the United States for the skin of a single animal. Today, thanks to quantity production of silver and platinum fox farms in the United States, Canada, and Alaska, the price is more reasonable.

Other extremely valuable furs include Russian sable, mink, and chinchilla. The Russian sable which belongs to the weasel family, is widely distributed throughout European and Asiatic Russia, and has lured trappers into the frozen wastes of Siberia. Even the Mongoloid tribes of Siberia regard the sable with esteem, and figures of the animals decorate their clothing. Large preserves have been set aside for the protection of these beautiful animals, and from time to time hunting is completely prohibited in all or at least part of their range.

The Russian species is relatively small, having a body length of some twenty inches. The color of the fur varies from grayish to yellowish brown, with an occasional individual almost black. Individual pelts, in spite of their small size, have sold for as much as $350.

Mink coats are priced from $1,800 up—mostly up. The mink was probably the first fur-bearer to be domesticated in North America (some say it was the fox) and today there are many mink ranches in various parts of the United States.

Mink is certainly one of the most popular furs on the market. The value of ranch-raised pelts as compared with the pelts of wild mink varies. Pelts taken from wild minks are more likely to be scarred from fights or the trap, and such furs will not bring as high a price as unscarred ranch-raised animals with pelts of the same quality. On the other hand, coats from wild mink are reported to be somewhat more expensive than those of the same type and quality made from ranch-raised animals. The term "ranch" as applied to mink coats can be misleading. In the fur trade this term is usually used to describe a color rather than to indicate that the minks have been raised on a ranch or farm.

Minks serve a useful function in controlling a variety of small animals including rodents, rabbits, and insects. Individuals are sometimes destructive to poultry if they can gain access to hen houses. Minks do not have as bad a reputation for wanton killing as do their relatives, the weasels, but they often kill far more than they can eat in a single sitting.

In the matter of value for completed coats, sea otters, foxes, and Russian sables must take a back seat to the chinchilla, a small rodent that is a native of South America. There are several reasons for its value. The fur is the softest, most delicate, and at the same time the most luxurious in the world. The color is silver-gray or blue-gray and so beautiful that in almost all descriptions of this small mammal the word "exquisite" appears. Chinchillas are quite small and it takes approximately 120 pelts to make a full length coat. Another reason that chinchillas are so valuable is that at present few pelts are available.

One of the last full length chinchilla coats to be offered for sale was purchased in England in 1929. It brought a whopping $110,000. A newspaper columnist remarked that the coat would not have been any more expensive if it had been made from thousand-dollar bills.

DUCKBILLS AND SPINY ANTEATERS

Only two types of mammals lay eggs: the duckbill and the spiny anteater. The duckbill, also called platypus, is found in southern Australia and Tasmania; the spiny anteater, of which there are several varieties, occurs in Australia, Tasmania, and New Guinea.

Duckbills lay their eggs in nests built in burrows in the banks of streams. The female probably incubates the eggs in some fashion, but the creatures are very shy and not much is known about this part of their activities. The female spiny anteater has a small pouch on the undersurface of her body, where the single egg is kept until it is hatched. The young anteater remains within the pouch for a time after hatching, and gets milk from the teats in the walls of the pouch.

KANGAROOS AND OPOSSUMS

What Are Pouched Mammals?

The pouched mammals include the familiar kangaroos and opossums besides several other animals not well known to the average person, such as the Tasmanian devil, the bandicoot, the marsupial wolf, and the phalanger. The females have a pouch on the undersurface of the body called the marsupium—hence the group name, marsupial. One of the most interesting features of marsupials is that the young are born in an extremely undeveloped condition; consequently, they must have a safe place where they can develop further until they are able to fend for themselves. This additional growth takes place within the pouch which contains the teats or mammary glands.

Living marsupials are found today primarily in Australia and adjacent areas, although a few are found in South America and one—the well-known opossum—in the United States. In former times marsupials probably had an almost world-wide distribution, but they were apparently killed off over large areas by other more efficient mammals. It is thought that they have been able to survive in Australia only because they are the only large mammals native to this country. The marsupials probably migrated to Australia at a time when the continent was connected with other land areas by a land bridge, which apparently disappeared before other mammals found their way across.

How Do Opossums Mate?

The fact that the reproductive organ or penis of the male opossum is forked has resulted in some interesting suppositions regarding the reproductive habits of the animal. At the time of mating, according to one story, the forked organ of the male is inserted into the nostrils of the female, and the male cells or sperm are deposited within the nasal passages. The female then supposedly thrusts her nose into her pouch and blows vigorously. In this way, the male cells are deposited in the pouch where, it is believed, fertilization of the eggs takes place, and the young pass through their complete development.

Actually, the forked penis of the male is correlated with the structure of the female reproductive tract, which branches into two parts a short distance from the outside opening; opossums mate in the same way as do other animals.

After they are conceived, however, the developing young remain within the body of the female for about 12 days, and are born in a very immature stage of development.

Each of the young (from eight to as many as twenty-one) is actually smaller than a honey bee, and so unlike the adults in appearance that no one unfamiliar with this type of reproduction could possibly recognize them as opossums. At one time it was thought that the female helped the young into the pouch, but direct observation has since revealed that they clamber into it by themselves, using their strongly developed front legs to scramble through the hair. Once within the pouch, each of the young opossums swallows one of the nipples or teats, attaching themselves so firmly that it is almost impossible to pull them loose. If there are more young opossums than there are teats, which happens occasionally, only those fortunate enough to locate a mammary gland will survive; the extra infants will all die.

After remaining within the marsupium for about 70 days, the young emerge, but remain with the mother for some time. As she travels from one place to another they cling to the hair of her body. Sometimes the female curls her tail over her back and the young attach themselves to it by their own tails and dangle head downward.

Are Opossums Fooling When They Play Dead?

If an opossum is captured or attacked, it frequently does not run or fight as the majority of animals do under similar circumstances. Instead, it sinks to the ground, partially closes its eyes, allows its mouth to gape,

and its tongue to loll out. During this procedure, its breathing becomes almost imperceptible. It is often said that when an opossum behaves in this way it is deliberately feigning death to deceive its attackers. Some people have doubted whether opossums have this much intelligence, and believe that they really faint with fear. By tossing them into water, or unceremoniously dumping a bucket of water over them, one can usually revive the creatures. Whatever the reason for their performance, it appears decidedly disadvantageous to future generations of opossums. Surely any attacker, whether human or animal, would rather contend with a passive victim than with a clawing, biting or fleeing antagonist.

How Are Kangaroos Born?

Young kangaroos, like young opossums, have been found within the pouch of the mother so firmly attached to the nipples that it is almost

impossible to remove them. From this has grown the belief that the young kangaroo is not born as other mammals are, but simply grows from the belly of its mother.

The birth and development of a young kangaroo are quite similar to the opossum's. At birth the infants do not even faintly resemble the adults, and the young of even the larger species are only about an inch in length. The grublike young have enlarged claws on the front feet which enable them, like the baby opossums, to scramble through the hair and find their own way into the pouch.

The length of time they spend in the pouch varies with the kind of kangaroo and, for the larger species, may be as much as several months. As the young kangaroo gains in size, it spends less and less time in the pouch, although even when it is quite large it sometimes bounces into the pouch when danger threatens, or occasionally sticks its head in for a drink of milk.

Can Kangaroos Climb Trees?

Some kangaroos are able to climb trees and, although they are quite awkward about it, even seem to prefer the trees to the ground. The tree kangaroos, or tree wallabies, as they are sometimes called, have long claws and their front legs are comparatively longer than those of other kangaroos. Some species are rather large, having a body length of approximately four feet and a tail of about the same length.

ARMADILLOS

Tourists, driving through the uninhabited sections of the southwestern United States, may occasionally see a peculiar looking animal shuffling across the highway. If the body is encased in bony plates from the tip of its snout to the end of the long trailing tail, the creature is an armadillo. It is the only mammal in this country that wears a suit of armor.

At one time the armadillo, which is common in Mexico, Central and South America, was found in the United States only in Texas. It has now spread north and east, however, and occurs in Oklahoma, Arkansas, and across the southern states to Florida.

The armor or shell is made of bony plates and bands covered with scales. There are few curio shops in the southwest that do not feature baskets, lamps, and other trinkets made from the shells. Biologists fear that the

popularity of these curios, plus the killing of armadillos as supposed pests, will cause their eventual extermination from the United States.

Many people believe that the armadillo has a continuous open season on the eggs of ground-nesting birds, and that such food forms a major part of its diet. However, eggs placed in the cages of captive armadillos have been completely ignored. In other cases the animals have refused to touch an egg unless the shell was broken. Examination of armadillo stomachs indicates that 80 to 90 per cent of the food is insects, including many harmful species.

Old and experienced armadillos sometimes raid the nests of quail or other ground-nesting birds, but this seems to be an infrequent occurrence. On the other hand, ants are among the favorite food of armadillos. These insects sometimes destroy the nests and newly hatched young of game birds, so even an old reprobate armadillo that eats an occasional bird egg probably makes up for these depredations through the number of harmful insects it destroys.

An occasional armadillo may do harm in a too-enthusiastic search for food. Many of the insects that it eats are found as the armadillo plows piglike through the soil with its nose. If the foraging occurs in a field of corn or other grain, considerable damage may be done to the growing plants.

Armadillos are eaten in some sections, but they are not widely held in esteem; the name "poor man's pig" is often applied to the mammals. The meat is edible, however. At a recent meeting of biologists in the southwestern United States, barbecued armadillo was one of the main dishes at a banquet, which also included fried rattlesnake and other delicacies.

The animal's name is a Spanish word meaning "little armored thing or creature," and the presence of the bony plates is sufficiently unusual to set the armadillo apart from most mammals. It has another more unusual feature: the nine-banded armadillo, the only species that occurs in the United States, almost invariably gives birth to quadruplets. Studies have shown that the youngsters are identical quadruplets which develop from a single fertilized egg. So far as is known, armadillos are the only mammals in the world in which this type of reproduction takes place as a natural routine.

RABBITS AND HARES

What Small Mammals Are Most Important as Food?

Most of the relatively numerous small mammals are used as food in some parts of the world, but by far the most important of these are the rabbits and hares. Biologists make a technical distinction between rabbits and hares, but the differences are sometimes hard to see, and most people use the words indiscriminately. For instance, all domestic rabbits, many of which are called hares, have been developed from the European species which is a true rabbit. Now we are told that the common cottontail of the United States is neither a rabbit nor a hare. Under these circumstances, it seems best to forget technicalities and to use the term *rabbit* in a general sense for all of these mammals.

Rabbits are not native to Australia or New Zealand. The European species (a true rabbit) was introduced into both countries about 1860 in what was probably one of the greatest mistakes of its kind ever made. The animals found themselves in areas with plenty of food and virtually no natural enemies to keep them in check. The rabbits reproduced at a fantastic rate. Within a few years they showed every indication of trying to take over both countries; areas of once lush vegetation were reduced to barren wastes as the munching hordes advanced.

Millions of dollars were spent in combating the multitudes, and sheep production was drastically reduced because of the vegetation destroyed by the rabbits. Estimates put the annual loss caused by these pests at about $100 million.

Government agencies and professional exterminators tried every method known to science in an effort to reduce the rabbit population to reasonable numbers. These efforts included the importation of foxes, which probably ate more of the rare native animals than rabbits; the distribution of poisoned fruits and vegetables; the use of poison gas in rabbit burrows; and the erection of a supposedly rabbit-proof fence about 7,000 miles in length in Australia. All these efforts proved to no avail, except to help upset the balance of nature with respect to other animals. The rabbits, thanks to their reproductive capabilities and other features, continued to hold the field against all comers.

About 1950 harried Australian scientists heard of a virus disease in South America that was fatal to domestic rabbits which had been developed from the European species. This disease, myxomatosis, is transmitted from rabbit to rabbit by certain kinds of mosquitoes and by direct contact. In some regions, it is transmitted by rabbit fleas. Some of this virus was inoculated into European rabbits which were released in Australia. For a time rabbits died from this disease by the carload, and the usually detested mosquitoes were hailed as benefactors. Then came the announcement that immune strains of rabbits were appearing. In the meantime, New Zealanders had found that crop rotation, sensible grazing of livestock and planting grasses discouraged rabbits.

The final act in the rabbit drama in Australia and New Zealand has not yet been completed, but at present the combination of myxomatosis and judicious use of land suggests that the expression "knee deep in rabbits" may not apply to Australia and New Zealand in the future.

Myxomatosis was eventually introduced into France and England. Again, European rabbits died by the millions, making landowners happy, and furriers, sportsmen, and those who depended upon rabbits for food, most unhappy. On the other hand, the European hare, which is immune to myxomatosis, and which is not as much of a pest as the European rabbit, increased in number. Perhaps this species will help establish a new and better balance of nature, but the possibility that the European rabbit will overcome all obstacles and return more pestiferous than ever must not be discounted.

Early in 1955 biologists sounded a warning to people in the United States about the European rabbit. For many years colonies of these creatures have existed on the San Juan Islands off the coast of the state of Washington, where they have made a nuisance of themselves.

Within recent years European rabbits have been introduced into several Midwestern states including Pennsylvania, Indiana, Wisconsin, and Ohio. Whether or not these creatures will chew up the landscape as they did in Australia and New Zealand remains to be seen.

The ecological imbalance was probably what produced such drastic results in Australia and New Zealand, but the mammals sometimes do considerable harm in their native lands. In the western United States rabbits, including various jack rabbits, often damage crops and fruit trees. If they become too numerous, rabbit drives and poisoning campaigns are organized to reduce the population. In a single Idaho county, 40,000 were killed during one such campaign, and a single day's drive in the San Joaquin Valley of California yielded 35,000 rabbits.

Rabbit fever (also called tularemia, because it was first discovered in Tulare County, California) can be transmitted to human beings by wild rabbits, which often get the disease. People can get tularemia by handling or skinning diseased rabbits, but they can also become infected from rats and other rodents, and from the bites of horse flies and deer flies.

In view of the well-known reproductive capacity of rabbits, and their adaptability to changing conditions, it is probable that they will be with us for some years to come. And they do make certain contributions to man's well being. In addition to their value as food, rabbits are in demand for their skins. Australia and New Zealand have exported millions of dollars worth of pelts, as well as large quantities of rabbit meat, and thus compensate on a small scale for the enormous destruction previously caused by the pests.

Individual rabbit skins do not bring a high price, but this is more than made up for by the tremendous numbers processed. The United States is not an especially large producer of rabbit skins, but on a world-wide basis it has been estimated that during certain years more rabbit skins are sold than those of any other animal.

Some rabbit skins are made into fur coats. Trade names that have been used for these variously processed coats include lapin, cape seal, chinchilla, muskrat, white fox, and French sable. The skins are in even greater demand by the hat industry; a large part of the material used for felt hats is made from rabbit fur.

The animals have an indirect but tremendous importance to man in that they, like small rodents, furnish many large carnivorous animals with food. When rabbits are numerous, more valuable species, such as deer and domestic animals, are not as likely to be destroyed. It has also been found that the number of valuable fur-bearing animals that is caught is often dependent upon the number of rabbits and rodents available for food. For example, one trader during two seasons when rabbits were abundant, bought more than 1,800 lynx skins at a trading post in southern Canada. The third season the rabbits were scarce, and he procured only 40 skins from the same territory. Certain varieties of rabbit are also used extensively as experimental animals, and for various tests.

HOOFED MAMMALS

The Most Important Big Game in the World

The deer family is the most important big game in the world. There are approximately a hundred different kinds of deer, and they are found in many lands. Members of this family range in size from the gigantic Alaskan moose, which may be over 7 feet high at the shoulder and weigh 1,800 pounds, to several small tropical species that weigh 20 to 25 pounds.

The Alaskan moose is, so far as we know, the largest deer that ever lived. The famed but now extinct Irish elk had larger antlers than the moose but a much smaller body. Several kinds of moose, smaller than the Alaskan species, occur in Canada, the United States, and parts of Europe and Asia.

Several species of the deer family occur in North America. These include the caribou and reindeer, the elk or wapiti, the whitetail, the blacktail, and the mule deer. Of these the whitetail deer is by far the most important species in the United States, for it is widely distributed and more numerous than the other species. The whitetail occurs over most of the United States, parts of Canada, Central and South America.

In the early days, deer of all kinds were probably more important to men in the United States than they are today. Venison was a routine article of food for the Indians who made use of practically the entire animal. The skins were made into moccasins, clothing, bedding, and tepees. The tendons were used for thread and fish lines, and the bones for needles, scrapers, and ornaments of various kinds.

Then came the white man, who also used the deer but not so economically as did the Indians. Many animals were slaughtered only for their flesh, and others for their skin, the flesh being unused. Elk, which have two large tusklike teeth in their upper jaw, suffered a special misfortune. The women of certain Indian tribes wore these teeth as ornaments, and a large organization adopted the teeth as its emblem. Untold numbers of elk were slaughtered by hunters who collected only the teeth and did not bother with the remainder of the body.

Fortunately, people at last awoke to the fact that deer of all kinds were becoming scarce, and regulations were imposed on the hunting of all species. Thanks to this protection, most species of deer have increased to such an extent that they are now again important sources of meat, buckskin leather, recreation, and income for state treasuries, as well as for sporting goods stores.

Recent estimates have placed the number of deer of all kinds in the United States at several million, of which several hundred thousand are killed annually. One authority states that the value of the meat alone will run between $20 and $30 million per year, and the hides are still in demand for making buckskin gloves and jackets.

Unfortunately, an abundance of deer is not always entirely advantageous. In the olden days when large predators, such as cougars, were numerous, the deer populations were kept within reasonable bounds. But the constant persecution of man has so reduced these natural enemies that deer overpopulate many areas. As a result, thousands often starve to death and large sections are stripped clean of vegetation. In Pennsylvania, for instance, it is believed that deer destroy more young trees per year than do forest fires. Deer are also attracted to crops of various kinds, and in some states the animals cause hundreds of thousands of dollars worth of damage per year. Certain states have partially solved the problem of this kind of destruction by erecting deer-proof fences and by paying for any damage done by the animals.

From the standpoint of business to the state, New York has placed a valuation of $1 billion on the deer within its boundaries. Multiply this figure many times for the value of all the deer in the world, and you can see why the mammals are considered the most valuable big game animals in the world.

Important deer in other parts of the world include the sambar deer of southwestern Asia; the red deer of Europe, Asia, and Africa; the fallow deer of Europe; and the sika deer of eastern Asia. These animals, like their relatives in North America, are of great value to the inhabitants wherever they occur in sufficient numbers.

Which is the Most Valuable Member of the Deer Family?

A sportsman who kills a buck with a prime set of antlers certainly considers his particular prize more valuable than any other deer. But on a world-wide basis, and from the standpoint of human dependence, the most valuable deer in the world are probably the caribou. Eskimos, Indians, and others living in the far north depend upon the caribou for the necessities of life. Without these deer, perhaps thousands or even millions of people could not survive in the arctic climates. Other deer, while admittedly of tremendous importance, can hardly compete with the caribou.

Once a caribou has been killed, very little of the body goes unused. The blood is used for soup, the hide and tendons for making clothes, the flesh is eaten, the horns are made into fishhooks, and the bones are fashioned into knives. Even the stomach contents do not go unnoticed; if it contains partially digested caribou moss, a type of lichen, the material is removed and consumed with relish.

When the Eskimos and Indians of these regions first acquired rifles they slaughtered wild caribou and other animals so enthusiastically that many forms of wildlife were virtually exterminated over large areas. As a result, people were in danger of starvation. Beginning just before 1900, several attempts were made to introduce domesticated reindeer into Alaska. The natives were taught to care for the herds and, probably even more important, they learned not to eat all the available reindeer in a rush. This experiment has been quite successful, and surprisingly, the once indispensable wild caribou is now regarded as an enemy where herds of reindeer are raised. Wild caribou are killed at every opportunity because they have the habit of enticing reindeer out of domestication.

Several different kinds of caribou are native to various parts of the world, including the northern parts of Europe, Asia, and North America. Caribou are sometimes indiscriminately called reindeer, but this name should be limited to the Old World species of caribou that has been domesticated for centuries. Wild reindeer still occur in parts of Siberia.

At one time caribou occurred in several regions in the northern United States. They are now considered to be virtually extinct in this country except for a few individuals and occasional stragglers from southern Canada. Several reintroductions have been tried without marked success.

The Lapps, living in the northern parts of Finland, Norway, and Sweden have, over the years, depended heavily upon reindeer. Here most of the reindeer are domesticated and they serve as food, clothing, beasts of burden, and for transportation. One of the principal methods of travel is by sled drawn by several reindeer; the animals can make surprising speed over the rough snowy terrain.

Reindeer, which are a type of caribou, are the only deer that have been domesticated. Caribou also differ from other deer in several additional respects. Both sexes have antlers, while in other species only the males are antlered. The caribou range farther north than any other species, and may be found within the Arctic Circle. They are the most gregarious of all deer and often assemble in herds of thousands. This congregating into herds is often a preliminary move to a mass migration which sometimes covers hundreds of miles. One of these migrating herds some years ago was estimated to contain at least 25 million individuals, and many biol-

Midwinter

Early Spring

Spring

Summer

Fall

Moose's Antler Development

ogists believe that the caribou in numbers then rivaled or even exceeded in numbers the herds of bison that roamed the western prairies at any one time. Today the caribou are not nearly as numerous as in previous years, but they are still common in the Canadian Rockies and other remote northern regions.

It is difficult to believe that the antlers of deer are shed and regrown each year, but there have been so many observations of the process in captive deer that we now know it is a normal occurrence. It might not seem so remarkable if the antlers were only a few inches long, but the antlers of the mature elk may be over 5 feet long and the antlers of the moose may have a spread of more than 6 feet. Even more astounding is the probability that the now extinct Irish elk, whose antlers had a spread of over 9 feet, also shed and replaced them each year.

Just before the antlers are shed, a portion of the main antler shaft near the head becomes weakened by the destruction and absorption of the bony material. The antlers eventually break at this weakened point without any loss of blood, and apparently without pain to the animal. The stumps that remain become covered with skin, and it is from these covered stumps that the new antlers begin to grow. The growth of the new antlers is unbelievably rapid. Observations have shown that they may grow as much as one-third to one-half an inch a day. Until development of the antlers is complete, they are covered by a layer of skin, called the velvet, which drops off in strips once full growth is attained, leaving a solid, bony sharp-tipped antler.

Cows, sheep, goats, antelopes, and gazelles have what are known as true horns. Those horns are not shed and they often occur in both sexes. The pronghorn antelopes of the United States have special kinds of horns. They usually have only two branches, and the outer covering is shed and replaced each year. Pronghorns occur in both sexes.

How Dangerous Is a Hippopotamus?

Hippopotamuses are generally mild, even timid, but they are also unpredictable. There are several known instances of their having made unprovoked attacks upon people, usually people in boats. In regions where the animals have not learned to fear man, there is always a certain danger from solitary individuals or from a herd aroused suddenly from their sleep.

Sir Samuel Baker, an early African explorer, writes that an irate hippopotamus once charged a steamer on which he was a passenger, knocking several parts from one of the paddle wheels, and breaking a number of holes in the bottom of the vessel with its tusks. On another occasion, some natives under his direction were driving cattle across a stream when a herd of hippopotamuses deliberately attacked the cows. They seized several of them and carried them under the water before they were finally driven off.

Does the Hippopotamus Sweat Blood?

Since biblical times there have been those who maintained that the hippopotamus could sweat blood. Various circuses with hippopotamuses on exhibit have encouraged this belief. During warm weather, the hippo's skin does secrete a reddish, oily liquid which probably makes the skin more resistant to water and also possibly protects it from the air. But this secretion is not blood, although it resembles blood in general appearance.

Guanacos—Mainstay of Patagonia

Guanacos belong to the camel family and are widely distributed in the mountains of Central and South America. They are much smaller than camels, weighing only about two hundred pounds, but they are of tremendous importance to the natives. It has been said, for example, that many inhabitants of the Patagonian region of Argentina would find life impossible if the guanacos were suddenly removed. The natives depend upon these mammals for food, clothing, shelter, and saddles, as well as for ornaments and utensils of various types. Guanacos are often hunted with bolos, and it is thought that these animals may have been the primary incentive in the development of this well-known weapon.

Many years ago Charles Darwin, while visiting parts of South America, discovered large numbers of guanaco skeletons in several restricted spots on the banks of a river. Darwin inferred that the animals had a common burial ground, comparable to the fictitious burial ground of elephants. This same idea was perpetuated by other naturalists, but it is now believed that the true explanation of the piles of these bones is less romantic.

Guanacos live in the highlands, but during severe winters when food is scarce they descend from the heights and take up winter quarters in groups along an unfrozen stream. Even here, there may not be sufficient food for all; as a consequence, hundreds of the unfortunate animals die, leaving great piles of bones that confounded the early naturalists.

Many people who have never heard of a guanaco are at least familiar with llamas and alpacas, which some biologists believe were derived from the guanaco through many years of selective breeding. Llamas are raised in South America primarily as beasts of burden, although the milk and flesh are also utilized, and the alpacas are valued for the fine long wool they produce. Both the llama and alpaca have been domesticated for hundreds of years, and today neither of them is found in the wild state.

Are There Any Wild Camels in the United States?

There are two kinds of true camels, the Arabian camel with a single hump, and the two-humped camel or bactrian. The term dromedary is often applied to the bactrian camel, but a dromedary is really a breed of one-humped camel that has been developed especially for riding and racing. Bactrian camels are never correctly called dromedaries. Neither the dromedary nor the bactrian has a hump at birth; the hump develops gradually as the camel gets older.

It is thought probable that neither species of camel now exists in the original wild state, although in some areas there are wild camels which are probably offspring of domesticated camels that escaped from captivity. Large numbers of these undomesticated camels existed at one time, and probably still occur in numbers in Turkestan, the Gobi Desert, and adjacent areas.

At one time there were several undomesticated camels in southwestern and western United States. These animals were descended from a herd that was imported by the United States government in 1856 and used as pack animals in expeditions across arid regions of the country. This experiment was eventually abandoned, but for many years an occasional camel appeared in the area to startle inhabitants and travelers. Some of these reports are relatively recent, but it is not recommended that a camel-hunting expedition be organized on the assumption that herds of camels are still roaming the deserts of the west and southwest.

Although no true camels are native to the Western Hemisphere, they have as we have seen, relatives in South America—the alpaca, the llama, the vicuña and the guanaco. These animals do not have humps, but only a glance at their facial expression and their feet is required to see the similarity between them and the camels.

How Long Can Camels Go Without Water?

It is true that camels can go without water for some time, but this capacity has been considerably exaggerated. The maximum time the creatures can survive between drinks varies and depends upon the temperature, the kind of food they eat, how hard they have to work, and so on. Most authorities agree that under usual desert working conditions, the average camel must have water every eight to ten days if it is to remain healthy. According to one writer, one group of camels considerably exceeded the usual period. This particular caravan was on the march for thirty-four days without water, and during this time covered 530 miles; however, the majority of the camels died before the end of the journey.

For many years people have been trying to explain how the camel can survive as long as it does without water. One suggestion has been that excess water is stored in the hump, the idea being that the hump is simply a built-in reservoir into which the water pours as the animal drinks. Another suggestion was that water could be stored in the small pouches that open into the camel's stomach. Somewhat more scientific theories have been that excess water is stored in the body as fat and other substances, much of which could be converted into water in time of need.

Recent experiments by physiologists, however, have shown that none of these ideas is correct. The camel does not have a built-in reservoir, the water is not stored in the pouches, and neither is the needed water obtained from the fat or other tissues. But the camel does have two capacities better developed than most animals that allows it to survive without water when many other creatures would die. First, the body temperature normally fluctuates from about 93° F. to more than 104° F.; second, camels can withstand dehydration or water loss from the body of as much as 40 per cent of their body weight. By comparison, to remain healthy, man must keep his temperature within a degree or so of 98.6° F., and he cannot navigate if he loses more water than about 12 per cent of his body weight.

I think it obvious that the more water an animal can lose, such as by sweating, and remain healthy, the longer it can survive without water. The fluctuating temperature of the camel also helps, because the camel loses water in the form of sweat more slowly than most animals. In the mornings the body temperature of the camel is low, and it is several hours before the temperature increases to the point where the camel must sweat to keep the body temperature down. Man and many other animals start sweating long before camels, since the body temperature of the camel must rise to about 104° F. before it starts sweating to any extent.

What Animals Never Drink Water?

Camels are not the only animals that can go without water for a relatively long time. A few others have this capacity so well developed that camels are rank amateurs in comparison. Many wild animals including giraffes, mountain sheep and goats, and wild cattle have been known to go without drinking for several days, and some desert species such as gazelles, ground squirrels, mice, and kangaroo rats do not drink at all, so far as is known.

A small gazelle which was kept for six months by the Central Asiatic Expedition in the Gobi Desert always refused water when it was offered. A colony of pocket mice from New Mexico, which were kept for a time in the American Museum of Natural History, consistently refused water, even though they were fed on seeds that had been thoroughly dried. These animals are apparently able to get enough water for their needs in the digestion and utilization of their food. But it is quite possible that even they would have to drink occasionally if they were forced to do the work of a camel.

Llamas Defend Themselves by Spitting

One of the most interesting, but not one of the nicest, habits of the llama, a relative of the camel, is its ability to spit with an accuracy that might well be the envy of human tobacco-chewing marksmen. Visitors who annoy llamas in zoological gardens are quite likely to receive a copious shower of saliva, which the llama can spit through its teeth for some distance. It has even been reported that at times a llama will chastise a persistent rider by turning its head and spitting full in the face of its astonished persecutor. Since the saliva is quite irritating, such a bath would be decidedly unpleasant.

Do Wild Sheep Land on Their Horns When They Jump?

Wild sheep never deliberately land on their horns when they jump. The sheep that does, does so by accident, and it will certainly end up with a broken neck. This belief, occasionally encountered, probably originated from the fact that, when frightened, mountain sheep do sometimes dive head first from a cliff, but to survive for other leaps the animals must land on their feet.

The head of a fine mountain sheep is one of the most prized trophies in the sporting world. A wild sheep found in the mountains of southern Russia and northern India, called Marco Polo's argali, grows the longest horns of any of the mountain sheep. The largest one known is 75 inches long, following the curves of the horn, and it has a maximum girth of 16 inches, an enormous size for animals weighing only 300 to 350 pounds.

Do Bulls See Red?

It is firmly ingrained in the average mind that anything red makes a bull beside itself with rage and incites it to immediate attack. No bullfight would be complete without the bright red capes which matadors flick under the very noses of their raging adversaries.

Biologists have recently punctured the balloon of this ancient belief, but it will be many years before all laymen accept the results of their experiments. They have proved, however, that bulls cannot distinguish red from any other color. They are, in fact, color blind. This fact is privately admitted by many bullfighters, and in some experiments matadors who used white cloths got the same reactions from the bulls as those who used red cloths. It is the movement of the cape that causes the bull to charge— not the color of it. Although the bulls cannot tell a white cape from a red one, bloodthirsty human spectators at a bullfight certainly can, and the bullfighter does not exist who would have the temerity to appear in the arena with an unromantic white cape.

With the exception of man and monkeys, all other mammals upon which any work in this connection has been done have also been found to be essentially color blind.

Why Do Cows Chew Their Cuds?

Anyone familiar with cows knows that when they are not actively eating they are usually contentedly munching their cuds, a process that is apparently not only pleasurable, but is also essential to the health of the animal.

The cow's stomach is divided into four compartments, but the statement that the cow has four complete stomachs is not, strictly speaking, true. When cows eat grass or other food, they chew it only enough to enable them to swallow it. The food passes first into the front division of the stomach, called the rumen or paunch, which is simply a storage place. From the rumen, it gradually passes into the second stomach division, where it is compacted into small masses or cuds. When the cow is resting, the cuds are regurgitated one by one, thoroughly chewed and mixed with saliva. When the cow swallows the cud, it goes by way of a valve in the throat to the third division of the stomach where digestion begins. The fourth stomach division plus the intestine completes the digestive process.

Other animals that chew a cud include deer, sheep, goats, giraffes, and antelopes. Animals of this type are called ruminants, because the first part of the stomach is the rumen.

What Mammals Have Four Horns?

There occurs in parts of India and Burma the only wild mammal in the world with four horns. This is the four-horned antelope, a relatively small animal that weighs about 40 pounds. Only the males have horns and, in some cases, even they have only two, or none. The rear pair, which may be 4 to 5 inches in length, are the longer and grow in essentially the same position as the horns of other mammals. The front pair are just above the eyes, and may attain a length of 2½ inches.

Several kinds of domestic sheep have been selectively bred and now have various numbers of horns. Perhaps the most interesting are the unicorn or one-horned sheep and the four horned varieties. The unicorn sheep is found principally in Nepal, India, and its one horn is really two, fused together for more than half the length. In many specimens of this breed, the horns separate toward the end and curve independently, occasionally even sweeping downward toward the neck. There has been considerable discussion about whether this peculiar horn condition is inherited or whether each sheep is given special treatment while young to induce the horns to develop abnormally. So far as I know this question has not been settled.

The four-horned sheep are equally spectacular. In some varieties one pair of horns grows upward and outward more or less normally, while the second pair, behind the first, grows outward and downward, with the points directed toward the sheep's nose.

Does the Giraffe Have a Voice?

Giraffes are traditionally considered to be as voiceless as the proverbial clam. Hunters have said that they do not make a sound even when wounded, and until recent years even biologists believed that they were as mute as they are popularly thought to be.

Recently, however, observations of giraffes in zoological parks have shown that at least an occasional specimen is capable of making certain types of noises. Female giraffes have been heard to moo or low softly, particularly when they were concerned about the welfare of their calves, and young giraffes, when hungry, have been heard to make sounds like those of a calf. The voice box or larynx of a giraffe is comparatively undeveloped, and it is possible that only some of them can make sounds. Perhaps the voice box is better developed in the young than in the adults, for according to reports the young produce more noticeable sounds.

What Is the Tallest Animal in the World?

The giraffe, thanks to its extremely long neck, is the tallest living mammal. It is possible that a few individuals 20 feet in height may exist, but the greatest height I have found recorded is 18 feet 11½ inches to the

tips of the horns. Perhaps surprisingly, the giraffe has only seven bones in its neck, the same number that most other mammals have. Seen in a mounted skeleton, they remind one of sticks of stove wood stacked end to end.

Although the giraffe is the tallest mammal alive today, at least one extinct species was taller—a type of rhinoceros, *Baluchitherium,* remains of which have been unearthed in Mongolia. Specimens of this old fellow reached a shoulder height of 17 feet 9 inches, as opposed to 10 or 11 feet for the giraffe. Added to this height at the shoulder, the giraffe has a columnar neck of some 7 or 8 feet, but our rhinoceros friend had a neck at least this long. In a tallest animal contest, it is believed that "Balucky" could have surpassed any living giraffe by several feet. A large specimen of the extinct rhinoceros would probably have measured nearly 25 feet from the soles of its front feet to the crown of its head.

What Is the Most Valuable Domesticated Animal of the Tropics?

Many animals that have been domesticated for centuries on a large scale become so changed that it is difficult to determine from what species they originally came. The water buffalo was almost certainly domesticated long before the time of Christ, and yet in many cases it is difficult to distinguish by appearance alone between wild and domesticated individuals.

Water buffaloes, also known as carabaos, Asiatic buffaloes, and Indian buffaloes, are certainly the most important domestic animal of the tropics. Next to the horse, there are probably more domesticated water buffaloes in the world than any other animal that is used as a beast of burden. There are perhaps as many horses in the tropics as water buffaloes, but the variety of ways in which the buffalo is used makes it much more valuable in these areas than the horse.

Water buffaloes originally occurred in the wild state in India and adjacent countries, but since their domestication they have been introduced into many other countries including Egypt, Italy, Turkey, Hungary, and the Philippine Islands.

In parts of the tropics life would be difficult indeed without these animals. They are used as draft animals and some are capable of carrying on their backs a load of over a ton in weight. They are especially valuable in cultivating rice, since their wide splayed feet are well adapted to the muddy fields in which rice is grown. The milk, flesh, and skins are also used. It has been estimated that there are more than twenty million domesticated buffaloes in India alone, with other millions scattered throughout the tropics.

Water buffaloes are considered to be more intelligent than our domesticated cattle, to which they are related. This comparison alone of course does not mean much, since it would be difficult to find a more stupid beast than the usual cow. Water buffaloes are said to learn tricks easily; one is reported to have learned to fetch water from a river with a bucket carried on one of its horns. Some claim that domesticated buffaloes develop an affection for their native masters; on more than one occasion, they are said to have ganged up on a tiger trying to eat their master and chased the big cat away.

Water buffaloes still occur in the wild state in parts of India, Ceylon, and the Malay peninsula. Domesticated individuals are docile and easily handled by their owners, but an aroused wild bull is one of the most savage and dangerous animals in existence. A wounded bull has been known to trail hunters by scent and once it has taken the offensive nothing will stop it except its own death or that of its enemy.

Are There Wild Pigs in the United States?

A species of peccary, also called the javelina, is the only native wild pig in the United States. Peccaries are small compared to the wild boars of Europe and Asia, and they are classified as a separate family. The javelina attains a maximum weight of about 65 pounds, whereas a large wild boar may tip the scales at more than 350 pounds.

Peccaries are most numerous south of the United States border, where two species occur, but at one time javelinas ranged as far north as Arkansas. Their present distribution in this country is confined to southern Texas, Arizona, and New Mexico. According to the Texas Game and Fish Commission, this reduction of range was caused by the unrestricted hunting that was practiced for a number of years. Much of this hunting was for the skins and bristles rather than for sport. The skin has been manufactured into various pigskin articles such as gloves, bags, purses, and shoes; the bristles are used for brushes. The peccary is now considered a game animal and, under the protection of hunting regulations, has been showing an increase in numbers within recent years.

Peccaries eat cactus, acorns, mesquite, nuts, and berries; they also consume lechuguilla, an undesirable range plant, insects, rattlesnakes, and other reptiles. Many ranchers in Texas are said to consider peccaries definite assets, helping to control plant and animal pests, and the little pigs have thus been encouraged to increase in numbers.

Although there are no native wild boars in the United States, the European wild boar has been introduced into several states. Introductions have been made in New Hampshire, North Carolina, Tennessee, California, and

Texas. Some of the descendants of these original wild boars still survive, but apparently they have crossed with domestic pigs to some extent.

Domestic pigs tend to revert to a partially wild state if given a chance. Examples of this situation are the razorbacks of the southeastern United States, and the diving pigs of Florida. Razorbacks are so called because many are lean, and the backbone forms a razor-like crest along the back. The diving pigs occur on several islands off the coast of Florida. One of their principal sources of food is fish discarded by fishermen; the hogs often plunge into several feet of water for their meals.

Some of the Hawaiian Islands have a rather large population of wild boars. It is believed that these boars were derived from domestic hogs originally introduced by the Polynesians who settled the islands many years ago.

Our attention has recently been called to a wild pig in southern Texas, the hunting of which is not regulated at this writing. This pig is apparently a result of crosses between several introduced European wild boars and wild domestic pigs. At present it seems well established in and near the Aransas National Wildlife Refuge in the vicinity of Corpus Christi, Texas. The boars weigh as much as 180 pounds, and wounded individuals have been reported to have charged men and to have crippled horses. An interesting feature of these boars is that their tusks are shorter than the tusks of either of their ancestors. The common name of these wild pigs? Texas *short*horns, of all things!

Wild boars armed with long sharp tusks have always been regarded as dangerous, especially if wounded or with young. Sportsmen have usually hunted them on horseback, therefore, but the horses and even the hunters do not always escape unscathed. During one year wild boars were responsible for the death of fifty people in India, some of whom were probably dehorsed "pig-stickers."

Much has been written about peccaries banding together and killing hunters, or keeping men treed for hours. These tales are largely fiction so far as the peccaries in the United States are concerned; or to be a little more charitable, if such occurrences have happened, they are rare. The white-lipped peccary, a different species that occurs in Mexico, Central and South America, is apparently somewhat pugnacious, but even its ferocity has been exaggerated.

What Animals Have the Longest Horns?

The Indian buffalo, with a record length of approximately 6½ feet for a single horn, has produced the longest horn of any living animal. Some of the wild sheep, relatively small animals, have horns almost as long, the record length of a single one being 6 feet 3 inches.

Figures on horn spread are scarce for many species, although some horns are rated almost entirely on the basis of spread rather than length. Two species appear to be outstanding as far as present data on living animals are concerned. These are the Indian buffalo and the longhorn steer. Possibly the longhorn should not be considered, since only the steer, a result of man's "tampering with nature," produces outstanding horns. A spread of over nine feet is on record for the Indian buffalo and, although I have not seen a positively established measurement of nine feet for the longhorn steer, several such sets have been reported, and it is believed that one or more of these reports is correct.

The antlers of moose establish a different kind of record. A pair of moose antlers may weigh as much as 85 pounds; they are believed to be heavier and to contain more material than the horns of any other living animal.

BATS

What Mammals Can Fly?

Bats are the only mammals that fly in the true sense of the word, although there are other mammals that can glide through the air to some

extent. Gliding mammals include the so-called flying squirrels and the flying lemurs, the latter peculiar monkey-like creatures about the size of a cat, found in the Malay Peninsula and adjacent areas and in Madagascar (now called Malagasy).

The wings of a bat are different in structure from the wings of a bird. Bat wings consist of leathery, membranous skin supported by the bones of the front limbs and by other enormously long bones that correspond to the finger bones of man. All the finger bones except those of the thumb serve as braces for the wings; the thumbs, growing near the middle of the front margin of the wing, are free and are used in clinging to surfaces and in crawling.

The "wings" of flying squirrels are not true wings at all, but simply folds of skin along the sides of the body, attached to the front and hind legs. Flying squirrels can sail or glide for a considerable distance by jumping from a tree and spreading this skin. The glide is usually downward, so that they alight on the trunk or branch of another tree lower than that from which they took off.

Do Bats Hibernate?

In temperate zones bats disappear as cold weather approaches, and reappear in the spring. During the winter insect-eating bats are forced either to hibernate or migrate, since the cold weather kills the insects upon which they feed. Those that hibernate hole up in caves, hollow trees or even under loose bark. The walls of caves in some regions may be literally covered by thousands of hibernating bats hanging from some projection by their feet, heads downward. Several species make rather extensive migrations, but as yet little is known about this. It is thought that some North American bats spend the winter in Bermuda, while others apparently go to the southern United States or even farther south.

During the summer most of the bats in the United States are active primarily at night and rest and sleep during the day in some secluded spot. Huge numbers sometimes use the same roosting quarters and emerge near dusk in hordes. One of the most famous of these nightly flights occurs at Carlsbad Caverns, New Mexico.

How Blind Is a Bat?

The expression "blind as a bat" indicates a general belief that bats are either totally blind or unable to see very well. This idea probably arose because many bats avoid bright sunlight and fly primarily at dusk or night.

But some bats are quite active during the day and some species, like the fruit bats or flying foxes, sleep at night and do practically all their foraging by daylight. Actually, even the night-flying species have excellent eyesight in semi-darkness and can see reasonably well in broad daylight.

Bats Have Always Used Sonar

Naturalists have known for a long time that bats can fly in total darkness without bumping into obstructions. Even before 1800 a biologist named Spallanzani reported that bats liberated in a dark room did not strike strings which he had strung across the room.

Various theories have been advanced to explain this ability, but only recently has the secret been partially solved. Blindfolded bats fly in the dark as well as those with unobstructed sight, but bats whose ears have been covered constantly bump into obstructions. It has been discovered that as bats fly they continuously emit cries that cannot be heard by human beings. These sounds are not the same as the irritated squeakings of a disturbed or captured bat, which are quite within the range of human hearing. The theory is that the inaudible or supersonic cries are reflected back to the bats and aid them in locating objects, which they are thus enabled to avoid. This principle is somewhat like that used by blind people, who avoid objects by tapping a cane and using the echo as a guide. It is said that sonar operates in a similar manner. The words *echolocate* and

echolocation have been proposed as descriptive terms for this method of locating obstacles by echoes. It is really not surprising that a bat, or for that matter any animal, is able to make and hear sounds that man cannot hear, for the range of hearing in human beings is quite different from that of many animals.

It is often said that bats use radar, but this is not correct according to the definitions of radar and sonar devices. Radar devices use electromagnetic waves, whereas sonar devices employ sound waves. Since no one has suggested that bats use electromagnetic waves in echolocation, the term *sonar*, rather than radar is the correct designation.

Do Vampire Bats Exist?

The vampire legend probably originated in eastern Europe long before the existence of a blood-eating bat was known. As originally described, a vampire was the restless soul of a dead person, which at night assumed one of several animal forms and stalked the countryside in search of a victim from which to suck the blood.

The bat was not associated with the vampire story until the early eighteenth century, for the very good reason that there are no European bats that feed on blood. The early explorers in South and Central America, however, encountered bats that did feed on blood, and their experiences, doubtless exaggerated, at last furnished a tangible basis for the amorphous vampire legend. Consequently, around 1725, a rash of vampire stories broke out in Europe, and since that time vampires have been thought of chiefly as bats.

There are several species of blood-eating bats to which the term vampire bat has been applied. So far as is known, bats of this type are found only in Mexico, Central and South America. The largest species has a wingspread of some twelve or thirteen inches and a body length of about four inches. The weapons of the vampire bat are its modified, needle-sharp front or incisor teeth, with which it makes small cuts in the skin of its victim. It does not suck the flowing blood, as formerly thought, but laps it up with its tongue as a cat laps milk. The bats feed upon a variety of animals, including horses, cows, goats, and chickens, and sometimes human beings. But they are not more partial to man than to other animals. For some unknown reason, however, they do exhibit preference for certain individuals, both human and animal. Thus, even though a number of men or animals may be available, the bats frequently attack only one or a few out of a group, night after night.

Very few people are awakened by the feeding of the bats, and the first indication that one has served as a meal for one of these winged leeches is usually the discovery of a bloodstained sheet in the morning. Possibly the saliva of the vampire bat contains something that deadens the pain of the wound; it probably does contain some substance that prevents the blood from clotting for, small as it is, the wound frequently continues to bleed for some time after the bat has stopped feeding. The vampire bat does not hover over its victim, and neither does it fan him to sleep with its wings. It may alight directly upon the body, or it may stop a short distance away and crawl up.

In some parts of South America goats, horses, cows, and chickens are so frequently attacked by vampire bats that it is almost impossible to raise them profitably. The bats also transmit diseases that kill large numbers of horses and cattle. One of the worst is the frequently fatal paralytic rabies, which has occasionally been transmitted to human beings.

There are no blood-feeding bats in the United States, but within recent years rabies has been discovered in some of the bats in this country. Human deaths have occurred from rabies obtained from bats in the United States, and because of this danger one should avoid handling bats.

The Values of Bats

Bats, of which there are some two thousand different kinds in the world, are as we have seen, the only mammals that can fly in the real sense of the word.

Bats are classified apart from other mammals, and only among rodents are there more different kinds than can be found in the bat group. They exist practically all over the world, but there are more species in the tropics than elsewhere.

It has long been known that some bats feed almost exclusively upon insects. Before extensive observations were made of their food habits, even some biologists thought that bats were important factors in controlling mosquitoes. The idea that bats could be utilized in controlling the insects, and that perhaps mosquito-borne malaria could be eliminated in this way gained some acceptance. Bat roosts of various types were erected in several cities, two of them in San Antonio, Texas, and Bakersfield, California. These projects became less popular when it was found that mosquitoes rarely make up a significant part of the bat diet.

Although insect-eating bats seldom emphasize mosquitoes in their feeding, the mammals do destroy myriads of other insects. A majority of the food consists of night-flying species, since most bat activities occur at night. Examinations of bat stomachs have revealed them to be literally stuffed with insects, many of them injurious species.

Some bats will eat practically any small animal they can overcome, and some feed primarily on fruit. To this latter group belong the flying foxes, the largest bats in the world, with a wingspread of as much as five feet.

In addition to their insect eating, some bats make other contributions to man. Caves are favorite roosting spots, and where the mammals have used the same spot for years, their droppings have gradually accumulated on the floor. When Carlsbad Cavern, New Mexico, was first discovered, it was found that bat droppings or guano had accumulated over the centuries. It was as much as a hundred feet thick in some places. Since that time, an estimated hundred thousand tons of the material have been removed and sold for fertilizer.

According to a reasonably reliable report, a bizarre military use for bats was discovered during World War II. A project was developed in which bats were used to carry small incendiary bombs. The idea was to release large numbers of bomb-carrying bats from planes in enemy territory; the bat's natural inclination to scatter and seek shelter in cracks and crevices of buildings was supposed to result in the bombs' being placed in many strategic spots. This project was classified as top secret to keep from giving "comfort" to the enemy, and apoplexy to animal lovers in this country. For the information of the latter group, however, we are assured that the canny bats would usually bite through the bindings of the bombs and escape. The bat brigade proved successful in tests, but I do not know whether it was ever used against the enemy.

RATS, LEMMINGS, WOODCHUCKS,
AND OTHER RODENTS

Are All Rodents a Menace?

In addition to rats and mice the rodent clan includes muskrats, beavers, chinchillas, gophers, prairie dogs, chipmunks, woodchucks, hamsters, guinea pigs, porcupines, and a host of others. Rabbits and hares, at one time considered rodents, are now classified in another group.

The annual total damage to crops by native rodents in the western United States has been estimated at approximately $300 million and, except for rats and mice, the most important of these culprits are probably gophers, ground squirrels, and prairie dogs. Marmots or groundhogs, chipmunks, and even the grunting shuffling porcupine may occasionally become so numerous that they destroy quantities of trees and crops.

In addition to the direct and easily seen damage caused by rodents, some are harmful indirectly. Many of the species are the reservoirs for organisms of such serious diseases as plague and spotted fever. The disease organisms are transmitted to the rodents and to people by ticks, fleas, and other parasites.

I doubt that even the most enthusiastic conservationist would shed a regretful tear if house rats and house mice were wiped off the face of the earth. Certain other rodents, however, are definite assets to man's economy. One point in favor of these animals is that they serve as food for meat-eating mammals such as foxes, skunks, weasels, coyotes, minks, bears, and wildcats. They thus become buffers, so to speak, between predators and domestic animals, and when rodents are numerous, farm and range stock are not as likely to be disturbed.

The burrowing gophers and the degus of Peru and adjacent countries have proved to be valuable soil conservationists in poor uncultivated areas. They bring subsoil to the surface and bury enriching vegetation. Their burrows help to reduce the runoff of surface water. It has been estimated that the gophers in Yosemite National Park alone bring 8,000 tons of subsoil per year to the surface.

Woodchucks, prairie dogs, and many other rodents, are edible, but aside from tree squirrels which will be considered later, few find their way to the American table. In West and South Africa, cane rats are staple articles of food. These rodents, which may weigh 10 to 12 pounds and are related to porcupines, are called ground pigs and cutting grasses by the natives. The mammals are often the objects of organized hunts in which dogs are used to round up the rats for easy killing.

Some short-tailed mice about 5 inches in length are called grasshopper mice for a very good reason: a majority of their food consists of grass-hoppers and other insects. Biologists once found that in 96 grasshopper mice, more than 78 per cent of the stomach contents were insects. In the southwestern United States these mice destroy large numbers of scorpions. Many other rodents, such as squirrels, chipmunks, and even prairie dogs, also eat insects.

Thus we find that some rodents are almost completely beneficial, others are beneficial to some extent, and still others have little to recommend them. With the possible exception of house rats and mice, it seems logical that man's goal should be control rather than extermination. If numbers are kept within reasonable bounds, most rodents not only form an interesting part of our landscape, but actually contribute to man's well-being.

What Mammal Is Man's Worst Enemy?

On a world-wide basis, no mammal can compare with house rats as enemies of man. At one time these rodents were confined to Asia, but within the memory of man they have spread by leaps and bounds. They are found now in practically all civilized and many uncivilized areas of the world.

There are many different kinds of rats, most of which avoid human company, but certain villains deliberately seek human habitations in preference to other living quarters. The two most important kinds of house rats are the brown, or Norwegian, rat and the black, or roof, rat. These species have been said to affect more people, directly or indirectly, than any other pest in existence, and to cause more damage in the United States than the combined depredations of all other mammals.

Rats will eat anything from live chickens to garbage, and they often contaminate with their droppings far more than they eat. The rat's gnawing activities damage furniture, floors, foundations, and water pipes, and the mammal may cause disastrous fires by its attention to electric wires. Rats have been known to attack infants, the sick, and the infirm, and there are instances on record of packs of starving rats killing healthy adults who were trapped in confined quarters. The animals eat and destroy enormous quantities of grain and other stored products. Rats and the fleas they carry are responsible for the transmission of human diseases; among the most important of these are endemic typhus, rat-bite fever, and plague. There are several forms of plague, the best known of which is bubonic. Plague alone is said to have caused more deaths than all the wars in history.

The reproductive capacity of rats is amazing and surpasses even that of the renowned rabbit. One biologist has estimated that, if all offspring from a single pair of rats lived and reproduced, 350 million rats would be produced within three years. Under similar conditions, according to the biologist, a pair of rabbits would produce a mere 322,000 rabbits within five years.

Fortunately, rats are relatively short lived. The average individual is old at two years of age, and if not killed and eaten by its fellows, will probably die of old age a few months later.

House rats have done man one favor, although the contribution was not deliberate. The white rat which is an albino form of the house rat, is one of the most widely used laboratory animals for medical research.

The house mouse, a much smaller cousin of the rat, is somewhat limited by its smaller size in the damage it does. But mice can cause appreciable damage to food, stored grain and other products, and even to field crops. Also, like the rat, the mouse, by its promiscuous deposition of waste products, contaminates much more than it actually eats.

Sometimes the populations of house mice build up to such proportions that damage in the millions of dollars is caused almost overnight. In Australia some years ago hordes of mice suddenly appeared around grain depots where sacked wheat was stacked awaiting shipment. They swarmed over the grain sacks gnawing away and creating havoc in general. Many control measures were tried unsuccessfully and incalculable damage was caused by the voracious little beasts before they were finally conquered. It was reported that eight tons of mice were killed In four nights around a single warehouse.

Meadow mice, sometimes called voles, were probably responsible for most of the ancient mouse plagues of the Old World, and in Europe they overrun the countryside intermittently during so-called vole years. The United States is subject to occasional eruptions of field mice. One year in Nevada it was computed that there were 12,000 mice per acre in some fields, which resulted in a $300,000-loss of alfalfa.

Do Migrating Lemmings Swim Out to Sea?

Lemmings are small mouselike rodents that live in most arctic and subarctic regions of the world. In Norway and adjacent areas enormous numbers of them make periodic migrations, eating everything edible in their path. According to the usual story, the migrations always end with the lemmings' plunging into the ocean and swimming out to sea.

There is considerable truth in many of the stories that are told about lemmings. Every three or four years when the feeding grounds become overpopulated by rapid reproduction, the lemmings boil out of the mountains in untold numbers and overrun the countryside. They tend to travel downhill, and the topography of Norway is such that a downhill direction eventually leads to the coast. During their migrations, they follow a rather direct route, and if streams or lakes lie across their path they attempt to swim rather than make a detour. Many, of course, are drowned; others die of a disease called lemming fever; and they are preyed upon by all kinds of animals, such as foxes, bears, hawks, owls, and even reindeer. Sometimes the total loss of life is so great that only a handful, sometimes none, ever reach the ocean. If they gain the coast, however, they frequently do plunge into the ocean and swim out to sea. Sometimes enough of them survive to cause consternation in all observers. In 1868 a steamer in Trondheim Fjord off the Norwegian coast encountered a swimming legion so large that fifteen minutes were required for the steamer to pass.

The reasons for many of their actions are not well understood. The final and fatal plunge into the ocean has been interpreted as a result of bad judgment on the part of the migrating hordes. It is possible that the lemmings believe the ocean is simply another small stream or lake to be quickly overcome, but this, of course, can be only a guess.

Is the Groundhog a Good Weather Prophet?

The groundhog, or woodchuck or marmot, is the most famous weather prophet in the United States. It hibernates in a burrow during the winter months and, according to tradition, emerges from hibernation on the second day of February, which for this reason has been designated ground-hog day. Once out of its burrow, the groundhog casts a knowing eye over the landscape. If the day is cloudy so that it cannot see its shadow, it stays outdoors and the general public heaves a sigh of relief: the weather will be mild for the rest of the winter. But if the day is clear and the groundhog sees its shadow, back it pops into its burrow for more sleep, for this weather-wise animal supposedly knows that there will be six more weeks of cold weather.

This is one of our oldest and quaintest traditions, but the chances are that very few people actually believe it despite the furor and publicity attached to groundhog day. It does furnish an interesting topic of conversation for a week or so each year, and it seems almost unbecoming to examine it with the cold eye of science. Aside from the groundhog's questionable ability to predict the weather, the best reason for not believing the story is that the time of the animal's emergence from hibernation varies from year to year and probably seldom occurs on February 2. During cold weather these animals sensibly refuse to come out of their burrows, even though they are eagerly awaited by their public. Several times in the East, newsmen have been forced to disturb the sleep of some poor woodchuck in a zoological park in order to take pictures for groundhog day. But despite all scientific logic the groundhog tradition is here to stay, and newspapers doubtless will continue to feature groundhog stories from time to time.

In parts of Europe, the hedgehog (page 64), an animal similar in habits to the groundhog, is supposed to be the champion weather prophet. It is thought that the hedgehog tradition was brought from Europe by the Pilgrim Fathers, who transferred their attentions to the groundhog when no convenient hedgehog could be found.

The groundhog is a medium-sized rodent, a foot and a half or two feet long with a weight of about eight pounds. It is related to the ground squirrel and prairie dog and is widely distributed over the eastern half of the United States. Related species occur farther west.

Is Marsh Hare Edible?

If you ever get a chance to eat marsh hare or marsh rabbit, be sure to try it. The flavor is excellent, somewhat resembling that of terrapin or wild-duck; it is actually a fat muskrat. From time to time muskrat carcasses have enjoyed tremendous sales in the markets of the large cities, such as Baltimore, St. Louis, Washington, and Philadelphia.

Muskrats supply more pelts to the fur market than any other American mammal—about ten million per year, on the average. Yet, surprisingly, the animal does not seem to be decreasing appreciably in numbers. It is extremely prolific, a single female muskrat has been known to produce thirty young in a year.

In marshy areas and along the banks of ponds and streams muskrats dig extensive systems of tunnels, which may create considerable difficulty for the human species. The animal was introduced into Britain in 1927 for the purpose of establishing a fur industry, the trade name for the pelts there being musquash. Some of the mammals escaped from captivity and within a few years were well established; so well established, in fact, that in certain river beds and important waterways their tunnels in banks, dams, and levees were threatening serious damage. The rodents also developed appetites for corn, potatoes, carrots, and other crops, and caused much local destruction.

The muskrat situation became so serious in England that laws were hastily passed prohibiting their further introduction. Campaigns were organized to exterminate them, or at least greatly reduce their numbers. Muskrats are hardy, however, and well able to take care of themselves under most circumstances; several years passed before there was an appreciable decrease in numbers. But the government trappers were persistent, and by 1937 the muskrats were virtually exterminated in England.

Are Tree Squirrels Harmful?

Certain tree squirrels were doubtless more harmful in the past than they are at present. Especially is this true of the gray squirrels of North America. Early colonists found them in untold thousands in the forests of the eastern United States, where the squirrels swarmed over the fields, causing so much destruction to crops that bounties were placed on the marauders. Over a period of years unrestricted slaughter and the clearing of forests brought the gray squirrel near extinction. Fortunately, however, restrictive legislation was enacted in time to save these mammals from extermination.

Tree squirrels of one kind or another are native to all continents except Australia. Wherever they occur in numbers they are hunted avidly for sport, food, and for their fur. Although the pelts are small, they are marketed by the millions. During some years it has been estimated that, on a world-wide basis, more squirrel skins are sold than those of any other rodent.

In spite of their values as a group, tree squirrels cause damage under some situations. For some unknown reason, the rodents are attracted to telephone cables and, on an average, cause a half a million dollars' worth of damage per year by gnawing through the outer sheathing. When other food is scarce, squirrels may destroy young trees by stripping the bark, and where the mammals are abundant, they occasionally cause some loss to pecan growers. In the United States red squirrels are accused of destroying the nests of birds, but it is not known how extensive this practice is.

Some years ago the gray squirrel was introduced into England and parts of Europe, where it became well established. Like many introduced animals, this one has become a pest in certain areas. It has been claimed that the gray squirrel is responsible for the decrease in England of a native species, the red squirrel, but most biologists do not believe that the former has been a major factor in this connection.

In some regions tree squirrels are the most important single game animal. In Texas, more than 600,000 are believed to be bagged annually, and in West Virginia, an estimated million pounds are killed during some years.

The habit of many species of burying nuts and seeds is considered an important element in reforestation. This contribution to conservation is not a deliberate one on the part of squirrels. The buried stores are supposed to be dug up and eaten later, but apparently the location of many caches is forgotten.

What Animal Helped to Settle North America?

Many animals in North America were of considerable importance as food and clothing to the early settlers of North America. The role of the bison in that expansion is known to every school child; not so well known but probably more important was the part played by the American beaver in the settling of remote regions of the North American continent.

The significance of this animal in the history of North America has often been recognized. The beaver is the central figure in the first postage stamp issued by the Canadian government, and several other beaver stamps have been brought out since. One historian remarked that the beaver was one of the most important facts in American history. This statement was hardly an exaggeration, since for many years the beaver was the backbone of the fur industry of the whole continent.

When the early colonists first landed in America, beavers were plentiful in the New England states and eastern Canada, where they were trapped in numbers by the Indians. The settlers established trade with the natives, who traded beaver skins for various trinkets and necessities. Because the Indians had trapped them conservatively, the beaver had maintained rela-

tively large numbers. This balance changed when the white trappers took over. As the beavers became scarce in the more civilized areas, trading posts dealing primarily in furs sprang up in remote regions. Many of these posts later became flourishing cities. The slaughter of beavers can hardly be condoned, but it must be admitted that it contributed greatly to the spread of civilization. If the animals had remained numerous on the east coast, the westward migrations might have been deferred for many years.

In Canada beaver skins became the basis of value, especially in the many posts of the famous Hudson's Bay Company. One beaver skin would buy a pound of tobacco, four a blanket, and twelve a rifle. Hudson's Bay blankets are still marked with four short stripes, the price in beaver skins, reminder of the days when beaver was king.

Although the fur of the beaver was the most important part of the animal, other parts of the body were not totally neglected. The flesh was eaten by many people, and for a time large numbers of carcasses were marketed in the larger cities. The tail was considered a special delicacy, although a visiting Englishman, who ate beaver tail in Canada, described the taste as resembling finnan haddie and fat pork. Whether this description was supposed to be complimentary or otherwise was never made clear.

Aside from the skin, a substance known as castorum probably found widest use. This material comes from two musk glands that occur in both male and female beavers. The odors from these glands probably help the animals in identifying individuals, or possibly it may attract the sexes to each other.

In the early days, castorum was used widely as a medicine, considered effective for almost anything that ailed a person. I can well remember as a child taking a patent medicine that had a name suspiciously similar to that used for beaver musk. I do not know if the main constituent was castorum, but I do know that I was stuffed full of the medicine at the least provocation. Thousands of pounds of castorum were sold until the medicine went out of style. It is no longer used as a medicine, doubtless to the relief of thousands of children.

The relentless hunt for beavers ultimately took its toll. The animals were exterminated over a large part of their ranges and became rare in others. Protective laws were passed in the United States and Canada, and under this protection the beaver has prospered. The animals have been reintroduced into many of their former territories, and have even become abundant locally.

A change in style was a major factor in saving the beaver from extermination. Until the beginning of the nineteenth century, a major use for beaver pelts was in the manufacture of men's hats known as castors or beavers. For many years no dandy, or businessman for that matter, was well dressed without one of these tall fuzzy monstrosities. Then an Italian invented the silk hat, French stylists adopted this with glee, and the demand for beaver pelts hit the skids. Only then could the few conservationists make themselves heard sufficiently to cause the passage of protective laws.

The beaver is the largest rodent in the world except for the capybara of South America; large individuals may weigh as much as a hundred pounds. A husky beaver can fell a tree five inches in diameter within three minutes, and even forest giants more than one hundred feet high have fallen before the chisel teeth of these industrious mammals. Beavers feed mostly upon bark, and the trees that are cut are used for food and for the construction of dams.

Beaver pelts are still in considerable demand for coats and for various kinds of trimmings, and from this standpoint the animals are definite economic assets. Their activities, however, may sometimes collide with human interests, and when this occurs, the rodents can cause considerable local damage. In Idaho some years ago, for example, fields and roads were being flooded over large areas because of the construction of beaver dams. The Fish and Game Commission promptly relieved the situation by capturing many of the culprits and transporting them to more remote sections. There have also been complaints that beavers destroy timber, orchards, and other valuable trees.

Under many circumstances the presence of beavers can be beneficial; their dams may prevent floods and conserve water. This was illustrated a few years ago, after some beavers were introduced into an intermittent stream in northeastern California. They built dams which prevented the spring runoff water from rushing downstream all at once and being lost. Now the stream runs all the year; the banks and adjacent meadows downstream are kept green with lush grass for cattle.

A more dramatic instance of water conservation comes from Colorado. During a year of drought, some resourceful individuals conceived the idea of using water that had been impounded by beavers some distance away. Irrigation ditches were constructed along dry stream beds, and the beaver dams upstream were opened. Life-giving water rushed into the irrigation ditches, and on one stream alone crops valued at more than $15,000 were saved.

Aside from man, beavers have few serious enemies. Coyotes, wolves, cougars, bears, and other large meat-eating mammals snatch an occasional beaver meal, but the mortality is not high.

The European beaver, similar in general appearance to the American species, has not been as fortunate as its American cousin. This species also was widely hunted for its pelt and the castorum, and until recently it was vigorously persecuted as a pest harmful to crops, trees, and fish. The animal was at one time widely distributed in Europe and parts of Asia, but is now relatively rare. Most of this species live in burrows in the bank and do not build dams and lodges. Some biologists interpret this as a result of the persecution it has received from the human species, which may well be the case, since in relatively remote regions of Norway, Sweden, and Russia, the dam-building habit still exists. European beavers are now protected over a large part of their range, and they, too, may once again become numerous.

How Does the Beaver Use Its Tail?

The ways in which a beaver is popularly believed to use its tail are many and various. It is generally thought, for instance, that it carries mud on its tail, and also uses it as a plasterer's trowel; that the tail serves as a prop when the beaver is gnawing a tree or waddling about on its hind legs; and further that it warns other beavers of impending danger by striking the water resoundingly with its tail.

As a matter of unadorned fact, no one has ever seen a beaver carrying mud on its tail or using it as a trowel. The mud for its lodge is carried in the beaver's front paws, with which it is also applied.

The other tail stories are true. A beaver, when alarmed, will smack its tail against the water with a resulting report so loud that every other beaver in the vicinity can hear it and dive under water to safety. While gnawing a tree, a beaver usually squats on its hind legs, propping itself with its tail. It also uses its tail for support when, its front paws full of mud, it has to walk on its hind legs.

The broad naked tail of the beaver is a positive mark of identification. The tail of the muskrat, a smaller but similar water-inhabiting animal, is slenderer and flattened from side to side.

Do Trees Cut by Beavers Always Fall Toward the Water?

In their necessarily extensive tree-felling operations, beavers have gained the reputation of cutting trees so that they always fall toward the water, thus saving the supposedly intelligent beavers considerable effort in hauling the logs. However, most of the trees along the bank of a stream or lake have a tendency to lean toward the water, and will fall toward the water no matter what the beavers' desires are in the matter. But trees growing some distance from the water are straighter and when cut down by beavers will fall in any direction.

Can a Porcupine Shoot Its Quills?

It is commonly believed that the porcupine can purposely shoot its quills, puncturing the skin of any creature that approaches it. When a porcupine lashes its tail at an enemy, some loose spines may become detached and be thrown a short distance; under exceptional circumstances, they may even stick into an animal. The story of the porcupine's quill-shooting ability is probably based on such rare occurrences, but ordinarily it cannot harm anything that stays beyond reach. It is not capable of deliberately throwing or shooting its quills.

Nevertheless, its quills serve the porcupine as excellent defensive armor against the mountain lions, lynxes, and other animals that sometimes prey on it. Some of these animals have been killed and have been found to have so many quills in their mouths and throats that they were probably unable to eat. The fisher, a relative of the weasel, is one of the few animals that has solved the porcupine's defense. It calmly turns the porcupine over on its back and quickly slits the unprotected belly with its sharp claws.

How Do Porcupines Mate?

Because the belly of the porcupine is relatively free of spines, considerable curiosity and a number of weird surmises have been expressed regarding the mating habits of the animals. Actually, porcupines mate as do other mammals without quills. Fortunately for the male porcupine, the female can control the spines and, during mating, pulls them tightly against its body. Of course, the female must be entirely cooperative for the process to be successful, and most males seem to have learned this, or perhaps they are born with that instinctive knowledge. Whatever the case, the females are the aggressors during the mating season, while the males continue on their stolid grunting ways until approached by an ardent female.

Are Porcupines Born Headfirst?

The fact that porcupines have quills when they are born has led to the supposition that they must always be born headfirst to prevent injury to the mother. However, the position during birth makes no difference, for the young at birth are surrounded by a relatively tough membrane that protects the female from injury. There is a similar birth membrane around the young of most other mammals.

SHREWS, MOLES, AND HEDGEHOGS

The Prodigious Eater

Shrews are rather numerous in woods and fields, but they are so secretive in their habits that they are seldom seen by the average person. Anyone seeing a shrew for the first time might easily mistake it for a mouse. Most shrews are smaller than mice, however, and they have a sharper snout and smaller eyes. A few species get to be as large as a rat, but most are very small.

Shrews are more closely related to moles than to mice, and both shrews and moles are classified in a group called the insectivores. This name is used because much of the food of shrews and their relatives consists of insects. They will also eat worms, snails, lizards, and practically any animal that they can kill.

It is not easy to measure accurately the contributions of such tiny secretive animals, but most biologists agree that shrews are definite assets to man. For their size, their appetites are certainly among the lustiest in the world. Shrews are believed capable of eating their own weight in food every few hours, and if deprived of food, they will literally starve to death in less than a day.

A shrew does not hesitate to attack a mouse or other animal more than twice its size, and it frequently manages to kill its larger opponent. If they cannot find something else to fight, shrews will fight each other; except for mating pairs, more than one shrew is seldom found in the same spot.

A biologist once placed three shrews together in a cage, and they began fighting almost immediately. Very shortly one was killed and eaten by the other two. Within a few hours one of the remaining two had killed and eaten its companion. The biologist made the sedate observation that the abdomen of the victorious shrew was somewhat distended.

Some of the shrews are the smallest living mammals, and the Virginia shrew of the eastern United States is considered by many biologists to be the smallest species. This tiny mite has a body length of less than two inches and weighs about the same as a thin dime.

What Mammal Has a Poisonous Bite?

One of the most interesting biological discoveries within recent years was that a certain kind of shrew has a poisonous bite. An amusing sidelight on the whole affair is that many laymen already knew that some shrews have a poisonous bite, whereas biologists who took the trouble to consider the matter were sure that their bites are harmless. The results of experiments show conclusively that this time the laymen were right, and it will be surprising if the shrew population is not shortly depleted by biologists eager to test all species they can lay hands on.

The shrew whose bite has been definitely established as poisonous is the short-tailed American species, which is found throughout the eastern part of North America. Extracts prepared from the shrew's salivary glands and injected into rabbits and mice caused death within a short while, and mice bitten by the creature showed marked effects and remained in a depressed condition for some time. The venomous bite of the short-tailed shrew probably helps it to overcome the mice and other small rodents upon which it feeds. It appears quite possible that other small animals will also be found to have a poisonous bite, especially some of the European shrews whose bites are popularly thought to be poisonous.

Are Moles Blind?

Few people ever see a mole, but many see the results of their work in the form of irregular ridges of soil that may appear overnight in lawns or gardens. There are many different kinds of moles in the world, their average length being about 6 inches. Most live beneath the surface. They have enormously enlarged and otherwise modified front legs that are used for digging. The unsightly ridges are formed as the industrious mammals burrow through the soil in search of food. In good soil, moles may dig tunnels at the rate of 12 to 15 feet per hour, and as much as 75 to 100 yards within 24 hours.

Moles have eyes, but in many species the skin has grown over the eyeballs so that they are almost completely covered. These moles, which include the common and western moles of the United States, and certain European species, are essentially blind. They can perhaps distinguish between bright light and darkness, but are not able to define objects.

This near-blindness does not seem to handicap the little animals in the darkness of their burrows; their hearing is acute, and they are sensitive to ground vibrations. The nose and front feet are well supplied with sensory hairs which prevent the animals from bumping into the sides of their tunnels. A few kinds of moles that venture above ground more than their relatives have eyes somewhat better developed, and it may be that they can to some extent distinguish objects.

Although some moles cause a certain amount of local damage to lawns, plant roots, and bulbs the little mammals as a group do far more good than harm. The food of most species is composed of insects and similar organisms, and like shrews, the eating capacity of a mole is enormous. One captive mole greedily ate more than its own weight within 24 hours. The food consisted of 50 white grubs, 45 larvae of another beetle, 13 earthworms, and several other miscellaneous insects. It is believed that this is about the average rate of food consumption, and if so, each mole is capable of eating more than 50 pounds of insects per year. Even the burrowing activities of moles are often beneficial. The soil is stirred and aerated as a result; and in dry areas, much rain water passes into the burrows and is conserved.

At one time it was estimated that more than six million mole skins were sold per year in the world fur markets. The pelts were used for fur trimmings and even for complete coats. The skins of these tiny mammals are not so much in demand now, but hundreds of thousands are still sold each year. Most of the commercial mole fur is from the European species.

Are Hedgehogs Immune to Poisonous Snakes?

The hedgehog, a spiny-skinned little mammal of Europe related to moles and shrews, does appear to have actual immunity to the bites of some snakes. It has been seen to kill and eat the venomous European adder without suffering any ill effects if bitten during the process. But immunity is not the only weapon in the arsenal of the wily hedgehog. Observers have seen the hedgehog cautiously approach a snake, make a sudden bite and then quickly turn its back. The snake, if it is still able to move, usually responds by striking fiercely, only to find that its bite falls harmlessly and unpleasantly upon the hedgehog's sharp quills.

A P E S

Is There a Manlike Ape?

If we are to believe some fiction writers, there is a kind of manlike ape in Africa of the same general type as the chimpanzee, except that it is larger and considerably more intelligent. It is not a gorilla, for the gorilla sometimes appears in the stories as the villain. These fabulous apes are supposed to feed chiefly upon meat, and when a large animal is killed they hold a tribal dance. The females squat about in a circle and beat upon improvised drums, while the males dance themselves into a frenzy before they dismember and devour their prey. The males or bulls also amuse themselves by fighting, beating their chests with their fists, and roaring challenges to the moon.

Of course, no such humanoid ape exists. There are only three types of apes to which the term manlike can be sensibly applied—the gorilla, the chimpanzee, and the orangutan. The gibbon is classified with these others, but it is smaller and not so well known to the average person. All these apes are primarily vegetarians rather than meat eaters, although most of them are not averse to eggs, grubs or even small mammals and birds. None of them kills large animals for food, so far as is known, and although apes are sometimes found in family groups, there is no evidence that any of them ever hold tribal or ceremonial dances.

How Big Is the Biggest Ape?

The gorilla is by far the largest of the great apes, but there is no evidence that it ever reaches a height of nine feet, as some sensationally minded writers have maintained. Captive gorillas, thanks to the inactive life that they are forced to live, are usually heavier than wild specimens.

There have been quite a few gorillas kept in captivity for a number of years in zoological parks and circuses. The greatest established weights I have found for captive gorillas in the United States are Mbonga, 618 pounds; Nagagi, 585 pounds; and Gargantua, 500 pounds. Until the times of their deaths, Nagagi and Mbonga were both in the San Diego, California, Zoo, and Gargantua in a traveling circus.

The greatest accurate weight for a wild gorilla that I have noted is 460 pounds, the greatest height is 6 feet 3¾ inches for a specimen that was estimated to weigh 450 pounds. This great animal had a chest measurement of 61 inches and an arm span of 90 inches from tip to tip of its outstretched fingers. While the average man cannot be compared with the gorilla in most measurements, human beings have comparatively longer legs, and a great cranial capacity.

Even the orangutan, sometimes called the Old Man of the Mountains, occasionally gets quite heavy, at least in captivity. Andy, an orangutan in the New York Zoological Park, weighed a hefty 450 pounds a year or so ago; in fact, so hefty that he was put on a reducing diet. His rations were cut from one bucket of fruit and vegetables per day to three-quarters of a bucket. After several months of this Spartan diet, Andy weighed a mere 415 pounds. I do not know if he was ever reduced to the svelte 375 pounds for which his dieticians were striving.

Are Gorillas Dangerous?

There has been considerable discussion regarding the temperament and ferocity of gorillas, and for many years it was thought that they held a continuous open season on man. When the existence of these enormous apes first became established, it was firmly believed that they habitually watched jungle trails from overhanging trees so that they could seize and kill unwary human beings who passed beneath.

Several men have recently studied the habits of gorillas, and it is now known that many of the early ideas about them were far from true. Although gorillas do sometimes climb trees in search of fruit, and occasionally build nests in low bushes or trees for the females and young, they apparently do not travel through trees to any extent. Indeed, their great weight makes tree life impossible.

In the majority of cases, gorillas will melt quietly into the forest rather than attack a human being without provocation. But they will certainly bluff, and they may do everything short of attack in trying to frighten a human being away. They have been known to stir up a frightful noise by stamping their feet and thrashing around in the bushes. To top off these preliminaries, gorillas are apt to charge with bloodcurdling roars, only to stop short suddenly, just before attacking, and make off quietly into the forest.

There have been one or two instances, however, which show that an occasional gorilla may not need much excuse to attack a human being. The late Harry Raven, who killed one of the largest wild gorillas ever weighed, had a hair-raising experience collecting the animal. He was crawling under a fallen tree when a terrific roar sounded almost in his ear. Scrambling to his feet, he saw an enormous gorilla looming above him and coming fast. Raven fired quickly, and the gorilla fell, then staggered to its feet. He fired again and the great ape went down, this time for good, but only fifteen feet away. I do not believe that this gorilla was bluffing.

W H A L E S

What Is the Most Dangerous Animal in the Sea?

Killer whales fully deserve their name, and are aptly described as the wolves of the sea. Many people who have studied them consider them the most ferocious animals in the ocean. They prey upon seals, porpoises, fish, and similar creatures, and their appetites are enormous, although their maximum size is about 30 feet, which is not large, as whales go. The stomach of one, variously reported to be from 16 to 21 feet long, was found to contain thirteen seals and fourteen porpoises!

One might think that the size of the larger whales would make them immune to attack from any animal, but a pack of killer whales does not hesitate to challenge any whale that crosses its path. Peculiarly enough, they seem to prefer the tongues of these enormous whales. Eyewitnesses to combats between them have seen killer whales slash continuously at the mouths of the larger whales, tearing off pieces of flesh until the tongue of the victim was exposed. A few more rushes and the tongue was torn out, leaving the hapless whale a floating dying hulk. Roy Chapman Andrews saw killer whales attacking a group of California gray whales, a species that attains a length of 50 feet. He later had a chance to examine thirty-five of these gray whales and found that, of this number, seven had contributed their tongues to the insatiable appetites of the killers.

Killer whales will attack anything in the water, including human beings, and although I have not noted any instances of their having killed a man it very probably has happened. Herbert F. Pointing, on an antarctic expedition, had an unenviable experience with a herd of eight of these monsters. He was standing on an ice floe photographing them when the whole group dived under him. The block of ice heaved suddenly, broke into several parts, and the heads of the killer whales appeared between the broken pieces. The whales then attacked, trying to dislodge him as he made his way frantically from piece to piece of floating ice. Just as he jumped to solid ground, the head of one of the whales rose out of the water and hung with wide-open jaws over the spot he had just left. The other seven, one after the other, broke the surface, but after seeing that the man was rapidly putting a safe distance between himself and the water they quit the spot for more fertile fields.

Killer whales belong to the so-called toothed whales, a group that includes the sperm whale or cachalot, the narwhal, and several types of dolphins and porpoises. They are rather easily distinguished from most of their relatives by a large triangular top fin, and their bodies are conspicuously colored with black and white markings.

The World's Largest Animals Feed on Some of the Smallest

Whalebone or baleen whales are the largest animals alive, but they feed upon very small organisms such as shrimplike crustaceans known as krill, small fish, and similar creatures. It is obvious that an animal the size of a whale would have trouble filling its capacious stomach with such tiny food particles unless it had a special way to concentrate the material. The

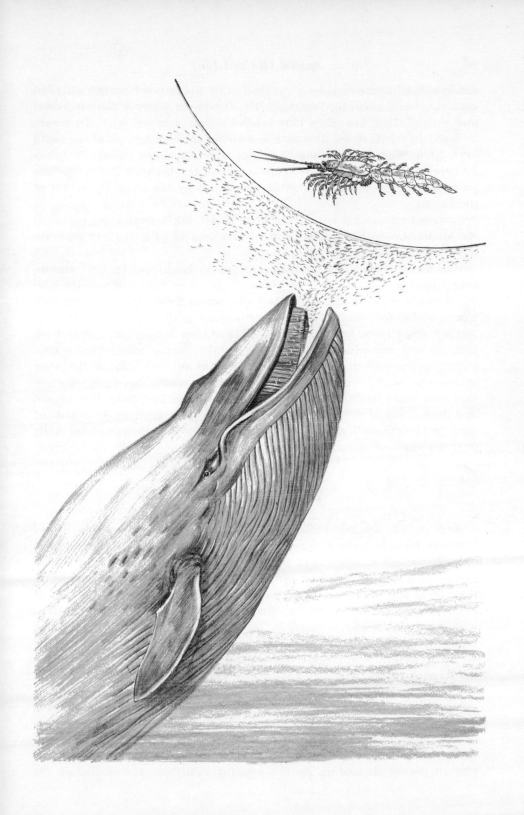

sheets of whalebone or baleen attached to its upper jaw help the whale in gathering these small food animals. The sheets are set very close together, and each of them has many long bristles attached to one edge. To secure its food, the whale opens its mouth and swims through schools of the small organisms. When it has a mouth full of water, it closes its mouth, raises its enormous tongue, and lets the water rush out between the plates, the particles of food being retained in the mouth by the straining action of the baleen.

So-called whalebone is not true bone at all, but a flexible horny material similar to the fingernails of man. The uses of whalebone to man are mentioned on the following page.

Whales, of course never ramble around on land, and for this reason, people have wondered how they obtain their water. One can imagine how much trouble even an ambitious biologist would have experimenting with a herd of 100-foot whales, and as a consequence, there is still much to be learned about these leviathans of the ocean. But some experiments have been carried out which indicate that whales, seals, and other aquatic mammals probably do not deliberately drink at all. It is believed that they get enough water from the aquatic organisms on which they feed, although they sometimes swallow sea water as they swallow their food. It is known that the kidneys of these aquatic mammals are more efficient than those of man, and it is thought that they excrete the excess salt taken in accidentally in this way.

What Is Ambergris?

Ambergris is a whale product now used chiefly in the manufacture of perfume. Its only known source is the digestive tract of the sperm whale or cachalot, but the details of its formation are not entirely understood. The presence of ambergris is generally considered evidence of illness on the part of the whale, and it probably is formed as a direct result of the animal's food habits. The sperm whale feeds principally upon large squids, whose mouths are surrounded by big horny beaks. Because undigested beaks are frequently found in a lump of ambergris, the theory is that they set up an irritation in the intestine or some other organ which stimulates the secretion of ambergris as a protective covering.

Aside from being found in the body of the whale itself, a lump of ambergris is sometimes discovered floating in the sea or washed up on a beach. presumably thrown off by a whale. Many seafaring men have felt their hearts jump into their mouths at the sight of a large, irregular-shaped grayish mass floating on the water, for the material is worth from $15 to $35 an ounce, depending on the amount available. The hearts of the majority, however, have shortly dropped into their boots when the substance was identified as a mass of soap, fat, or other valueless material. Nevertheless, anything found in the ocean or on the shore that resembles fat or soap should be taken for identification to a museum or university despite the possible apoplectic comments of the overworked staff.

Most pieces of ambergris that have been found have been rather small, but a few large masses have been discovered. The largest of which there is definite record weighed approximately 900 pounds, and was found near the coast of New Zealand. The largest piece known to have been taken from the body of a whale weighed about 750 pounds. This lump was found by the crew of a whaling ship and was probably of sufficient value to make the men forget all about whaling for the remainder of the voyage. A few years ago a 252-pound piece was found by two Long Island fishermen.

What Other Useful Products Are Obtained from Whales?

At one time whales were hunted for two principal resources: oil obtained from the fat or blubber, and baleen or whalebone that occurs in the mouths of certain species. The oil was used for light and fuel, and in the manufacture of paints. The whalebone was employed as stiffeners in bustles, for collars, umbrellas, and corsets. At the present time many more valuable products than formerly are obtained from whales, and very little of the body is discarded. The value of the products obtained varies somewhat with the many different species. Most important to the whaling industry are the sperm whale, the blue or sulphur bottom, the right whale, the humpback, and the finback. Porpoises and dolphins, which are sometimes caught on a small scale, are also members of the whale group.

The sperm is a type of toothed whale, so-called because it has true teeth. These teeth are in some demand as ivory.

The other important whales we have mentioned are all baleen or whalebone whales, named because they have strips of whalebone in their mouths rather than true teeth. At one time the right whale (named because it was considered to be the best or "right" whale) was the backbone of the whaling industry. But it was hunted so persistently that it is now relatively rare. Today the finback, which attains a length of 60 to 80 feet, is usually the species most frequently caught.

The value of individual whales, and the products obtained from them, vary with the size and species. Most large whales, however, if processed correctly, will probably yield products worth from $5,000 to $6,000 each.

Whale oil, a general term used for the oil from baleen whales, is still the most valuable single product usually obtained, but it is now used in many more ways than formerly. In Europe, whale oil has been used in the manufacture of margarine, but in the United States the cheaper vegetable oils are usually employed. The principal use of whale oils in the United States is in the manufacture of soaps and glycerine. Some of the material is also used in making candles and lard substitutes. Oils for delicate instruments, such as watches, are obtained from dolphins, blackfish, and porpoises.

Oil from sperm whales is not considered suitable for conversion into edible substances, but is valuable for other materials. The thinner oil is made into lubricants, and the thicker material known as spermaceti, is used in the manufacture of cosmetics.

All whale meat is edible, and the people of a few countries, such as Japan and Norway, have long included it in their diets. During World War II whale meat became popular in England as a substitute for beef and other scarce meats. It has been eaten in Canada and as a novelty in the United States. However, whale meat has seldom proved popular as a staple food when other meats are available.

In view of the efficiency of modern whaling methods and the large number of whales killed annually, it may seem strange that these enormous mammals have not become extinct. In 1953 a Japanese whaling fleet established a world record, catching 67 sperm whales in a single day —more than had ever been captured before in a similar period. Recently, whalers killed more than 40,000 whales in one season. Several factors including stricter hunting regulations, a short gestation period, and rapid maturity have operated to the whales' advantage in their battle to maintain the species. However, even stricter regulations will probably have to be applied eventually if the creatures are to survive.

What Is the Largest Animal That Ever Lived?

The sulphur bottom or blue whale is the largest animal alive today, and so far as is known, the largest animal that ever lived. The longest whale of which I have found authentic record measured 113 feet in length. Another more corpulent specimen of 89 feet was weighed aboard ship, piece by piece; it tipped the scales at approximately 300,707 pounds. Sperm whales, the largest of the toothed whales, do not grow as large as their toothless cousins. The largest sperm whale of which I have a record was a male that was washed ashore near Port Arthur, Texas, in 1910. It was 63½ feet long—without question a fine specimen—but Dr. H. H. Newman, the good professor who measured it, became too enthusiastic when he stated that the sperm whale was probably the largest animal that ever lived.

Some extinct reptiles belonging to the dinosaur group—the thunder beasts or thunder lizards—were very large, but there is no evidence that any of them approached the size of the blue whale. Several rather complete skeletons of these reptiles have been found, from which it has been possible to estimate the maximum size they attained. One of the largest known skeletons measures 87½ feet in length. It has also been estimated that the heaviest of the dinosaurs may have attained a weight of 50 tons which is considerably less than the known weights of several kinds of whales.

What Is the Biggest Baby in the World?

A young whale at birth is often almost half as long as its mother. A female sperm whale only 32 feet in length was found to contain a calf that was 14 feet 8 inches long. Another baby, taken from an 80-foot blue whale, was 25 feet in length and weighed 16,000 pounds. This tremendous size is possible only because the water in which the whales live helps to support the weight of the developing embryo. No land mammal could possibly carry such a large embryo. Indeed, the size which adult whales attain is possible only because they live in a supporting medium.

The whale's growth to maturity is unbelievably rapid. It may double its length within a year and, in some species, the female may become mature at the end of the second or third year of life. This rapid growth is probably one reason that whales have not become extinct as a result of the enormous numbers killed by man. It is thought that the pregnancy period is from 11 months to a year or so, but more observations on this point are needed.

How Are Young Whales Fed?

Young whales are fed on milk, like the young of other animals. Because the teats of the females are on the undersurface of the body near the rear end, for a long time it was a mystery how the young whale, which breathes air, could procure a meal without drowning. It is now known that at feeding time the huge mother rolls over on her side to bring the nipples close to the surface of the water. The young whale then grasps one of the nipples in its mouth, its nostrils remaining above the water. Special muscles pump the milk down its throat, which relieves it of the pulling effort that the human infant must exert.

How Does a Whale "Blow"?

The expression "thar she blows," shouted by a lookout in the crow's-nest of a whaling ship, is probably familiar to most people, who also generally take it to mean that the whale is spouting water from its nostrils. That is not what happens. Whales never deliberately take water into the breathing passages; if they did, they would drown just as surely as would a human being. When a whale starts to dive or sound, it fills it lungs with air, which it retains while it is under water; then when it comes to the surface it expels the air with some force, or "blows." The air that is expelled, warmed and moistened from being in the whale's lungs, condenses on contact with the colder outside air and forms streams of vapor resembling water which can be seen for some distance. The same thing happens on a small scale when our own breaths condense on a cool frosty morning. If the whale happens to blow a short distance below the water surface, a considerable amount of water may be carried upward with the escaping air; and people seeing this have thought that the water came from the whale's nostrils.

How Deep Can Whales Dive?

Protected as they are from the terrific pressure of the water by a layer of fat or blubber sometimes 20 inches thick just beneath the skin, whales can dive to tremendous depths. This was suspected long before it was proved, since the large squids upon which the sperm whale feeds are usually found in very deep water. Positive proof of the whale's deep-diving ability, however, was obtained when in 1932 a blundering sperm whale became entangled in a submarine cable on the ocean floor, 3,200 feet down. The cable was broken and, when it was hauled to the surface for repairs, the drowned whale was still caught in it. Some authorities believe that whales can dive even deeper than this.

Such an accomplishment by a mere flesh-and-blood mammal may be appreciated when we note that this sperm whale reached a depth almost 200 feet deeper than that reached in 1934 by the famous metal bathysphere, an object especially made for deep-sea diving. Especially constructed diving globes have now passed the 35,000 foot mark, and it is doubtful if even the fabulous sperm whale will be able to do better than that.

Can a Whale Swallow a Man?

The question of whether or not a whale can swallow a man has been discussed since the time of Jonah. As far as Jonah is concerned, there is also the problem of whether a whale or fish was involved. It is not possible for the whalebone or toothless whales to swallow a man, because their throats are less than a foot in diameter. Any human being larger than a small child or a midget would cause them considerable embarrassment if they were to become ambitious enough to try. Small penguins are the largest animals that have ever been found in the stomach of a toothless whale.

The great sperm whale or cachalot, however, is an entirely different matter, for the throat of this whale is large enough to swallow a man whole. Captured sperm whales have been found to contain pieces of squid larger than the body of a human being.

Some people doubt that there are any verified accounts of a whale's swallowing a man, but two reports are of interest. In 1891 the boat of a whaling ship was upset by the flip of the tail of a large sperm whale, and when the crew was rescued one of the men was missing. Despite this loss, however, the rest of the men rallied and several hours later captured the whale that had wrecked their boat. They fell to work upon the carcass, and by the next morning they had reached the innards of the creature. Deciding to remove the whale's stomach, they hauled it on deck. Something inside started to move, much to everyone's astonishment, and when they opened it up there was their lost comrade, unconscious, but still with sufficient vitality to have made the movement that saved him. The man eventually recovered, so the story goes, but parts of his skin remained a dead white color for the rest of his life, supposedly as a result of the action of the whale's gastric juices upon the body surfaces not protected by clothing.

The most unbelievable part of the whole story is that the man should have been alive after he had been in the whale's stomach for so many hours. Perhaps the whale obligingly swallowed enough air for the man's needs, and his nostrils conveniently remained above the digestive juices while the rest of his face was being digested!

An account of a whale swallowing a man appeared some time ago in *Natural History Magazine*, related by a man who was allegedly a former ship's surgeon. According to the story, a sperm whale swallowed one of the crewmen. The whale was later captured and the badly mangled body of the man was recovered. However, later investigation by Dr. Edward M. Weyer, then editor of the magazine, indicated that the storyteller used a fictitious name. Chances are good that this instance never did occur.

Did the Unicorn Ever Exist?

The unicorn, according to mythology, was a horselike creature with a single horn growing from its forehead. No such creature has ever existed; but the term unicorn or unicorn fish is sometimes applied to the narwhal, a type of toothed whale, which grows to a length of 15 or 16 feet and is found primarily in arctic waters. The peculiar development of one of its teeth is responsible for the name of unicorn. At birth, both male and female narwhals have a few teeth, but they very shortly degenerate, except for two in the upper jaw. These two seldom become functional in the female, but in the male the left tooth continues to grow. It grows forward straight through the upper jaw and lip, spiraling upon itself in a clockwise direction. The right tooth normally does not develop even in the male, but occasional specimens have been collected in which both teeth had grown into tusks, and for some unknown reason both the tusks spiraled in the same direction. Exact measurements are scant, but it is probable that the tusks sometimes grow to a length of 9 to 10 feet.

The function of this enormous tooth is not definitely known. There have been reports that it is used as a weapon for fighting, for punching holes in the ice, and for spearing fish, but, so far as I am aware, none of these reports has been confirmed.

The narwhal has figured rather conspicuously in connection with the mythical unicorn of European folklore. Norsemen from Iceland, where the narwhals were at one time rather numerous, collected some of the teeth and took them to Europe, trading them as genuine unicorn horns to the delighted Europeans. The chances are that no true description was given of the original owner of the "horn," since, according to mythology, the unicorn was supposed to be a graceful, horselike creature, not at all like the legless, clumsy, blunt-faced narwhal.

SEA COWS

How Did the Mermaid Legend Originate?

The story of mermaids is one of the oldest legends to be told by seafaring men. According to romantic descriptions these fabulous creatures have the faces and bodies of beautiful women, while the legs and feet have been replaced by fishlike tails. Strangely, descriptions of male mermaids or mermen seldom appear, possibly because the originators of the stories were more interested in the fair sex during a long ocean voyage.

Such creatures do not exist, but animals live in the ocean that could very well have been the basis for the story. There are a few species of aquatic mammals, called sea cows, that are found along the coasts of various areas of the world. These include the dugong, widely distributed in parts of the Indian Ocean and near the shores of Australia, and two kinds of manatee occurring in the rivers and along the coast of South America, and sometimes are found in Florida. Although even a drunken sailor could not mistake the face of a sea cow for that of a beautiful maiden

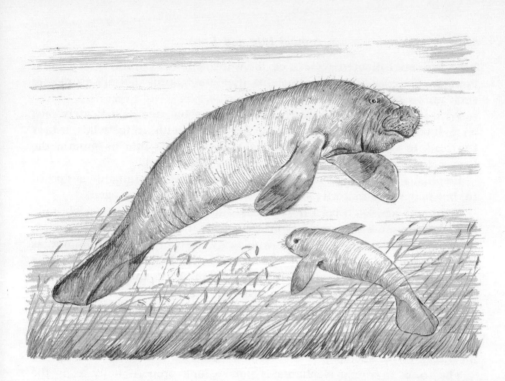

at close range, it is believed that these animals are responsible for the mermaid story. When the creatures come to the surface to breathe, they stick their rounded heads above the surface, and they may remain in this upright position for some time. At a distance the head might easily be mistaken for that of a human being, and this resemblance is heightened when a female appears at the surface holding a youngster in her front flipper. A nearer view of such a female would certainly cause the observer to hope that this ugly old sea hag was only the nurse maid carrying the youngster out for a stroll, although it is a mystery how anyone could think that any relative of the youngster could possibly be beautiful.

ELEPHANTS

Do Elephants Drink Through Their Trunks?

Elephants do not drink through their trunks, as people sometimes suppose, but they do suck water up into their trunks and then squirt it into their mouths. They also use their trunks as a spray. If undisturbed, they may spend hours in a lake or river enjoying the cooling and cleansing effect of the water. Captive elephants who were being teased by human beings have been known to fill their trunks with water and squirt it firehose fashion full in the faces of their tormentors. Contrary to popular opinion, however, a young elephant uses its mouth—not its trunk—to suck milk from its mother's teats.

With its trunk an elephant can pull down a big tree or delicately pick a small peanut from the floor and pop it into its mouth. In the wilds, it uses its trunk to strip from trees and bushes, and thrust into its mouth, the leaves, twigs, and other vegetation upon which it feeds.

Elephants do not grow nearly so slowly as they are commonly supposed to, but may reach maturity when twelve to fifteen years of age.

Elephants are often born in captivity, and one of the most widely publicized of these events occurred in the Zoological Park in Portland, Oregon, in 1962. According to reports, the whole city knew of the situation, and as the time approached, radio bulletins kept the populace up to date as to the condition of the expectant mother. At last in April, the birth occurred, and all interested parties including the attending veterinarians, the elephant "midwives"—female elephants that took an interest in the affair —the general public, and the mother, doubtless breathed a sigh of relief. The youngster is said to have weighed 225 pounds, and to have measured 35 inches at the shoulder.

The trunk in young elephants is not so long proportionally as is the adult's, and observers say that it is an almost useless appendage, continually getting in the way until the elephant has learned how to use it. I doubt whether even a biologist would have the patience to count the number of muscles in an elephant's trunk, but one writer says that there are more than 40,000. In view of the varied and manifold ways in which an elephant employs its trunk, this seems a reasonable estimate.

Circuses Use Indian Elephants

The elephants seen in circuses are almost invariably Indian rather than African elephants. African elephants are not domesticated to the extent that Indian elephants are; consequently, the former species are much more difficult to obtain.

It is not difficult to distinguish between these two kinds of elephants. In profile, the back of the Indian elephant is strongly arched, and there is a definite depression between the head and the shoulders. In the African species there is no depression, and the back is not arched. The highest point of the back of an African elephant is just above the shoulders instead of near the center of the back. Also, African elephants have larger ears than the Indian species; in large males they may be more than 3 feet wide. Finally, there are four toenails on each of the hind feet of the Indian elephant, while its African cousin has but three.

How Do Elephants Use Their Tusks?

Elephants' tusks are modified teeth, the longest and heaviest teeth in the entire animal kingdom. They are used in fighting and in digging up roots, bulbs, and similar plant products that elephants eat. It has also been reported that the African species occasionally picks up the young elephants with its tusks and carries them for some distance.

Practically all male African elephants have tusks, and even the female often develops them. The female Indian elephant, however, seldom has tusks and even the male of this species is frequently without them.

The longest known tusks from present-day elephants are a pair from an African elephant now in the National Collection of Heads and Horns, of the New York Zoological Society. The longest of the pair measures 11 feet 5½ inches; its mate, 11 feet. Their combined weight is 293 pounds, which is rather light for such long tusks. The heaviest tusk known is in the British Museum and weighs 226½ pounds, and the second of the pair weighs 214, for a combined record weight of 440½ pounds.

The tusks of some of the extinct mammoths were much longer than those of living elephants. The longest known tusk is one from an imperial mammoth and is a fraction of an inch over 16 feet. Discovered in Texas several years ago, this enormous tooth is now on display in the American Museum of Natural History.

Besides being longer, the tusks of the mammoths were considerably more curved than those of present-day elephants. In some species the tusks grew outward and downward from the base, then curved inward toward each other. Frequently, the ends of the tusks crossed in front of the head. In long tusks, the curvature was sometimes so great that the points were directed back toward the bases of the tusks. It is difficult to understand how they could have been of use to their owners at this stage.

Are Elephants Afraid of Mice?

It is popularly believed that an elephant is extremely afraid of mice, presumably because it fears the mouse might get into the end of its trunk and either suffocate it or injure the delicate inner lining of the nasal passages. But the actions of elephants in zoological gardens and circuses do not confirm this belief. Mice are frequently seen running about in elephants' stalls, sometimes very close to the ends of their trunks, but the elephants totally disregard them. Since their eyesight is rather poor, it is possible that they cannot see a mouse at a distance; but since their sense of smell is one of the keenest in the entire animal kingdom, the chances are that they can smell it, small as it is, especially when it is only a few inches from the end of the trunk. In any case, it is very doubtful whether a mouse could cause an elephant much injury, even if the rodent had the courage to crawl into the end of the trunk. In all probability the elephant would simply take a deep breath, blow vigorously through the trunk and splatter the mouse over the walls of the stall.

Do Elephants Ever Forget?

Elephants do have a good memory, and some of them may remember an injury for a long time. The late Dr. Raymond Ditmars used to tell of an elephant in the New York Zoological Park which, for some unknown reason, took an intense dislike to one of the attendants. The attendant left the park, but returned some years later. When he visited the elephant house, he was almost instantly recognized by the enraged elephant, which tried to break out of the enclosure to get at him. But the elephant's memory has been considerably exaggerated. The process of training wild elephants may be quite severe, and if they never forgot injuries and abuse very few of them would ever be tamed. Some elephants doubtless have better memories than others, but that an elephant never forgets is a statement without foundation.

Have Elephants a Common Graveyard?

All old and dying elephants have a special place where they go to die, according to legend. However, no such graveyard has ever been found except in movies and highly imaginative stories, and the chances are that the acres and acres of tusks supposedly reposing therein exist only in dreams. Why, then, are dead elephants never found? The answer is that they are sometimes found, despite popular belief to the contrary. The bodies of those elephants that are never found are probably quickly eaten by the other animals of the jungle, and their skeletons and tusks rapidly covered by forest litter and growing vegetation.

How Large Are Elephants?

Elephants are the largest living land animals. Jumbo, the African elephant that toured with a circus many years ago, was certainly the most publicized and ballyhooed elephant the world has ever known. For this reason many people believe that Jumbo was the largest elephant that ever lived.

So far as I know, Jumbo's height and weight were never made public during his life, although at least one well known biologist, who requested permission to measure the elephant, was turned down flatly by the outraged owners. It is believed, however, that in life Jumbo measured 11 feet to 11 feet 6 inches at the shoulder.

Several wild elephants have measured higher at the shoulder, including one of 12 feet 4 inches, which held the record for some years. Then, in 1955, an elephant was killed in Angola, in southwestern Africa, that topped all previous records by almost a foot. This enormous pachyderm measured 13 feet 2 inches at the shoulder, and weighed an estimated twelve tons. The skin, which weighed more than two tons, was shipped to the United States where it took several years to get it properly mounted. The lifelike figure, depicting an alert elephant moving along with trunk and ears extended, was unveiled in March 1959. Today the elephant stands in the rotunda of the Natural History Building of the Smithsonian Institution, Washington D. C., a model of the world's largest present-day land animal.

At least two extinct mammals were somewhat larger than living elephants. These include the imperial mammoth, which probably attained a shoulder height of more than 14 feet, and an extinct rhinoceros, *Baluchitherium* (p. 42).

RHINOCEROSES

How Dangerous Is a Rhinoceros?

There are several different kinds of rhinoceroses in existence. The largest of these include two African species, the black and the white rhinoceroses, and the Indian rhinoceros of India and adjacent countries.

The black African and the Indian species have the worst reputation for unprovoked attacks, and there has been considerable debate among big game hunters as to the dangers of hunting them. Some believe that rhinoceroses are the most dangerous of all animals, whereas others insist that hunting these big mammals is no more dangerous than hunting ducks.

Of African mammals, most hunters consider the elephant, lion, buffalo, hippopotamus, and black rhinoceros the most dangerous; the black rhinoceros has been ranked both at the head and at the foot of this list. The rhinoceros has a good sense of smell and hears well, but its eyesight is supposedly on a par with that of a nearsighted man who has lost his spectacles. And, it has been claimed by some that because of poor eyesight, the rhinoceros solves the problem of distinguishing friend from foe by treating any disturbing element as an enemy. Others believe that many so-called charges are actually retreats, but that because of relative blindness these retreats take place in the wrong direction. One thing is certain, any man or animal in the path of such a charge, accidental or not, would very likely be spitted by a horn or trampled in the dust.

I feel, therefore, that the larger species of rhinoceroses are dangerous, if for no other reason than that their actions are unpredictable. One or two happenings should help to confirm this point of view. When roads were first built through rhinoceros country, there were many reports of their blindly charging automobiles and reducing the cars to wreckage, and there is at least one record of an irate rhino's actually attacking a train. The passengers were made rudely aware of the attack by a tremendous jolt and, looking out of a window, saw a rhinoceros scramble to its feet and stagger off with much snorting and head shaking.

White rhinoceroses are not considered to be as pugnacious as their black cousins, but the following story, related by a hunter, shows that even they can be dangerous if provoked. The hunter, on horseback, sighted a fine male some distance away. Putting spurs to his horse, he came within shooting distance, took aim and fired and expected the rhinoceros either to fall dead or retreat as members of this species often do. But this rhinoceros had other ideas. It lowered its head and charged the horse and rider so quickly that they could not escape the rush. The longest horn caught the horse in the side, completely penetrated its body, and struck the man's leg on the other side. Horse and rider went down in a scrambled heap, but fortunately the hunter managed to disentangle himself in time to kill the rhinoceros before it could finish what it had started.

As this story would suggest, the horns of a rhinoceros are lethal weapons, and they are much in demand as big game trophies. To a white rhinoceros, and a female at that, must be awarded the prize for having produced the longest rhinoceros horn known. This prize trophy, collected in South Africa, is 62¼ inches in length and it has a maximum girth of 22¼ inches. Its nearest competitor, also from a white rhinoceros, has a length of 56½ inches. The horns of other species are shorter than those of the white rhinoceros, but one black rhinoceros horn of 53½ inches is on record.

The blundering rhinoceros has not escaped the eagle eyes of certain mixers of alleged drugs. A good rhinoceros horn has been known to bring as much as $2,000 in an Oriental market. A cup made from such a horn is supposed to purify a poisonous drink, and some believe that it will even detect the poison. Powder made from the horn is mixed with various concoctions and taken as a medicine for a variety of ills. The powdered material is also much in demand by aged individuals as a reputed aphrodisiac.

It has often been stated that, aside from the elephant, the white rhinoceros is the largest living land mammal. The authors of such positive statements seem to have forgotten that overgrown pig, the hippopotamus. In spite of short dumpy legs and a shoulder height of 5 feet, as opposed to a shoulder height of 6½ feet for the rhinoceros, the weight of the hippo is remarkable. One in the London Zoo is said to have weighed 8,600 pounds.

BEARS, WOLVES, CATS, AND OTHER CARNIVORES

How Dangerous Are Bears?

There are many species of bears scattered throughout the world, and these vary considerably in temperament. Some are easily trained, and make attractive circus and carnival performers. Others are so grumpy that teaching them to perform is a virtual impossibility. European bears are among the most easily trained and the famous dancing and performing bears are mostly of these species.

If unprovoked, bears as a group are not considered to be as dangerous as several other kinds of animals. Most are not aggressive unless wounded or cornered, and they usually avoid man if given half a chance. A majority of the reportedly unprovoked attacks, upon investigation, proved to have been made by wounded bears, or by those that apparently thought their homes, their food supply, or their young were in danger.

The North American species considered most dangerous are the polar bears and the grizzlies. The grizzly group includes the true grizzly of the United States and Canada and several brown bears that are found in Alaska and on some of the adjacent islands.

At least one big game hunter considers the Alaskan bear the most dangerous wild animal in North America, and he has awarded it eighth place among the most dangerous mammals of the world. Even the smaller grizzly has been known to break the neck of a bull bison with a single blow of its paw.

A farmer in Montana once caught a grizzly bear in a trap, and proudly announced to his wife that he was going out to finish off the victim. No one saw the details of the tragedy, but a day later the badly mutilated body of the man was found, with signs indicating that the bear had broken free of the trap, killed the man, and escaped. The biologist who wrote this story stated that although it showed how dangerous bears could be, he still believed that the grizzly is relatively harmless if left alone.

Although bears occasionally kill people, most species seldom do so for food. Polar bears are exceptions. These bears eat a greater percentage of meat than other species. Their normal food consists of young walrus, seals, caribou, and practically any animal they can catch. When the usual food is plentiful, polar bears often disregard human beings, but in remote regions, when food is scarce, these bears seem to regard people as legitimate prey.

The black bear, most common species in the United States, is not thought to be as dangerous normally as the other species. However, there are several instances of black bears injuring tourists who, against the rules, were feeding them in national parks. There are also cases of these bears' attacking human beings unprovoked.

Do Bears Hibernate?

Bears are said to hibernate during the winter, particularly during the extremely cold weather in the northern parts of their range. Strictly speaking, however, the winter sleep of bears is not true hibernation. Their temperatures and breathing remain relatively normal, and during warm spells some bears may emerge and remain outside for a day or so before returning to their sleeping quarters. Bears are much more easily disturbed during their winter sleep than is commonly thought, and may scare the wits out of a trustful human being who approaches too closely. If the investigator is persistent, he may be severely injured by the outraged bear whose sleep he has disturbed.

The cubs are born during this winter sleep. If one considers the size of the parents, they are very poor excuses for offspring, being smaller than the young of a porcupine and sometimes weighing no more than six or eight *ounces* at birth.

Although polar bears are exposed to far worse weather conditions than other bears, only pregnant females sleep during the winter. They dig a hole in the ice and snow and remain there for several months, during which time the young are born and develop sufficiently to be taken outside.

The Bear Hug

According to popular fiction, when a bear attacks it first seizes its victim and squeezes him to death with the famous "bear hug," and then devours him. However, there is no evidence to back up the story at all. A bear kills with its front paws—with which it can strike one of the most lethal blows in the animal kingdom—sometimes aided by claws and teeth. Inasmuch as a bear has been known to break the neck of a huge bison bull with a single blow, it is apparent that it would be ridiculous for it to try to kill any animal or human being by squeezing it to death.

Grizzly bears seldom eat human beings whom they have killed, although they will eat anything else, from insects to putrid flesh.

Can Adult Bears Climb Trees?

Bears have a reputation as tree climbers, and I well remember listening as a child to an elderly friend describe how he climbed a tree with a bear after him. In this particular escapade, according to my friend, the bear pursued him to the topmost branches and, balked by the smaller limbs, was trying to shake him from the tree when friends arrived conveniently and shot it.

The black bear is an excellent tree climber, even as an adult, and will sometimes sleep astride a limb barely large enough to support its weight, but grizzlies seldom climb trees even when they are young. Thus the only bears in North America that would normally be able to climb a tree after a man are the black bears. These creatures are usually inoffensive, however, and I have never heard of an authentic instance of their doing so.

A completely different association between black bears and trees has recently come to the attention of irate lumbermen in the state of Washington. For some reason, bears have developed a fondness for the cambium layer of young Douglas fir trees, and in getting to this juicy layer, the culprits may completely girdle the tree, thus dooming it to death. It has been found that one black bear may damage as many as twenty trees in twenty-four hours.

This development obviously made lumbermen most unhappy, and as a consequence, the game commission of the state removed all protection from black bears in five counties of the Olympic Peninsula in northwestern Washington. In 1961 professional trappers and hunters killed at least 336 bears by actual count. To sportsmen this seems like needless slaughter of a valuable game animal, but no one has come up with a better suggestion for the protection of the young trees in the region.

How Much Do Grizzly Bears Weigh?

One cannot read much about grizzly bears before coming upon a statement that someone has killed one weighing from 1,700 to 1,800 pounds. Most of these alleged weights are based upon hunters' estimates, and the following instance illustrates why the estimates should be regarded with suspicion. Several years ago a very large grizzly bear in a zoological park was weighed and found to tip the scales at 1,153 pounds. Several hunters who saw it admitted that it was larger than some which they had estimated to weight 1,800 pounds. This captive specimen is probably the largest grizzly bear that has ever been weighed by an unbiased person, and it was doubtless considerably fatter than it would have been in the wild state.

The great brown bears of Alaska, relatives of the grizzlies, are larger than the true grizzlies, but even they fall short of the fabulous 1,800 pounds mark. The largest specimen of which I am aware weighed 1,656 pounds; and it is said that they sometimes attain a length of 10 feet 6 inches. The polar bears are close competitors of the brown bears in size, and some people believe that they may even be larger. They too have been measured at 10 feet 6 inches, and weights of approximately 1,600 pounds have been recorded.

Will Wolves Attack Human Beings?

Most of the gruesome stories about wolves that adorn the pages of literature have dealt with the species of Europe and Asia, and many of these apparently originated in Russia, Austria, and adjacent countries. The United States and Canada, however, have contributed a share of legends about North American wolves. According to popular opinion, largely influenced by these blood-curdling accounts, wolves prefer human flesh to all other food.

The United States Fish and Wildlife Service has published a report covering twenty-five years' careful investigation of stories about wolves attacking human beings. None of these accounts was ever verified.

Since the publication of this book, however, there occurred a reasonably well-documented case of a single wolf attacking an unarmed man in Ontario, Canada. Fortunately, help arrived in time to save the victim.

There is still disagreement among experts, both real and self-styled, on the question of the possible dangers of wolves in Europe and Asia. European and Asiatic wolves, it seems, are more likely to be dangerous than those of North America.

Wolves in the past were widely distributed over North America, Europe, and parts of Asia. They were exterminated from the British Isles several hundred years ago and now occur in very limited areas of the United States. They still occur in some numbers in parts of Europe, Asia, Canada, and Alaska. With the recent emphasis in the United States upon the training of army personnel to withstand the rigors of cold climates, the demand for wolf pelts for cold weather clothing has greatly increased.

The animal makes another small contribution to man's well being. The best arctic dog teams are those that are part wolf. Captive wolves are crossed with sled dogs and the breeding of the offspring is controlled to achieve the desired combination.

The wolf is a powerful predator that sometimes attains a weight of 175 pounds. The animals often run in family groups that are capable of pulling down large game animals. In the far north caribou are their principal food, whereas various kinds of deer, rabbits, and even smaller game are taken in some regions. Most situations that have been investigated show that wolves are not a serious menace to herds of deer and other big game animals. In some instances they have even been regarded as beneficial in reducing excess populations of other animals on limited ranges.

The wolf is the only animal that has been deliberately exterminated from all national parks in the United States. This action was taken some years ago and is probably regretted now by government officials.

Today ranchers and stockmen in the United States seldom have to worry about the depredations of wolves, but this has not always been true. Wolves are among the cleverest of mammals in avoiding traps, poison baits, and the guns of irate cattlemen, and many are the tales of individual wolves living for years on cattle and horses before they were finally killed. One such outlaw, called Three Toes because of a maimed foot, was claimed to have destroyed $25,000 to $50,000 worth of stock during his infamous career.

Should the Coyote Be Exterminated?

Ever since the white man moved west of the Mississippi River, the coyote has been one of the most hated of animals. For years this creature has been the target of traps, poison baits, special gadgets called coyote-getters, and the guns of government hunters and irate stockmen. The numbers of coyotes have been reduced in some sections, but coyotes do not seem to be in any immediate danger of extinction.

At one time these animals were confined to central and western United States, but recently they have spread east and north. Many people believe that this range extension was due to the persecution the coyotes received in their original home. Established populations now occur in many eastern states and across Canada into Alaska.

The food habits of coyotes have probably been studied as much as those of any other mammal. They seem to have a preference for meat, but they will eat anything from vegetables to garbage. Living animals that they consume include rats, mice, rabbits, ground squirrels, prairie dogs, and, unfortunately, sheep, goats, and cattle. Coyotes weigh only twenty to thirty pounds as a rule, and probably because of their relatively small size, most of their attacks on livestock are directed against sheep and goats. They will sometimes pull down a calf, and they have been known to develop a liking for chickens, turkeys, and other birds.

In the considered opinion of many investigators the normal food habits of most coyotes are more beneficial than harmful, but occasionally villainous habits are developed by individuals. The coyote problem is usually a local one, and although this may be serious, it is doubtful if this should be taken as an excuse to persecute the whole coyote clan.

Coyotes that have been crippled by traps, or those that are old, often take the easiest path by turning to livestock as their source of food. One crippled coyote was blamed for most of the killing over a two-year period of 448 goats owned by three ranchers in California. Even biologists, who have not lost valuable livestock to hungry coyotes, must admit the necessity for control.

But what can be said in favor of these yapping denizens of the West? About twenty years ago, irate citizens in central California put on an unrestricted wholesale poisoning campaign against coyotes. They succeeded in killing many coyotes, as well as numerous other predators, such as foxes and skunks. The poisoners were settling back to enjoy the fruits of their slaughter when there erupted over the countryside an unprecedented plague of mice. More than 82,000 mice per acre were estimated as the hungry rodents ate everything in their paths. Even a sheep, in an enclosure that prevented its escape, was overwhelmed by sheer numbers and eaten by the little demons. Millions of dollars worth of grain and other products were destroyed, and tons of mice were killed before they were brought under control.

The coyote-control campaign was apparently an important factor in the mouse plague, but it cannot be stated positively that this was the only cause. Food supply, weather, reproductive activities, and many other things probably contribute to such outbreaks, and in most cases it is not possible to say which single factor is the most important.

Extensive studies of coyote stomachs and droppings have shown, as might be expected, that the food varies in different situations and localities. It has been found that even in stock country a majority of the food is made up of rabbits and harmful rodents, although livestock remains do appear now and then. In game preserves, rodents are preferred in the fall, spring, and summer, but in winter some deer, elk, and other big game are taken, One investigator claims that much of the game eaten by coyotes consists of weak or dying animals. The general conclusion has been reached that, away from livestock, coyote feeding habits are about 70 per cent beneficial, 18 per cent neutral, and 11 or 12 per cent harmful.

Coyotes not only make a considerable contribution to the control of harmful rodents; they are also important scavengers. The scavenger role is especially noteworthy in protected, overcrowded refuges where starvation takes its toll of deer and other game animals.

At the present time, state and government hunters kill numerous coyotes, and the bounty system is still in effect in many states. Thousands of the animals are killed annually, but some people believe that the number killed simply keeps the population static, rather than reducing it materially. Thanks to the cunning and resourcefulness of the average coyote, the mammal seems destined to remain a permanent resident of our western states.

How Does a Cat Purr?

Purring is caused by the vibration of the cat's vocal cords. When air is taken into the lungs, it passes through the voice box that contains the vocal cords. Purring is, of course, under the control of the cat. When it wishes to express its contentment, the vocal cords are allowed to vibrate as the air passes in and out of the lungs during breathing. When the cat is asleep, or if it does not want to purr for some reason, the passage of air does not affect the vocal cords and no purr is produced.

The Cat of Many Aliases

The cougar has a wider distribution than any other American land mammal, which probably explains why it is known by so many different names. Cougar, puma, panther, mountain lion are among the most familiar designations, although catamount and painter are also used. At one time these mammals were widely distributed in southern Canada, the United States, Mexico, Central and South America. Now essentially eliminated from many civilized sections, they are still fairly numerous in remote areas.

There are those who believe that cougars are no more dangerous than rabbits, and this might be true for most of these big cats. But there are notable exceptions. One of the most clearly established modern instances of an attack on a human being occurred in the state of Washington in 1924. The victim was a boy of 13 who was attacked during the day on his way home from a neighboring ranch. When he failed to arrive home, a search was made and his partly eaten body discovered. Tracks in the snow showed that the killer was a mountain lion. An organized hunt failed to find the villain, but sometime later a cougar was caught in a trap a few miles from the scene of the tragedy. The stomach contained bits of clothing and a trinket known to have been carried by the boy.

In 1951 a newspaper account from Campbell River, British Columbia, Canada reported that a 63-year-old man had been attacked by a cougar. In this case the big cat had hurled itself through a window to get at its victim. The man fought it bare-handed until he managed to reach a butcher knife, which he used to stab the mountain lion. This distracted the attacker so that the badly mangled man could stagger outside in search of help. He ultimately found assistance; two men returned to the scene and dispatched the wounded cougar which was still in the cabin.

The incident of the trapper was one of a series of verified cougar attacks in this part of Canada over a period of several years. Such incidents are apparently rare, and just what impels the occasional cougar to attack a person is not known. It is thought that excessive hunger, mistaken identity, and possibly rabies have all been important factors.

Cougars feed upon a variety of wild and domestic animals, but deer seem to be their favorite food. Under most conditions mountain lions do not seriously reduce the number of deer. The occasional cougar that develops a taste for livestock, has brought the wrath of man down on the whole race. The big cats often kill much more than they can possibly eat. In Colorado some years ago, one cougar killed 192 sheep in a single night, and another accounted for 45 sheep and goats within 48 hours. Colts are one of their favorite foods and in the early days it was practically impossible to raise horses successfully in parts of California because of the depredations of the carnivores.

While admitting that stock-eating mountain lions should be controlled, most biologists do not believe that these predators can be completely eliminated without seriously upsetting the balance of nature. Most of the deer killed by cougars have been shown to be deformed, diseased, or otherwise below par, and the removal of these unhealthy individuals is considered beneficial. The cougars help to keep the deer population from becoming too abundant on limited range. Therefore, no attempt has been made to exterminate cougars in our national parks.

The animals vary considerably in size, generally weighing from 100 to 175 pounds, but extra large specimens may weigh more. The greatest reasonably authentic weight I have noted was 276 pounds, although several have been known to weigh over 200 pounds. In size, the cougar must take second place among North American cats. The jaguar of Central and South America, Mexico, and the southwestern United States is larger, and, among cats of the world, is surpassed in size only by the tiger and the lion.

There seems to be a general agreement that in parts of South America the cougar is temperamentally different from its brothers and sisters farther north. There are numerous reports to the effect that even a cornered South American specimen does not defend itself from man, but simply resigns itself to its fate. There are also stories that mountain lions have tried to make friends with people by approaching travelers with the playful attitude of kittens.

What Mammal Is the Greatest Man-Killer?

Tigers probably kill more human beings than any other mammal. During one year 882 people were recorded as being killed in India alone by the big cats.

Authorities agree that a majority of tigers turn to man because circumstances make it difficult for them to kill their usual prey. One well-known hunter claims specifically that nine out of ten man-eating tigers have developed the habit because of wounds, and that the tenth does so because of old age.

The wounds that presumably cause tigers to become man-eaters may appear relatively insignificant. For instance, one tiger that killed 24 people before being killed itself was found to have several porcupine quills in one of its paws. This probably caused the difference between successful and unsuccessful pursuit of its normal food.

Once a tiger gets a taste of human flesh, and realizes how easily this potential meal is overcome, chances are good that the killer will remain a man-eater for the remainder of its life. A single tigress is reported to have killed 200 people in one province in India before moving into another section. Here she is said to have accounted for 234 more for a total of 434 victims before she was killed by a professional hunter.

Tigers often take a fancy to man's livestock. In some years these predators are said to have killed more than 60,000 sheep, horses, and other animals. The depredations are especially serious in poverty-stricken countries, such as India, where only one or two domestic animals may stand between the native and starvation.

In defense of tigers it must be said that they make certain contributions to the natives. The normal prey of the cats includes deer, antelopes, wild pigs, and an occasional buffalo. Some of these animals have a fondness for cultivated crops, and may cause considerable damage if they become too numerous. In districts where the tigers have been systematically re-

duced in numbers, there has often been an increase in the damage to cultivated crops by foraging deer, antelopes, and wild pigs.

In the past, and perhaps even today, certain parts of the tiger's body
have been used for charms, amulets, and even for medicine. The tiger's
heart, if eaten, was supposed to give the consumer the courage and strength
of the tiger; and various concoctions, from clotted blood to tiger kneecap,
have been recommended for many ills. This demand for all parts of the
tiger has caused its virtual extinction in its once common habitat of northern China.

The King of Beasts

Lions are much more sociable than either tigers or leopards. Lions
sometimes hunt in groups, or prides. This habit is not found among the
other big cats, although they sometimes hunt in pairs. In Africa, any lion
that overcomes its fears of human beings sufficiently to capture livestock
in a tribal village is recognized as a potential killer of men. Hunting parties
are then organized to hunt down the animal before it turns to human flesh.

Like the tiger, most man-eating lions are old or otherwise handicapped,
but this is not invariably true. One lion that accounted for 37 people in
South Africa was found, when killed, to be young and healthy. Before
killing human beings became a necessity for it, this lion had discovered
how easily people could be overcome.

Two lions in East Africa near the turn of the century became among the
best known in history. During the construction of the Uganda railroad, the
two big cats acquired a taste for the Indian coolies who had been imported
for the work. The animals killed so many of the workmen that the work
on the railroad was completely halted for three weeks. When the lions were
at last killed they had accounted for 28 Indian workmen, in addition to an
unknown number of African natives.

Contrary to popular opinion, lions are not confined to the African continent. At one time they were relatively common in parts of India and the
Middle East, and are reported to have occurred in parts of Europe during
the past several hundred years. Today these Asiatic lions are virtually
extinct. A few still survive in a small protected area in western India, but
with the advance of civilization even these few remaining lions may soon
be gone.

Black Panthers

The usual large black cat sometimes seen in zoos and often called a
black panther is really a leopard. To people in the western hemisphere, the
word *panther* usually means the cougar or mountain lion, but leopards are

also called panthers in the countries where they are native. Leopards are widely distributed in parts of Africa and Asia, and they vary in color in different parts of their ranges. Black leopards or panthers are most common in Ethiopia and the East Indies. The usual leopard is somewhat brownish with black spots.

Leopards are about the size of cougars, and are thus smaller than lions, tigers, and jaguars. Their ability and ferocity, however, somewhat makes up for their small size. The general concensus is that man-eating leopards are relatively rare, but that once the animal gets a taste of human blood it may cause frightful havoc before it is killed. During one year leopards are reported to have killed 366 people in India, and two man-eaters are believed to have accounted for 525 people over a period of several years.

For some unknown reason leopards are especially fond of dogs, and they have been known to snatch a dog in broad daylight from under the very noses of their human masters. There are actually no dogs at all in some Indian villages around which leopards are common, for all have fallen prey to the hungry carnivores. The extent to which leopards are attracted to dogs is illustrated by the following incident. A man in a small Chinese village had the habit of tying his dog to his bed at night. One night a leopard came through the window, captured the dog and made off before it could be apprehended. The next night the same thing happened to another dog. Still a third dog was tied to the bed and the owner kept watch. The leopard did not appear the third night, but it did on the fourth, and successfully escaped with its third victim. About this time the man apparently ran out of dogs, or perhaps he prudently kept his window closed. At any rate, there is no record of a fourth attempt by the leopard. People naturally do not approve of the leopards' attraction to dogs, but they can be glad that their taste is thus directed rather than to human beings.

Over the years the demand for leopard skins for coats and jackets has probably been greater than that of other cat skins of comparable size. The popularity has vacillated from time to time, possibly because the spots give the garment a somewhat garish appearance. But the routine demand has been sufficient to cause difficulty in parts of Africa where large numbers of leopards have been killed. When leopards are fairly numerous, many animals that have a taste for native crops are held in check. Baboons are among the "problem children" with which natives have to contend. They are somewhat oversized monkeys and certain kinds are brilliantly colored at both ends. Within recent years baboons have increased so greatly in numbers that successfully raising crops has become a major problem in parts of East Africa.

Many people believe that the leopard is the most important single factor in keeping the baboon population within respectable bounds, and developments certainly support these beliefs. The regions suffering most from raiding baboons are those in which leopards have been drastically reduced in numbers.

Chemical Warfare—The Skunk

Skunks, or polecats or wood pussies, as they are sometimes called, are best known because of their ability to emit one of the most malodorous secretions in the entire animal kingdom. This secretion is released by two glands, one on each side of the digestive tract. Ducts lead from the scent glands into the digestive tract close to its outside opening.

When the skunk gets ready to discharge its secretion, it turns its back toward the object of its wrath, raises its tail, and stamps its front feet in warning. They are sometimes quite hesitant to discharge the fluid, and it has been suggested that the stuff smells horrible even to a skunk. If warnings do not suffice, however, muscles contract and squeeze the scent glands, and the skunk lays down a barrage of spray which may be thrown for ten feet, sometimes with disconcerting accuracy. Although a relatively small amount of material is released at each discharge, usually only two or three drops if it is concentrated, it is so powerful that it can be smelled for more than half a mile in all directions.

How Not to Capture a Skunk

It is claimed that one safe way to capture a skunk is to sneak up behind it, seize it suddenly by the tail, and hoist it triumphantly into the air. A skunk held in this position is reportedly unable to discharge its secretion, and apparently this method of capture has succeeded in some instances. But success cannot be guaranteed, as some people have learned. Probably skunks vary in their ability to discharge their secretion when held by their tails, or possibly those that have been caught safely in this way were not in a spraying mood. At any rate, this method of capture is not recommended unless one is fully prepared to take the consequences of possible failure.

What Mammal Is the Greatest Insect Fighter?

Moles, shrews, armadillos, and many other mammals include insects in their diets, and all of these make contributions to man's fight against his insect enemies. Skunks, of which there are several species in Canada, the United States, Mexico, Central and South America, may be the most important of all. One biologist has said that skunks are the most important mammalian enemies of insects, and another, even more enthusiastic, has stated that skunks destroy more insects than all other mammals combined.

Whether or not the first prize in this contest should be awarded to skunks is still debatable, but the smelly little fellows should certainly be placed near the top of the list. Harmful insects that skunks consume include grubs, cutworms, and other caterpillars, grasshoppers, potato beetles, and crickets.

From an intensive survey in Canada on an eight-acre tract, it was estimated that skunks were responsible for the destruction of more than 115,-000 white grubs within a relatively short time. During an outbreak of the range caterpillar in New Mexico, the food of skunks was found to be made up of from 60 to 95 per cent of these pests. In New York skunks were so effective in controlling the hop grub, a serious pest of hop plants, that the people showed their appreciation by pressuring for legislation protecting the mammals. The growers succeeded.

When insects are not common, skunks will eat a variety of other foods. This miscellaneous fare often includes mice and other rodents, but the mammals will also eat fruits, reptiles, amphibians, and almost any other small animal that they can overcome. An occasional skunk has been caught red-handed in poultry houses, and the animals sometimes destroy the eggs and young of quail, pheasants, and other ground-nesting birds. On the other hand, they are not guilty nearly as often as many people believe. In 1,000 skunks whose stomachs were examined, it was found that less than 1 per cent contained the remains of poultry; and not a trace of a game bird egg was found in another study involving 1,700 skunks.

Skunks that get too friendly can be discouraged by sprinkling moth balls or naphthalene flakes under houses where they have taken up residence. Closing cracks and crevices through which they enter should also have the same effect.

Skunk skins are widely used in the fur industry, but the demand fluctuates considerably. On an average, however, the number of skunk skins processed in the United States is exceeded only by those of muskrat and opossum.

The secretion that the animals use to produce their horrible odor is deodorized and employed in—of all things—the manufacture of perfumes. It seems possible that the material added to some of the cheaper varieties has not been completely deodorized.

In parts of southern and southwestern United States the spotted skunk, a relatively small species, is called the hydrophobia cat. An occasional pugnacious individual has been known to bite sleeping campers, and some people believe that hydrophobia or rabies follows these bites. During the mating season the males of these skunks are apparently seized with a desire to do something unusual, and these actions have been interpreted to be a result of rabies. Male skunks have been known to squirt full in the face of an astonished bull minding its own business, or to dash into a wolf's den and bite the young wolves. These actions probably are not caused by rabies, but apparently are the result of a "mating frenzy."

Do Raccoons Wash Their Food?

There is some truth in the story that raccoons wash their food before eating it. If water is available, most raccoons do wash their food, and some have been known actually to refuse food when they could not find any water. But refusal is not the rule; if a coon comes upon food some distance from water, he will usually eat it, though he may be unhappy about it. This washing habit is not always practiced even when it is possible; some men who have studied the habits of raccoons have never observed it.

The reason for the raccoon's peculiar action is not known. It does not indicate cleanliness, since the water used in washing the food may be dirtier than the food. Also, frogs, crawfish, and similar tidbits caught in the water may be scrubbed as efficiently as other types of food. Some people believe that the raccoon washes its food because it enjoys feeling the food in the water; if this is true, it would explain why the animal sometimes almost wears the food out in its enthusiasm. A piece of meat, for instance, is sometimes mauled and scrubbed so thoroughly that it is an unrecognizable mass by the time the raccoon is ready to eat it. Whatever its reasons, however, it seems to derive considerable pleasure from the procedure.

Virtues and Vices of the Raccoon Family

Raccoons are widely distributed over the United States; they also occur in parts of Canada and in South America. And raccoons will eat almost any type of food, including frogs, birds, chickens, insects, berries, eggs, turtles, acorns, corn, and melons. They are essentially opportunists, and what they eat depends upon what can most easily be found. In one area where waterfowl were abundant, vegetable matter made up more than 70 per cent of the food of coons before the hunting season opened. During the hunting season, another study revealed, ducks and other animals accounted for almost 90 per cent of their food.

Unfortunately, the mammals have a taste for watermelons, cantaloupes, and tender corn. They will occasionally eat other crops, and have been known to raid hen houses. In some regions, coons have also been reported as destroying many diamondback terrapins and other commercially important species of turtles.

Most damage caused by raccoons, however, is local rather than general, and all things considered, the mammals are definite assets. Even their indiscriminate food habits cannot be entirely condemned because of the large numbers of insects that they consume.

Their greatest value lies in their fur. Today thousands of people hunt them, both for recreation and for profit. The demand, and hence the price, for raccoon skins has varied widely during the years, but over a long period of time raccoon furs have been among the most important in the fur industry. During pioneer days coonskins were used for currency in the Mississippi Valley states, and the coonskin cap was an accepted article of apparel. Raccoons were quite popular as food at one time, and are still eaten in many sections of the country.

Some twenty-five years ago, no college man's wardrobe was complete without a raccoon coat, nightmarish in appearance, but reasonably efficient in protecting the wearer from the weather. Recently, the director of the Indiana Conservation Department wished publicly for the return of the raccoon coat; his complaint was that since the coats were no longer popular, raccoon hunting had diminished, allowing the mammals to increase numbers and do considerable damage to crops. It may be that he will get his wish sooner than expected. In the fall of 1962, furriers gleefully announced that for the winter, women's coats would be trimmed with more long-haired fur, including raccoon. How long the fad for long-haired monstrosities will stay in vogue remains to be seen.

The raccoon is one of three animals in the United States with a black-ringed tail. The other two, the coati or coatimundi, and the ringtail or cacomistle, are relatives of the raccoon. These mammals are more slender than coons, and have comparatively longer tails.

Coatis occur mostly in Mexico, South and Central America, but they are also fairly common in Arizona and New Mexico. An occasional straggler has been found in Texas. Like their relatives the raccoons, coatis will eat almost anything that is edible. They sometimes raid the nests of birds and chickens, but, on the constructive side, they polish off a large number of insects.

The ringtail, also called the ringtailed cat and miner's cat, is common throughout the southwest, but the mammals are so secretive in their habits that they are seldom seen. Few mammals can compete with ringtails in ability to capture rats, mice, and other rodents. Favorite hunting spots are abandoned mine shafts and tunnels, and an occasional ringtail overcomes its natural timidity and takes up residence in a prospector's cabin or hunting lodge. Their presence is often encouraged by men who know that rats and mice will be kept at a low ebb as long as the miner's cat is around.

What Is the Most Bloodthirsty Mammal?

There are many kinds of weasels in the world, and wherever they occur they have a well-deserved reputation as bloodthirsty killers. Smallest of the carnivorous mammals, they more than make up for their lack of size by their agility, strength, and courage.

Biologists believe that the animals kill for the sheer joy of killing. They have been known to enter and completely destroy a colony of rats, and not infrequently they are forced to move from one place to another because they have killed all the natural prey in the vicinity. One weasel nest was found to contain eight dead mice plus the remains of six other rodents, and a weasel whose tracks a biologist was following in the snow left eleven dead rabbits along its trail. Weasels usually drink a little blood from each victim before continuing the slaughter.

Adult weasels may weigh less than half a pound, but the courage and tenacity of these mammalian mites is amazing. They do not hesitate to attack animals several times their size, and not infrequently they will emerge victorious—or die trying.

Sometimes weasels will raid a chicken house. One of the little demons has been known to destroy more than forty fowls in a single night. This occasional outlaw has brought the wrath of farmers down on the heads of all weasels, and many people kill the mammals on sight.

But scientists who have investigated the food habits of the weasel disagree with the commonly held opinion of the mammals. For weasels are great enemies of harmful rodents. One authority asserts that, except for weasels, rats and mice would multiply so rapidly that they would overrun the earth. It has been estimated that there are approximately 300,000 weasels in New York state, and that they could account for 60 million rats and mice per year.

Although weasels are small, large numbers are captured for their pelts. This is especially true of the species called ermine, whose fur changes to white in winter.

The Mongoose, Famed Killer of Snakes

Since the time of Rudyard Kipling and his mongoose, Rikki-Tikki-Tavi, the mongoose has been the best-known killer of venomous snakes in existence. In fact, many people believe that mongooses deliberately hunt for poisonous snakes, and that the little mammal always wins in these encounters. Until recently, some biologists partially accepted these beliefs, but investigations have now exploded several of the myths of the mongoose.

Dr. James A. Oliver, director of the American Museum of Natural History, who has studied the mongoose situation, states that the little mammals seldom deliberately seek fights with large venomous snakes. There are actually few verified reports of fights between a mongoose and a venomous snake in nature, and staged fights between the two are seldom very successful. Sometimes no fight develops; when it does, the battle often ends in a draw with both combatants exhausted.

The strike of a cobra is much slower than that of a pit viper, such as a rattlesnake, and the agile mongoose can often avoid the strike, seize the cobra behind the head, and enjoy a meal at the expense of its erstwhile enemy. However, mongooses are not immune to snake venom, and they do not always win, even against cobras; their record is considerably worse against large pit vipers. An attempt was once made to film a fight between a mongoose and a bushmaster, the dreaded pit viper of Central and South America. A bushmaster strikes more rapidly than a cobra, and eight mongooses were used before the picture was completed.

That mongooses do not look for snakes specifically was shown by a study of food habits in Trinidad, West Indies, a short time ago. The stomachs of 180 mongooses were examined and many animal remains were identified. These included birds, lizards, frogs, rats, insects, and snakes. The remains of only eighteen snakes were found, and these were all of non-poisonous species.

We must, therefore, conclude regretfully that although mongooses sometimes do kill venomous snakes, they are not the traditional invincible enemies of all kinds and sizes of serpents.

Why the Mongoose May Not Immigrate

There are many species of mongooses in Africa and Asia, and one species in southern Spain. In their native lands they are probably as well known as killers of rats, mice, and other pests, as for their alleged ability to kill snakes. In some sections natives encourage mongooses (not "mongeese") to live about their houses in order to discourage serpents and rodents.

Because of the reputation of the mongoose as a destroyer of rats, it was introduced into the West Indies and the Hawaiian Islands some years ago in an attempt to control the rodents. For a time the mongooses slaughtered the rats and everyone was happy. Then rats became scarce, and those that remained cleverly took to the trees to avoid the earthbound mongooses. The hungry mongooses turned to native ground-nesting birds, waterfowl, chickens, and even young sheep and pigs. This turn of events has caused great destruction and the near extermination of several valuable wild species. The mongoose problem in these islands is regarded by biologists as so serious that the introduction of the mammals into the United States is strictly prohibited.

Which Mammal Keeps the Largest Harem?

The males of many mammals have several mates, but the champion of them all is the fur seal. Forty to sixty wives is an average, but an exceptionally strong bull may have more than one hundred. The only mammals that can compete with the fur seal in harem size—excepting man—are the elk and the caribou; but the seal is usually given first prize.

Of the two distinct kinds of fur seals—the northern and the southern species—the northern one is by far the more important. The southern species has now been almost completely exterminated by fur hunters. The important herds of this species that remain occur on the coast of South Africa, and on some islands off the coast of Uruguay. These have been saved only through regulated hunting.

During the winter, northern fur seals do not get on land, but they occur in various parts of the Pacific Ocean. As spring approaches, the seals head north toward their breeding grounds. For some reason, yet unknown, approximately 80 per cent of all the northern fur seals breed on the Pribilof Islands in the Bering Sea near Alaska. The old bulls arrive first and each one appropriates a section of the beach for his future wives. Later, when the females appear, each bull captures as many as he can and herds them to his selected spot on the beach. He then remains on guard for the months they are on land, fighting any other bull that approaches his territory, and driving errant cows back into the fold.

When the Pribilof Islands were first discovered, it was estimated that there were at least 5 million seals using them for breeding purposes. Due to unrestricted hunting, they have been on the verge of extinction on two separate occasions. The lowest ebb was reached about 1910 when less than 125,000 animals remained. At what seemed the last minute, international treaties were agreed upon, and since that time the killing of the fur seals has been strictly regulated. Only a limited number, mostly young bulls, are killed each year under United States government supervision. For the past several years the number of skins taken has averaged about 65,000 annually, and a recent estimate places the number of seals in the herd at more than 3.5 million. Under governmental protection, the fur seal seems well on its way toward regaining its former numbers.

The northern fur seal is the most important species of seal, and the pelts, which are used largely in the manufacture of fur coats, are its most valuable products. The carcasses of the seals are also used to obtain oil and meal after the pelts have been removed. There are several other seals and seal relatives that are of some significance, including the hair seals and the sea lions.

The most important of the several kinds of hair seals are the harbor or leopard seal, the harp seal, the hooded seal, and the Caspian seal. The hair seals, as their name implies, do not have the fine fur of the fur seals, and as a consequence their pelts are made into leather rather than being used for fur coats. The hair seals contribute most of the leather for seal-skin articles such as jackets, brief cases, wallets and an occasional pair of shoes. Strips of hair seal skin, with the hair intact, are also often used on skis for climbing.

Sea lions, closely related to the fur seals, have been hunted for their hides, for oil, and for other portions of their anatomies that have been called the "trimmings." These consist of the gall bladder, the sex organs or genitalia, and the whiskers, and were for many years in demand in the Orient. The gall bladder was used as a medicine and the whiskers for cleaning opium pipes. The genitalia were ground up, made into a concoction, and relished by aged Chinese on the theory that this was a rejuvenator.

Commercial fisheries for sea lion products are now practically non-existent, but the trained seals of circus, carnival, and zoological park are really sea lions, most of which come from the western coast of the United States.

Seals and sea lions eat a variety of marine animals. There has been discussion as to their possible destruction of commercially valuable fish; consequently, in Alaska and some western states, bounties have been offered for harbor seals. Perhaps under special conditions some seals and sea lions cause damage, but stomach examinations have seldom borne out the contention that they are excessively destructive. Apparently most of the food consumed consists of squid, some fish, and other marine animals with no commercial value. On several occasions the mammals have been found stuffed with lampreys, parasitic fish that often destroy large numbers of valuable species.

Where they occur in numbers, seals and sea lions have been of importance to the natives of many lands. The flesh is eaten and the skins used for making boats, clothing, and shoes. Raincoats have even been made from the intestines of some of the larger species, and the stomachs used as pouches for storing oil.

The greatest natural enemies of seals and sea lions are probably sharks and killer whales. The latter have been called wolves of the sea because of their ferocity and voracious appetites. Killer whales doubtless take considerable toll from the seal herds. One of these whales that was killed had eighteen fur seals in its stomach, and another had twenty-four—tremendous meals even for such gluttonous animals and, in view of the value of the fur seal's pelts, very expensive ones.

What Can You Do with a Walrus?

In addition to the ivory that once made walrus hunting a highly profitable pursuit the animal's skin was tanned for leather and valuable oil was obtained from the body. But as usual, wasteful methods and indiscriminate killing took their toll. Even the Eskimos, many of whom were dependent upon the walrus for food and clothing, contributed to the needless slaughter.

Today walrus hunting is regulated in many areas. Eskimos and other inhabitants of the far north still find use for the walrus, and some villages are almost entirely dependent upon these mammals for their existence. The meat is used for food, the skin for boats and for dwellings, the oil for light and fuel, and the tusks for tools and ornaments. In some places at least, the natives have learned their lesson. They kill only enough for a season's use, and leave the herds strictly alone at other times to prevent them from becoming frightened and leaving the vicinity.

Two BIRDS

Birds are probably easier to identify than the members of any other vertebrate group because they are the only animals having feathers. It is well known that the front limbs of birds are modified into wings. It is perhaps not so well known that the bones of the wings are not very different from those in the human arm. As in the arm, a single bone at the upper end connects the wing to the body. At the lower end of this single bone two bones are attached; these correspond to the two bones in the human forearm.

The bones of the bird's wing that represent man's wrist and hand are more modified. In the bird, only three fingers are represented. These bones are bound together by tissue. They probably correspond to the human thumb, the index finger, and the third or middle finger.

What is popularly called the wishbone in the bird can be compared with the human collarbones or clavicles. In man, the bones are separate; in birds, they are fused together at one end. This modification doubtless is correlated with the flight habits of birds.

Compared with mammals, other modifications of birds include hollow bones, the presence of air sacs, and enormously developed pectoral muscles which form the "breast." All of these features and others combine to make birds remarkably efficient flying machines, though there are some birds that do not fly.

Birds, like mammals, are warm-blooded: their body temperatures remain relatively constant despite the temperature of the air. Many birds migrate to warmer climates in the fall and return to their homelands in the spring, but others remain in temperate and even arctic climates throughout the year. This they are able to do because of their warm-blooded condition.

If a person holds a bird in his hand, the body of the bird will feel warm. This is because the normal body temperature of birds is higher than that of man. If the body temperature of a man were to become as high as that of many birds, he would have a raging fever; if he survived after attaining the maximum temperature for birds, he would be a medical curiosity. Normal bird temperatures that have actually been taken range from 101.3° F. to 112.7° F., as compared with 98.6° F. for man.

All birds lay eggs; none that we know of gives birth to living young. The eggs are usually deposited in a nest of one kind or another, and in most cases they are incubated by one or both parents. But there are exceptions to both of these statements. Birds that do not build nests include certain shore birds that lay their eggs on the sand, cowbirds and cuckoos that lay their eggs in the nests of other birds, and a few other species. The fairy tern, a bird that occurs on some islands of the Pacific Ocean, probably has the weirdest egg-laying habit of all. It lays only a single egg, which is deposited on the branch of a tree with no nesting material around it. The parents incubate the egg, and they must be expert balancers, for they lose no more eggs than the average bird.

The incubation time required for hatching varies markedly among birds, and much more information is needed for many species. At one end of the scale we find 11- to 12-day periods for several species, such as cowbirds, some sparrows, and cuckoos. The royal albatross, a large sea bird, probably has the longest known incubation period: its eggs require approximately 80 days to hatch. The kiwi of New Zealand is a close second with 75 days.

In general, large eggs require longer to hatch, but the incubation time for the smallest and the largest eggs known are between the extremes just given. The eggs of the tiny hummingbirds take from 14 to 15 days; those of the ostrich, the largest eggs of living birds, will hatch in 42 days. The incubation time for the hen or domestic chicken, a medium-sized bird, is approximately 21 days.

Birds are of value to man in several ways, including the more obvious ones of their use for food, as targets for hunters, and as subjects of the pastime known as bird watching. In a final analysis, wild birds are probably of most importance to human beings because of their food habits.

The value of birds as destroyers of harmful insects, rodents, and other pests was recognized by biologists even before detailed studies had been made of the food preferences of the various species. And at one time erudite gentlemen amused themselves by estimating what would happen to the human race if all birds were suddenly eliminated. One such learned scientist stated that without the aid of birds, human beings would become extinct in less than a year. It is now believed that this calculation was somewhat exaggerated.

Over a period of years United States government biologists have examined and analyzed the stomach contents of more than 100,000 birds in an effort to learn more of the food habits of the various species. These and other studies now make it possible for biologists to make quite accurate estimates of the over-all importance of many species of birds.

How Scarce Are Hens' Teeth?

"Scarce as hens' teeth" is an appropriate description for nonexistent objects, because teeth are entirely lacking, not only in hens, but in all birds. The lack does not seem to inconvenience them, however, as they swallow their food whole without any ill effects. This process is made possible by the gizzard, a muscular organ that substitutes for teeth and which is really part of the bird's stomach. The principal function of the gizzard is to break up the food into small particles so that it can be digested, and the birds occasionally swallow small stones that are of assistance in the process. With the gizzard, they are able to grind up even such hard food as grain and other seed.

The craw, or crop as it is sometimes called, like the gizzard, is a modified part of the bird's digestive tract. It is a saclike enlargement of the food tube, or esophagus, just in front of the gizzard in the region where the neck joins the body. It is used principally for storing food, although in some birds digestion starts in this organ. A hen or other bird can rapidly gobble up large quantities of food without danger of indigestion because the food is held in the craw for a time before passing on into the gizzard. A well-filled crop is quite noticeable in young chickens and can be easily felt even in adult birds. A few birds, such as pigeons, doves and their relatives, secrete a milky substance in the craw called "pigeon's milk." This the parent bird regurgitates and feeds to its young.

Birds Have More Neckbones than a Giraffe

The neck of a chicken is not considered choice eating by most people, but it is a part of the bird that should be looked upon with a certain amount of respect. There are more bones in the neck of any bird than in the neck of a giraffe. The number of bones varies with the kind of bird, those with long necks usually having the greatest number. The English sparrow has 14, ducks 16, and swans 23. The long-necked giraffe has but a paltry 7.

Do Birds Carry Any Diseases?

There are few diseases that are directly transmittable from birds to man, but a couple of these can be serious. The best known has been called ornithosis and psittacosis; it is a virus disease that has been classified as a type of pneumonia. This malady has also been called parrot fever, because the first known human cases were traced to sick parrots. Since that time, it has been found that the same or a similar disease also occurs in pigeons, parakeets, canaries, and certain other birds. Man apparently gets the disease in most cases when he breathes in dust or other material with the virus on it. As might be expected, the disease often strikes people who work in pet shops.

Psittacosis occurs wherever parrots or parakeets are found, either in the wild state or where they are kept as pets. The number of reported cases is usually rather low, but the death rate may be high. During one year in the United States there were 33 deaths from 170 known cases. Within recent years human cases have been traced to pigeons, but the mortality rate of cases from this source is much lower than the parrot-transmitted type.

Birds such as quail and grouse sometimes catch tularemia or rabbit fever, and occasionally someone has become infected with the disease while cleaning such a bird.

Within recent years it has been found that several kinds of wild birds, as well as domestic chickens, harbor the virus of several forms of encephalitis, sometimes called sleeping sickness. These diseases, which occur in the United States and other parts of the world, are different from African sleeping sickness. Encephalitis is not transmitted directly to man by contact with birds, but it is carried by the bites of certain kinds of mosquitoes, which pick up the virus from birds.

Certain kinds of encephalitis may have a high mortality rate compared with some other diseases. For example, in 1959 there were approximately 33 confirmed cases of eastern equine encephalitis (sometimes abbreviated EEE) in New Jersey. Twenty-one of the patients died. During some years hundreds of cases of insect-borne encephalitis occur in the United States, but in 1961 only 73 cases were reported to the Communicable Disease Center of the United Public Health service. Birds are hosts to mites, ticks, fleas, and many other parasites; occasionally, some of these pests will attack domestic fowls and human beings.

On the credit side, however, birds help in controlling many maladies and pests. Some species eat flies, mosquitoes, and other potentially disease-carrying biting insects. There is also evidence that birds help to keep some human parasites in check by eating their intermediate host. The parasite causing snail fever (or schistosomiasis) must pass through stages in freshwater snails before it can attack man; various water birds eat large numbers of snails. The ibis, which was common in ancient Egypt, consumes large numbers of the snails in which the snail-fever parasite passes part of its life. The ancient Egyptians did not know what connection there was between bird and disease, but it *is* thought that they did recognize that the ibis helped to keep the incidence low. Perhaps this was one reason the Egyptians considered the bird sacred, and rigorously protected it.

What Birds Eat Insects?

Half of the approximately 8,600 different species of birds in the world eat a certain number of insects; many species depend primarily upon insects for their food.

Birds certainly help to keep many harmful insects in check, and in some instances they have actually averted disaster. Perhaps the best-known case occurred in Utah many years ago. The Mormons, who had settled in the area, had suffered a severe crop failure; they were watching the results of their second planting when hordes of Mormon crickets appeared on the scene and started munching on the plants. Before the crickets could do much damage, thousands of gulls flew into the fields, ate the insects, and saved the farmers from probable starvation. In grateful appreciation the Mormons erected a monument to the birds. It still stands in the heart of Salt Lake City.

Some birds, such as warblers, swallows, flycatchers, and nighthawks eat insects regularly, whereas others eat the pests when available in large numbers. During a plague of the Rocky Mountain locust in the Midwest some years ago, more than two hundred different kinds of birds were seen feeding on the insects. Meadowlarks were given primary credit for destroying an infestation of the Coulee cricket in the state of Washington, and woodpeckers cleared up a heavy concentration of spruce beetles in Idaho.

Most insects are destroyed during the nesting season when the parent birds have several hungry mouths to feed. In order to develop normally at certain stages, young birds must eat at least their own weight in food each day. One or both parents will usually feed their brood many times per hour. From dawn to dusk the busy adults shuttle back and forth stuffing food into gaping mouths. In Utah, during an outbreak of the alfalfa weevil, it was estimated that a single brood of English sparrows accounted for 1,980 larvae of the beetle or this equivalent in other insects.

Unfortunately, birds do not deliberately hunt out harmful insects. As a consequence, some beneficial types are also eaten. Kingbirds occasionally eat honey bees (whence the local name bee martin), but stomach examinations have shown that in most instances the birds eat only drones, which make no contributions to the colony except to fertilize the eggs of the queen. Ground beetles, lady bird beetles, and other beneficial insects are also eaten at times, but few instances are known where large enough numbers are destroyed by birds to upset the balance of nature.

What Are the Most Important Enemies of Birds?

The enemies of birds range throughout the animal kingdom, from insects to human beings; they include many species of birds themselves. Obviously enemies will vary among different species of birds, and the harm that is done will often depend upon the habits and distribution of the birds involved. In southeastern United States, for instance, certain ants take a tremendous toll of the eggs and young of the bobwhite quail. The bird nests on the ground, and surveys have shown that in some regions 15 per cent of the nests are destroyed by ants. The insects attack the nestlings shortly after they are hatched; the ants may even gain access to a hatching egg before the youngster has a chance to get out of the shell.

Foxes, weasels, skunks, armadillos, some lizards, snakes, and even other birds make use of eggs for food if they can find the nests. Crows, magpies, and blue jays are probably the worst offenders on this score.

Young birds have to contend with an assortment of natural enemies that range from turtles to hawks. Temperature, storms, and disease also inflict a toll. Some years ago one coastal storm in the state of Washington was estimated to have killed 50,000 water birds, and severe winters in other areas have destroyed approximately 95 per cent of the quail population.

Why, even without man's intervention, are more birds not extinct? The following illustration of the balance of nature may have some bearing:

A marshy area in New York state containing snapping turtles, ducks, skunks, and other animals seemed well balanced until man came along. The turtles doubtless caught an occasional duckling, but the skunks presumably ate enough turtle eggs to keep the number of turtles within reasonable bounds. The price of skunk fur suddenly skyrocketed. People invaded the swamp and killed large numbers of the mammals. The snapping turtle population increased rapidly, and the reptiles killed more and more young ducks. This development apparently made the adult ducks unhappy, because they left the marsh for more satisfactory nesting grounds. The bottom then dropped out of the skunk fur market; the number killed became fewer and the skunk population increased. Snapping turtle soup became popular, and the hunters shifted their attention to the reptiles. The skunks and people so reduced the population of snappers that the ducks returned and started using the marsh again as a nesting site. The situation thus became essentially what it was before man invaded the community.

Biologists agree that natural losses of bird life will normally be taken care of by the reproductive capacities of most species. Many birds, however, find it difficult to survive the additional pressures for which man is responsible. For various reasons man has slaughtered birds by untold millions and, by clearing woodlands and swamps, has destroyed or narrowed the natural habitats of certain species.

The introduction of the domestic cat and other animals that prey upon birds has been another factor. The half-wild alley cats that eke out a meager existence from garbage cans, back fences, fields, and young birds probably account for the greatest losses of bird life. One estimate shows that, on an average, each cat will kill from 10 to 50 birds per year. During a single day, 226 cats under close observation were seen to kill 624 birds of various kinds. Three and one-half million birds, it is believed, are destroyed this way each year in the state of New York alone. Biologists have suggested everything from manicuring to complete extermination of cats in an effort to decrease the destruction of birds by these animals. The Society for the Prevention of Cruelty to Animals and similar organizations have made great progress here by having unclaimed cats destroyed. But the cat situation is still one of the major problems facing the bird conservationists.

Before leaving the general subject of bird enemies, one point should be made clear: any animal that kills birds or eats their eggs must be classified as an enemy, even though these actions occur only occasionally. Some of the species that have been named as bird enemies actually do a tremendous amount of good in other ways.

What Bird Products Are Useful to Man?

Birds have always been used for food. But the products that have probably been most in demand over the years are the plumes and feathers, used primarily for decoration of women's hats. Feather merchants answered the charge of barbarism by asserting that most of the plumage was obtained by gathering molted feathers, or by plucking living birds on bird farms. These claims were open to dispute: much of the plumage that was used had pieces of wing bones or skin still attached.

Hummingbirds, egrets, herons, birds of paradise, terns, swans, condors, and even albatrosses were in demand for their plumage. The birds were hunted so enthusiastically that several species were completely exterminated, and several others were threatened with extinction. In one season, the skins and feathers of fifty-five million birds were purchased in the United States; England accounted for another eleven million.

This appalling slaughter continued until 1913. Finally the Audubon Society and similar organizations persuaded the American government to adopt a law prohibiting the importation of bird skins into this country. This and similar laws now make it illegal to use wild bird plumage commercially in the United States and several other countries.

Ostrich farms have been flourishing in Africa for many years, and since the decline of the wild plumage trade, farms have been established in Europe, South America, and parts of the United States, where the feathers and plumes are the most valuable products produced. The skin, too, is sometimes used for the manufacture of articles such as belts, wallets, and purses—much to some people's distaste.

Two other bird products are the nests of certain species used for soup, (page 156) and the accumulated droppings or guano that are used for fertilizer (page 137).

The down and soft feathers of many ducks, geese, swans, and even chickens have been used for centuries for making feather beds, and for the insulation of sleeping bags and cold-climate clothing. The most valuable down is that of the so-called eider duck that nests in the far north. At one time these ducks were slaughtered mercilessly, a practice that fortunately has now been largely discontinued. Much of the commercial down now comes from Norway and Iceland, where the ducks are rigidly protected. The eiders, like most ducks and geese, line their nests with down that they pluck from their breasts. In Norway and Iceland the down is collected from the nests. There is some disagreement among authorities as to whether the down is collected after the nest is built but before the eggs are hatched, or only after the ducklings have left the nest. The last method seems most logical in order to insure the survival of the youngsters, and to perpetuate the colonies and the fortunes of the natives.

Birds as Food

With few exceptions, almost all species of birds that occur in relatively large numbers have been used for food at one time or another, and the availability of birds and their eggs has saved human lives on more than one occasion. Today certain primitive people are largely dependent upon birds for their major food supply. It is said that the little auk or dovekie makes it possible for the Eskimos to live in certain parts of Greenland. In more civilized countries ducks, quail, pheasants, and many other birds are important articles of diet.

How has man repaid his benefactors? In many cases by slaughtering the birds by untold millions, and in the cases of the passenger pigeon and the dodo, by literally eating the birds out of existence. Many game birds, such as quail, prairie chickens, and plovers were at one time killed for the market in large numbers. Not so well known is the fact that many songbirds were also included. Robins, meadowlarks, bobolinks, and even flickers were often served in restaurants as "rice birds."

From the standpoint of edibility, there are few birds that cannot be eaten. Most people would hesitate to eat a buzzard or other animal that feeds on carrion; a few, such as the stink bird or hoatzin of South America, have a foul taste.

Some birds not generally thought of as edible actually have an excellent taste. Some years ago my father, a school superintendent, decided to try an experiment. He obtained several birds from a farmer, and invited some women teachers to dinner. The birds had been cleaned previously. My father told my mother and the cook that they were "birds," a term which, according to popular usage, implied that they were quail. The dinner was a marked success; the guests as well as my mother enjoyed the birds immensely.

An unfortunate incident exposed the secret. One of the teachers, some days later, reprimanded the son of the farmer from whom my father had obtained the birds. This indignity broke the boy's resolution to keep the secret. He started chanting with considerable pleasure,

"You ate a crow! You ate a crow!"

How Dangerous Is a Bird in Flight?

People who seldom travel by plane probably do not realize that birds are an actual hazard to air transportation. The exact number of planes that have collided with birds is not known, but at one time as many as two collisions per week were reported in the United States by airline pilots. Sometimes the planes suffer only minor damage, but there are numerous instances on record of plane crashes caused by birds, resulting in the death of one or more passengers.

Large birds, such as swans, cranes, and eagles cause the most difficulty, but because of the force of impact even small birds can cause serious trouble. One such small bird passed through the windshield and two wooden walls of a transport and ended up in the baggage compartment. Another, size unstated, is reported to have penetrated the bullet-proof windshield of an English fighter plane.

Most collisions with birds are accidental, but a few birds have been known to attack planes deliberately, a fact that probably gave rise to the suggestion, reportedly originated in France during World War I, that eagles be trained to attack enemy aircraft. Absurd as it may sound today, this idea might not have been so far-fetched in the days of the much slower canvas-covered airplanes, and possibly more effective in bringing down enemy planes than bricks heaved at the propellors, a practice that was reported to have been occasionally successful.

Not only are birds a danger in mid-air, but they sometimes become a problem by congregating on and around airfields, and competing for landing and take-off space. In late 1954 the United States Department of Defense appealed to the Fish and Wildlife Service for help in solving a knotty problem on Midway Island. The naval airbase there had been invaded by thousands of gooney birds, a type of albatross. The birds had nested on the island and had become alarmingly friendly, perching on planes and sometimes swooping full into the propellers. Within a few months they had caused ten plane crashes.

An expert from the Fish and Wildlife Service was dispatched to Midway Island to match wits with the gooney birds. He planned to make a three-pronged attack against the feathered foe: pilfering nests in the vicinity of the airstrips, sprucing up other parts of the island as nest-building sites, and broadcasting high frequency noises to drive the culprits away. Egg-smashing tactics succeeded during World War II when terns, another type of sea bird, threatened to take over Ascension Island off the west coast of Africa.

Until recently at least, all efforts to discourage the gooney birds had met with ignominious defeat. Nests were robbed and the birds proceeded to lay more eggs. Marked birds taken thousands of miles away returned within a short time. Nearby islands and other areas made into "ideal" nesting sites were almost completely disregarded. Within the last year or so, authorities have turned to the last resort of killing the birds. This development will doubtless cause bird lovers to be most unhappy, but it seems to be completely justified under the circumstances. I can see no logical reason why a batch of stubborn gooney birds should be treated any more gently than would a human enemy trying to take over the airbase.

Do Birds Spoil the Fisherman's Sport?

There are large numbers of birds that eat fish, although most of them supplement their diet with other items such as worms, insects, and even berries and seeds. Some of the best known fish-eating birds include kingfishers, herons, loons, grebes, ospreys, some eagles, mergansers, gulls, terns, and other sea birds.

In the past there has been much unjustified persecution of fish-eating birds. In many instances the fish that are eaten are non-game species, or, as in the case of the bald eagle, often dead or dying individuals. But occasionally certain species such as kingfishers, herons, and mergansers become too attentive to fish hatcheries, and under such circumstances they must be discouraged.

Recent studies indicate that fish-eating birds and animals may in many instances actually improve fishing. The concept is that if no fish are removed, there will often be too many in ponds and streams for the available food. Fish will, consequently, be numerous but undersized. On the other hand, if birds and other animals are allowed to share the fish, those remaining will have plenty of food and will rapidly attain a size lusty enough to satisfy any angler.

This theory seems justified by experience and observation. Reservoirs around which fish-eating birds have been slaughtered have contained large numbers of fish, most of them so small they could barely swallow a hook. In other areas, however, where fish-eaters have been tolerated, fishing remained good even though the birds caught fish estimated at many thousands of pounds per year.

Old-squaws, a type of duck, are an irritating hazard to fishermen. These ducks can probably dive deeper than any other bird, and in the Great Lakes they have been known to reach a depth of two hundred feet. Commercial fishermen, using enormous nets, have on more than one occasion laboriously hauled in a heavy catch only to find that the net was filled with dead or gabbling old-squaws. Not only do such catches limit the fish that are caught, but the birds often object to the indignity so strenuously that they manage to tear the net.

Birds that eat clams, mussels, and oysters apparently seldom cause great economic losses; however, their difficulties in opening the uncooperative shellfish deserve brief mention. Sea gulls, for instance, carry the clam or oyster into the air and drop it on rocks to crack the shells. The birds do not always distinguish between hard and soft landing spots, but sometimes, to the annoyance of motorists, select concrete bridges and highways.

Gulls are not the only birds that drop potential food from a height to reach the contents. The lammergeier or bearded vulture, an Old World species, drops the bones of animals on rocks in order to get at the marrow inside. They are also reported to drop turtles in this way to break open their shells. According to legend, the famous Greek poet, Aeschylus, was killed by a dropped turtle when a bearded vulture supposedly mistook the poet's bald head for a rock.

What Is the Largest Bird in the World?

The largest living bird, as far as height and weight are concerned, is the African ostrich. It does not even have any close competition for this honor. Large males have been found to measure 8 feet in height, and the maximum size is probably over 8 feet, with a weight of more than 300 pounds.

At least two groups of extinct birds were considerably larger than ostriches. These were the moas of New Zealand and the *Aepyornis* or elephant birds of Madagascar. Almost complete skeletons of the moas, 9 to 10 feet in height, have been found, and some biologists believe that the largest species may have attained the incredible height of 18 feet. The elephant birds were not so tall, but they were more massively built. Based upon skeletal remains, a biologist recently computed that the largest of the elephant birds probably weighed almost 1,000 pounds.

What Birds Have the Greatest Wingspread?

The two groups of birds that have the largest spread are the albatrosses and the condors, but there is no evidence that either of them has a wingspread of 17 or 18 feet, as has been reported. A recent edition of a well-known encyclopedia, for instance, states that the albatross may have a wingspread of 17 feet, but an expert on birds of this type, Robert Cushman Murphy of the American Museum of Natural History, says that this figure is far too high. The maximum spread for the wandering albatross is probably 11 feet 4 inches, a figure that represents the wingspread of the largest of hundreds of specimens measured by several different men. As for the condor, although greater spreads have been reported, the largest recent measurement that I have found was a fraction over 10 feet, for a condor shot by Murphy off the coast of Peru. The bird weighed 28½ pounds. Some biologists still maintain that the condor has the greater wingspread, but others, including myself, favor the albatross.

The wingspreads of a few species of large birds are indicated in the table on the next page.

CHART OF WINGSPREADS

Species	Probable Maximum Wingspread	Remarks
Wandering albatross	11 to 12 feet	11 feet 4 inches is the largest spread by actual measurement that can be accepted at present.
Condors	10 to 11 feet	The largest recent measurement of a South American condor which I have found was slightly over 10 feet.
Trumpeter swan	10 to 11 feet	One measurement of 10 feet 2 inches is on record.
Bearded vulture or lammer-geier	9 to 10 feet	Largest bird of prey in Europe; also found in parts of Asia.
King vulture	9 to 10 feet	Found in northern South America, Mexico, and Central America.
White pelican	8 to 9 feet	Found in Canada and south to Yellowstone Park. In winter seen along the Gulf Coast of the United States.
Great bustard	8 to 9 feet	A large gooselike game bird related to the cranes. Rather widely distributed in parts of Europe, Asia, and Africa.
Bald eagle	7 to 8 feet	Widely distributed over Canada, the United States, and on south into Mexico.
Golden eagle	7 to 8 feet	Widely distributed in North America, Europe, and Asia. In the United States, more common west of the Mississippi River.
Man-o-war or frigate bird	7 to 8 feet	Found in the United States chiefly off the coast of Florida. Also occurs farther south.
Whooping crane	7 to 8 feet	Found chiefly in Canada, although it migrates as far south as Texas in winter. Now exceedingly rare.

CHART OF WINGSPREADS—*Continued*

Species	Probable Maximum Wingspread	Remarks
Sandhill crane	6 to 7 feet	Rather widely distributed in Canada and the United States, but quite shy and seldom seen by the average person.
Brown pelican	6 to 7 feet	Occurs along the Atlantic and Gulf coasts of the United States and south into Central and South America.
Turkey vulture or buzzard	6 to 7 feet	I once measured a specimen with a wingspread of exactly 6 feet. Found over most of the United States and south into Central and South America.

How Fast Can Birds Fly?

There have probably been as many squabbles over the maximum flight speed of birds, as about any other characteristic of bird behavior. One reason for this is that before the development of accurate measuring devices, possible flight speeds were based on estimates. Some of these estimates were ridiculous in the light of present-day knowledge, since even some biologists believed that migration flights were made at speeds of as much as 400 to 500 miles per hour.

Today, even with the use of stop watches, airplanes, automobiles, and other devices, ornithologists are far from agreement as to which are the fastest flying birds. The main arguments seem to center around the methods used for making measurements and the accuracy of the instruments employed. A few of the fastest speeds reported should be of interest even though some of them are now questioned by various authorities.

Some years ago two species of swifts—birds related to the chimney swifts of the United States—were timed over a measured course of two miles in India. It was stated that the birds covered the distance in from 36 to 42 seconds, or at rates of approximately 171 to 200 miles per hour. Some swifts in Mesopotamia overtook and circled an airplane which was traveling at 68 miles per hour; estimated speed of the swifts was about 100 miles per hour. Other high speeds recorded by various methods include the following in miles per hour: frigate birds, 244; green plover, 120 to 185; godwits, at 150; and a curlew, 240. A European peregrine, a species frequently used in falconry, was timed with a stop watch during its dive after quarry and was estimated to have been diving at 165 to 180 miles per hour.

Colonel R. Meinertzhagen, well-known English authority on flight speeds, dismisses most of the above records as "pure fancy," and some of them do appear a bit excessive. Colonel Meinertzhagen believes that the fastest reliably measured flight speed is for a homing pigeon recorded at 94.3 miles per hour. He also states that there are several records for pigeons of over 90 miles per hour over a distance of 80 miles, and that one bird covered 182 miles at the rate of 73 miles per hour.

After this report appeared, Max C. Thompson of the Arctic Health Research Center published a paper on the flight speed of the red-breasted merganser, a type of duck. He stated that for a short distance one duck stayed ahead of an airplane traveling at 80 miles per hour and flying into a 20-mile-per-hour wind. Mr. Thompson calculated the ground speed of the bird at approximately 100 miles per hour.

It is true that homing pigeons have been selected for years for their speed as well as for their homing instincts. It is also possible that at least some of the reported high flight speeds are inaccurate. I suspect that a good homing pigeon could outdistance most species over a distance of 50 to 100 miles, but I would still put my money on some of the swifts and falcons in a race of a few miles.

Naturally, controversies among the experts do not make our task of deciding the true flight speeds of birds any easier. I, for one, believe that some birds can fly faster than the speeds listed in the table, and that some may even approach the top speeds previously noted. Until more positive proof is available, however, I must string along with the conservatives.

CHART OF FLIGHT SPEEDS

Species	Possible Speed in Miles per Hour	Remarks
Peregrine falcon	65 to 75	Used in falconry in Europe.
Ducks and geese	65 to 70	Usual speeds listed are 55 to 60 m.p.h. Higher reports include 66 m.p.h. for a ring-necked duck, 72 m.p.h. for a canvasback, and 100 m.p.h. for the merganser previously mentioned.

CHART OF FLIGHT SPEEDS—*Continued*

Species	Possible Speed in Miles per Hour	Remarks
European swift	60 to 65	
Golden plover	60 to 65	A record of 60 m.p.h. was obtained when these birds were chased by airplane; 70 m.p.h. speeds have also been reported.
Mourning dove	60 to 65	One bird timed at 60 m.p.h.
Hummingbirds	55 to 60	One speedometer reading gives 60 m.p.h.
Starlings	45 to 50	One report of 55 m.p.h.
Wading birds (sandpipers, curlews, etc.)	45 to 50	
Gannet	45 to 50	A large white, gull-like ocean bird with black-tipped wings. One measurement of 48 m.p.h. is on record.
Swallows	45 to 50	Usual flight speed 24 to 31 m.p.h.
American quail	40 to 45	One record of 44.5 m.p.h. with special radar device.
Crows	40 to 45	Usual speed 20 to 30 m.p.h.
Heron	35 to 40	One record gives 41 m.p.h.
Pheasant	35 to 40	One timed at 38.2 m.p.h. with special radar device.
English sparrow	35 to 40	One record of 35 m.p.h. with car speedometer.
Wild turkey	30 to 35	Special radar device reports one at 31.7 m.p.h.
Blue jay	25 to 30	One reading gives 20 m.p.h.; another 26 m.p.h.

How Long Do Birds Live?

Parrots and various kinds of eaglelike birds and swans are credited with sometimes living for 100 to 300 years. Even in relatively recent publications one finds reports of a vulture that lived to be 118 years old; a parrot, 120; and a golden eagle, 104. Most of these reports are for birds that were alive several hundred years ago; not even 75 years has been claimed for a bird in a relatively modern zoological park. Men who have investigated bird ages admit that some may live longer than presently established ages indicate, but until such extreme ages are verified these reported centenarians must be looked upon with suspicion.

Established bird ages include an eagle-owl of 68, a black-backed gull of 63, a condor of 52, a parrot of 54, an eagle of 55, and a white pelican of 51. Even some of the smaller birds live for a surprisingly long time. Accepted ages for small birds include a starling of 17, a canary of 22, an English sparrow of 23, and a red-crested cardinal of 30. The late Major Stanley Flower, who has probably done as much work investigating animal ages as any other man, believed that birds in general live longer than mammals. This same belief is shared by Dr. Alex Comfort, present-day authority on animal ages.

E G G S

What Is an Egg?

The egg of any bird is a more complicated production than superficial consideration would lead us to believe. The yellow or yolk of the egg is formed within the bird's reproductive organ or ovary. The yellow breaks out of the ovary, enters the upper end of the reproductive tract or oviduct, where the white is added; then travels down to the lower part of the tube where the membranes and shell are applied around the yellow and white. The egg then is ready to be laid—an accomplishment that the hen announces to the world with loud cacklings.

Only a small part of the egg is living material that will develop into a young bird or chicken. This is the small whitish spot in the yellow, which can easily be seen if a hen's egg is removed from the shell. During incubation the young chicken or bird is formed from the small living part of the egg, while the yolk and white serve as food material for the developing embryo. In fertilized eggs—and most eggs are fertilized unless roosters and hens are separated—a certain amount of development occurs before the egg is laid. Therefore, when one breakfasts upon a platter of eggs, one is in reality eating embryonic chickens.

What Makes Double Eggs?

Hens sometimes lay what is called a double egg, a large egg containing two yolks. The method of formation of the most common type of double egg is relatively simple. As a usual thing, only one yellow is discharged from the ovary at a time, the next one being released a day or so later. Sometimes, however, two yolks are liberated at once and pass down the reproductive tract very close together. The white, membranes, and shell are applied around both yellows, thus forming a double egg.

Sometimes a complete egg with a shell is found within another shell which also contains a white and yolk. An egg of this kind may be formed in one of several ways, as has been pointed out by the late Dr. J. T. Patterson of the University of Texas and other workers. In one method of formation, it is thought that one yellow is discharged from the ovary as usual and passes down the egg tube where white, membranes, and shell are applied to the outside. Then, instead of discharging the egg in the normal way, the reproductive tube goes into reverse and carries the fully formed egg back to the upper end near the ovary. By the time the egg has reached this part of the tube, another yellow has been discharged. When the movements of the egg tube again become normal, the complete egg and the recently liberated yolk are carried downward very close together. The glands in the wall of the tube apply white, membranes, and shell around both the yellow and the complete egg. The resulting oversize egg is then deposited as a double egg, probably to the pride, and certainly to the relief, of the responsible hen.

Do Roosters Ever Lay Eggs?

Very small eggs, sometimes only one-tenth the normal size, are occasionally found in hens' nests. Some people believe that these small eggs are laid by old roosters or cocks, and they are therefore sometimes called "cock" eggs. However, no rooster is capable of laying an egg of any size. The small eggs are laid by hens and are thought to be the result of a disturbance of the egg-producing mechanism. In some instances, a yolk smaller than normal is discharged from the ovary; in other cases, a loosened piece of tissue or other substance gains access to the oviduct, passes downward and in the regular way is coated with white, membranes, and shell. Usually the disturbance is temporary and the hen shortly produces normal eggs again.

What Bird Lays the Largest Eggs?

The egg of the ostrich is larger than that of any other living bird. Some investigators have amused themselves by breaking hens' eggs into the empty shell of an ostrich egg and, from these experiments, have found that an ostrich egg shell will hold from twelve to eighteen hens' eggs. Ostrich eggs measure 6 to 7 inches in length and 5 to 6 inches in diameter and, incidentally, require about forty minutes or longer for thorough boiling.

Although the ostrich egg seems huge when compared with the eggs of most living birds, there are some extinct species that would have probably been chagrined if they had laid an egg so small. The extinct elephant bird of Madagascar produced the largest egg that anyone knows anything about. Almost complete shells of these eggs have been discovered, some of them measuring 13 inches in length and 9½ inches in diameter. The shell will hold more than two gallons, which is six times as much as an ostrich egg will hold, and nearly 150 times the capacity of a hen's egg.

Hummingbirds produce the smallest eggs. Some of the smallest species, the vervair hummingbirds of Haiti and Jamaica, lay eggs that are only a quarter of an inch in length.

The kiwi, a flightless bird of New Zealand that weighs five or six pounds, holds another kind of record. It deposits an egg larger in proportion to body size than any other kind of bird. This tremendous nugget may weigh one-fourth as much as the proud bird that deposits it! Just before the egg is deposited, the hen kiwi would have trouble winning a race with a snail. Observers have stated that the great weight of the egg causes the female to stagger about as though she were inebriated. This great handicap limits escape from their enemies; small wonder that kiwis have become rare in many areas.

How Many Eggs Can Birds Lay?

Under normal conditions most birds lay a fairly definite number of eggs in a given batch or clutch. After this number is deposited the eggs are then incubated until they hatch. Some like the California condor, some of the sea birds, and certain penguins lay but a single egg per "sitting." Others, such as the American quail or bob-white, will lay twelve to twenty per batch.

Some birds, however, will lay considerably more than the usual number under special circumstances—if, for example, one continuously sneaks the eggs out of the nest after they are laid. Such nest robbers have obtained the following numbers of eggs from certain birds: grouse, 36; English sparrow, 51; flicker, 71; mallard duck, 146; American quail, 128; and, one jungle fowl, the species from which our domestic chickens were derived, actually deposited 309 before she became discouraged.

So far as domestic or wild fowls are concerned, the constant removal of the eggs not only assures the owner of fresh eggs for breakfast, but delays the development of the mother instinct—preventing the "biddies" from becoming broody. Surprisingly, champion ducks often outlay chickens. Some years ago, the domestic duck record was 363 eggs in 365 days; the champion hen for the same year produced 351 eggs. Some years later, the chicken record was increased to 361, and it may be that eventually a duck or chicken will reach the ideal of one egg per day for 365 days.

What Birds Do Not Incubate Their Eggs?

Although most birds incubate their eggs by sitting on them, a few species have found ways to relieve themselves of the chore. One of the most ingenious methods has been perfected by the mound birds or brush turkeys of Australia, the East Indies, and adjacent areas. These birds scratch together a large pile of sticks, leaves, and dirt, lay their eggs near the top of the mound, and then cover them. The heat from the sun and the heat generated as the vegetation decomposes hatches the eggs. Several birds use the same place year after year, building a community incubator, so that some of the mounds are 14 or 15 feet high and 30 to 35 feet in diameter. The crocodile bird of Africa makes use of a similar principle; it lays its eggs in the sand where they are hatched solely by the heat of the sun.

Husbands That Do the Household Chores

The males of several kinds of birds help in the incubation of the eggs, but the outstanding example of a henpecked husband is the phalarope, several species of which are found in the United States. Phalaropes are medium-sized birds with long beaks and long legs and have the same general appearance as sandpipers, except that the female is more brilliantly colored than the male, a condition that seldom occurs among birds. The male builds the nest, is courted by the female and, after the eggs are laid, takes over the entire responsibility of incubating them.

The assistance given by any male bird during incubation is not entirely unselfish. During the incubation season, some birds develop areas of inflammation on their breasts, called hatching spots, which are somewhat irritating, and it is believed that the coolness of the egg surface relieves the irritation. In those species in which only the female develops the spots, the male does not help in the incubation process. When such spots occur the male invariably takes his turn on the nest.

MIGRATION

Do Any Birds Hibernate?

Before it was known that many birds migrated, various weird theories were advanced to explain their disappearance from certain regions during a part of the year. One idea was that birds hibernated during the winter in caves, hollow trees, and similar places. Swallows, for instance, were said to hibernate in the mud at the bottom of lakes and streams. In fact, one list of books and articles dealing with the hibernation of swallows contained no less than 175 titles. Until recently biologists did not believe that any bird hibernated. But within the past few years, birds known as poor-wills, related to nighthawks and whip-poor-wills, have on several occasions been found hibernating in caves and other secluded spots. Ornithologists now accept the fact that at least some poor-wills hibernate, and there have been unconfirmed claims that other species do also. Migration, however, is the way that most birds in temperate countries avoid the inclement weather of winter.

Even after some of the facts of migration were known, a number of strange theories prevailed. One of the most interesting was that the larger birds, especially cranes, carried the smaller birds on their backs during the migratory flight. It is now known that this does not happen, but the belief is still prevalent in some places. During the past fifty years a considerable amount of work has been done on bird migration, but it still presents many unsolved problems. Many factors are known to influence migration—amount of food available, relative length of day and night, temperature, and changes in the birds' reproductive organs at different periods of the year—but a number of other factors not yet discovered probably also play a part.

What Bird Travels 20,000 Miles a Year?

Several species of birds have long migratory routes, but the champion migrants of them all are the arctic terns. These amazing birds make a round-trip migration each year of 20,000 to 22,000 miles, although probably not all of them fly quite that far. They nest over a wide range, from the arctic circle as far south as Massachusetts; in winter some are found even within the antarctic circle. It is thought that the tern makes the trip in about twenty weeks, averaging over 1,000 miles a week. This seems even more remarkable when one remembers that much of the time is spent searching for food. The arctic tern experiences more daylight than any other animal. Traveling back and forth between the arctic and the antarctic, and in its nesting and winter quarters, it is constantly in areas where the daylight hours are longest.

Most land birds make comparatively short hops during their migrations, but some must fly for long distances over open water with no chance to alight on land. The golden plovers make the longest nonstop flight over open ocean. The American golden plover, which nests in the arctic region of North America, starts its southern flight from Labrador or Nova Scotia and, so far as is known, flies directly to northern South America, a distance of 2,400 to 2,500 miles. This is thought to be a nonstop flight, but some biologists suspect that the birds may rest occasionally on the water. The Pacific golden plover also takes a remarkable migratory route over open ocean. After its nesting season is over in Alaska, Siberia, and adjacent regions, it migrates to Hawaii.

Do Birds Migrate on the Same Day Each Year?

No birds begin their migration on the same day each year, but there are some that do not vary the day a great deal. Probably the most remarkable in this respect is the slender-billed shearwater or mutton bird, a marine bird that nests in countless thousands on Phillips and Green Islands between Tasmania and southern Australia. Year in and year out there may be a few days' difference in the time of their arrival, but once a few strag-

Migration of Arctic Tern
(*The birds nest in the far north, winter in the Antarctic region.*)

glers start flying in, the time of arrival of the rest, according to Ludlow Griscom, well-known ornithologist, can be predicted almost to the quarter hour. If a few birds arrive on, say, Monday, November 22, the mass of the breeding population is almost sure to arrive at Green Island on Wednesday, November 24 at 8 P.M.

The cliff swallows of Capistrano, California, also have a famous reputation for regularity; they furnish material for sensational newspaper articles once or twice each year. Cliff swallows nest in colonies and build their flask-shaped mud nests in a variety of places including banks, the eaves of buildings and other sheltered spots. Some of these birds have nested for years at the San Juan Capistrano Mission, and an interesting tale has grown up regarding the regularity with which this colony enters upon its migration. According to the story, the swallows always leave the mission on October 23 for their southward migration and, as regular as clockwork, return on March 19. Nor does the extra day in leap years confuse them; if we are to believe reports, they take this change into consideration, since they still depart and arrive on their favorite dates! Observations of biologists have failed to confirm the reported regularity of their migration; the dates of departure and arrival have been found to vary from year to year. Despite scientific opinion, however, newspapers will continue to have a biennial field day with the legend.

EXTINCT BIRDS

Was the Roc a Real Bird?

Many readers will doubtless recall the adventures of Sinbad the Sailor of Arabian Nights fame, who was carried away by a huge bird called a roc. The existence of such a bird was also supported by Marco Polo, who wrote of a legend of the natives of Madagascar. According to this story, birds of tremendous size had been seen to seize elephants in their claws, carry them, struggling, to great heights and drop them, then settle on the carcasses and eat their fill. Like the thunderbird of Indian legend, the roc was also said to prey upon human beings and domesticated animals.

There is no evidence that enormous birds of this type ever existed, but skeletons and egg shells of a large extinct species have been found in Madagascar, which may have given rise to the story of the roc. These birds, however, could not have flown away with a field mouse, much less an elephant, for they could not fly at all. Variously called rocs, elephant birds, or giant birds, they were larger than ostrichs, but the most remarkable thing about them was the size of their eggs, mentioned on page 124.

The Dodo Was a Real Bird

Most everyone knows the meaning of the expression "dead as a dodo," but many people do not realize that the bird was once very much alive. A peculiar, clumsy, flightless bird about the size of a turkey, it was first discovered in 1507 on the island of Mauritius off the west coast of Madagascar. Sailors used them for food, killing them with such ease that they called the birds "doudos," or stupid. Today, the term *dodo* is frequently applied to stupid people. Dogs, rats, pigs, and people killed the young birds indiscriminately and ate the eggs, with the result that less than 200 years after their discovery the dodos were extinct. The few restorations in various museums were made long after the last bird was dead. It is thus possible that the real dodo was somewhat less ridiculous in appearance than the restorations would lead us to believe.

How Did the Passenger Pigeon Become Extinct?

Seventy or eighty years ago there were probably more passenger pigeons in the United States than any other single species of bird. Today not a single living specimen remains. The last wild bird was seen in 1906. The last one in captivity was "Martha," a female hatched at the Cincinnati Zoo where she lived to the ripe old age of 26. When it grew apparent that the passenger pigeon was rapidly becoming extinct, the zoo made efforts to save the species and offered large rewards for a male, but without results. Efforts to cross the female with other species also failed, and on September 1, 1914, Martha died, the last representative of a once numerous race. Fortunately, Martha was not tossed into an ash can, as are many dead birds. She was mounted and is now on exhibition at the Smithsonian Institution in Washington, D.C.

This pigeon, larger than the common mourning dove but similar in general appearance, ranged at one time over most of the eastern part of the North American continent. The birds flew in huge flocks, some of which were estimated to contain between one and two billion birds; when they were on the move, they literally hid the sun. Unfortunately, they nested in great colonies, a habit probably more responsible for their extinction than any other one factor. The birds were a popular food, and their nesting areas were raided and the young and adults killed and shipped by the carloads. When the food markets became glutted, the birds were fed to hogs or were used for fertilizer. Even countless millions could not withstand this ruthless slaughter. Today a few unexciting specimens, peering vacantly through glass eyes from museum cases, are all that remain of the passenger pigeon.

FLIGHTLESS BIRDS

What Birds Cannot Fly?

Birds that cannot fly include the well-known ostrich, a native of Africa, the emu and cassowary of Australia, the rhea of South America, and the kiwi or apteryx of New Zealand. With the exception of the kiwi, however, these birds have fairly well-developed wings. The wings of the kiwi are mere stubs, so that the bird appears to be entirely wingless.

The running speed of some of these flightless birds somewhat compensates for their inability to fly. The two chief competitors for the title of the fastest running bird are the ostrich and the emu. The ostrich has been said to have run 50 miles per hour when chased by a car, but this is questionable, and biologists believe that other recorded speeds of 28 to 37 miles per hour are more accurate. Emus have been timed at approximately 40 miles per hour, and some biologists believe that this bird can outrun the ostrich. Ostriches at top speed have been known to take strides as long as 28 feet, and I have an idea that they can move their knobby feet just as fast as the emu. At any rate, if the chips were down, my choice would be the ostrich.

The name emu is probably more familiar to crossword puzzle fans than the name of any other flightless bird, with the exception of the ostrich. Emus are natives of Australia, but they have become rare in some areas. The male is smaller than the female; after the eggs are laid, he incubates them and takes care of the resulting brood of chicks.

Do Ostriches Stick Their Heads in the Sand?

One of the most prevalent beliefs about ostriches is that, when frightened, they stick their heads in the sand and feel perfectly content that they are safely hidden. When an ostrich has its head in the sand, so the story goes, one can walk up to it and pluck its feathers or capture it easily.

Stupid as the ostrich undoubtedly is, even the most critical authorities do not believe it is stupid enough to stick its head in the sand, and no one has ever observed this action in either captive or wild birds. However, they do have an interesting habit which may have given rise to the story. When sighting possible danger from afar, ostriches sometimes drop to the ground, stretch their necks out parallel with it and watch intently. When the danger is imminent, however, the ostrich reacts as other animals do and beats a hasty retreat.

Is It True That Ostriches Will Eat Anything?

Ostriches are likely to swallow practically any small or medium-sized object that is offered to them. Being perhaps too trustful of human beings, who offer them ice picks, files, and other "delicacies" to eat, they cannot be relied on to judge what they can digest successfully, and many zoological parks have lost valuable birds as a result of this indiscriminate appetite.

Ostriches can survive a reasonable amount of foreign substances and, like many other birds, actually require stones and pebbles for the proper functioning of the digestive system. It may be that captive ostriches swallow the harmful object offered them because they do not get enough pebbles or the proper food in captivity. Certain it is that if wild birds ate as much indigestible material as do captive birds, the ostrich clan would shortly become extinct.

ALBATROSSES

Do Sea Birds Drink Sea Water?

At least some sea birds can drink sea water without harm, and in many instances they prefer it to fresh water. In fact, some species cannot live without sea water. Penguins, shearwaters, terns, and albatrosses are among those birds that drink marine water. Even though some penguins drink either salty or fresh water, at least one young penguin is known to have died presumably because it drank too much fresh water. Certain albatrosses will die if they are not given sea water soon after being placed into captivity.

For a long time physiologists doubted that sea birds drank sea water. Even after this fact was established, it was not known how they accomplished it and remained healthy. It is now known that the birds can do this because they have glands in the nasal passages that excrete the excess salt. The body processes involved in taking in sea water and excreting the excess salt are apparently necessary to the health of many birds. Observers have stated that some albatrosses are happiest when their salt glands are discharging excess material so rapidly that they have a dripping nose! Other birds, such as certain sparrows that frequent salt marshes, are also known to drink sea water on occasion.

Fledglings That Are Larger than Their Parents

Some young birds actually shrink in the process of becoming adults. This phenomenon has been investigated in several species. The young of some swallows, for instance, have been found to be as much as 25 per cent larger than their parents. The characteristic is probably true of other birds also, including eagles, hawks, and several of the sea birds; for the young birds appear considerably larger and heavier than the adults.

It is easy to see that such an arrangement could be an advantage. Many sea birds, such as the albatrosses and the shearwaters, feed their young until they are almost bursting with accumulated fat. When the young birds have completed their growth, the parents fly away over the ocean, leaving the fledglings to shift for themselves. The layers of stored-up fat are now of prime importance, since the sudden shift from dependence to enforced independence is quite drastic. By the time the young birds have learned the tricks of obtaining food and of flying, they have used up most of the reserve food supply in their bodies and are approximately the size of their parents.

PENGUINS

Are There Penguins at the North Pole?

Penguins are found only in the areas south of the equator where, as a group, they have a fairly wide distribution. Some species are found on various South Sea Islands, in parts of Australia, New Zealand, and in some parts of South America. At least one species is found as far north as the coastal regions of Peru. Auks and puffins, found in the arctic regions, greatly resemble penguins, and the two groups may be confused by people who are not biologists. Penguins are flightless, but auks and puffins are able to fly.

What Birds Have a Common Burial Ground?

One of the most persistent animal stories, chiefly heard in connection with elephants, is that some animals have community graveyards. Though much talked about, however, none was ever found until Dr. Robert Cushman Murphy, of the American Museum of Natural History, recently discovered a penguin burial ground on South Georgia Island in the antarctic.

There was a large colony of penguins on the island, but Dr. Murphy noticed that there were seldom any dead birds to be found. Before leaving the island, he discovered why. One day he found a small clear lake on top of a hill some distance from the ocean. Around the edge of the lake were several droopy penguins, obviously sick or seriously injured. Further examination revealed that the bottom of the lake was literally covered with dead penguins, the icy cold water having preserved the bodies in perfect condition. Apparently most of the seriously ill or injured birds of the colony came to this quiet spot and enjoyed a few moments of peace before consigning themselves to their watery graves.

So far as I know, this penguin graveyard is the only common burial ground of animals that has ever been discovered. I have not found a report of a similar practice among other groups of penguins.

CORMORANTS AND PELICANS

What Wild Birds Are Responsible for an Industry?

The Chincha Islands lie off the west coast of Peru. On these small dots of land live the most valuable birds in the world. For centuries great numbers of sea birds have been nesting on these islands, and their droppings accumulated until the material was many feet thick in some places. At last someone got the bright idea that this guano would make excellent fertilizer, and it was consequently removed and sent all over the world by the shipload. For many years guano from the Chincha Islands supplied much of the world's fertilizer, to the great satisfaction of the Peruvian government and everyone connected with the industry. Within recent years other types of fertilizer have tended to replace guano, but it is still used to some extent.

The majority of the birds that nest on the islands are a kind of cormorant, appropriately called guanjays, or guanays; other sea birds, such as gulls, terns, and pelicans are well represented. In some parts of the islands the birds produce guano at the rate of 750 tons an acre per year, which gives one an idea of the tremendous numbers of birds involved.

Visitors who have seen these islands say that the nesting birds are not especially afraid of human beings, and that in some places the nests on the ground are so numerous that one has difficulty walking through the pecking, squawking females. But such man-made vehicles as airplanes and steamships do bother them, and now rigid laws prevent the approach of airplanes and the blowing of ships' whistles in the vicinity of the islands, lest the disturbance cause the birds to seek more isolated areas for their nests.

Birds That Catch Fish for Men

Cormorants are large birds with webbed feet and hooked beaks that feed almost entirely on fish. They capture their food by diving into the water and using both legs and wings to overhaul their prey. They frequently seem to fish for sheer enjoyment, for they sometimes continue fishing after they have stuffed themselves to capacity.

In parts of the Orient natives have taken practical advantage of the cormorant's ability as a fisherman. Young birds are caught and trained to fish for the natives rather than for themselves. At first, each bird has a ring around its neck to prevent it from swallowing the fish it catches, but eventually some of them become so well trained that they can be trusted without ring or leash and will not swallow a fish until given permission to do so. The birds are trained to bring their catch to the boats, where they are frequently rewarded with bits of fish or with fish too small to be of commercial value.

Sometimes several cormorants may cooperate and round up scattered fish into compact and more easily caught shoals, and two or more may gang up on a fish too large for a single bird to manage. Well-trained birds are of considerable value to their owners; it has been said that some cormorants may catch as many as one hundred fish in an hour.

How Does the Pelican Use Its Pouch?

The long beak of the pelican, with the large pouch attached to its lower jaw, makes it one of the most peculiar looking of all birds. However, not only is the large pouch of considerable use to the adult pelican, but without it the young pelicans would not get fed nearly so well.

Pelicans feed primarily on fish, and the pouch is a very efficient fish net. If the bird, as it flies along, sights a fish in the water below, it drops like a rock with a splash that can be heard for half a mile. If there is only a single fish the pelican will seize and swallow it, but if there is a shoal, the pelican is really in its element. It swims forward, using its pouch as a scoop net. When the pouch is full of water and fish, the bird closes its mouth, and the water drains out leaving the fish safely caught in the pouch. If the fishing is good, the pelican may not stop to eat, but may rush back into the game until its bag is bulging. The capacity of the pouch is enormous, and it can be stretched considerably; one writer states that it can hold as much as forty pounds of fish. However, I doubt if even such a large bird as a pelican could keep from falling on its face with so heavy a load; certainly it could not fly.

The pouch, like all good fish nets, is dried or at least aired occasionally. The bird tilts its head backward and opens its beak widely, causing the pouch to spread out over its chest. There the pelican stands, with its mouth agape and its bare pouch hanging out, certainly one of the most ridiculous sights in the bird world.

Young pelicans are fed by regurgitation, and the pouch makes a handy serving bowl. The mother pelican opens her mouth, burps, and a quart or so of ill-smelling, but wholly enjoyable, fish soup flows into the pouch. The

young stick their heads in and greedily consume the contents of the pouch, sometimes almost falling into it in their eagerness to get their stomachs full. It was at one time thought that live fish in water were carried in the pouch to the young, but there is no evidence to support this theory.

SHOREBIRDS AND GULL-LIKE BIRDS

What Bird Picks the Teeth of Crocodiles?

The black-backed courser of Africa or Egyptian plover, a medium-sized bird related to the sandpipers, has earned the name of crocodile bird because of its association with crocodiles. Crocodiles have a habit of basking in the sun for long periods and frequently lie with their mouths partially open. Parts of their bodies, including the inside of their mouths, are sometimes infested with leeches, parasitic worms related to the familiar and considerably less detestable earthworms. Crocodile birds are quite fond of these leeches, and pick large numbers of them from the crocodiles' bodies. If the body pickings are slim, the bird will enter the partly open mouth of the crocodile and gobble up any leeches lurking within as well as bits of food lodged between the teeth. As soon as its meal is finished, the bird, which apparently does not put too much trust in the crocodile, flies out backward, not even taking the time to turn around. Some authorities doubt the reports of this habit, but it has been observed in at least one captive bird and is apparently accepted by most biologists who have investigated the matter.

A Bird That Walks on Water

One of the oddest sights in the bird world is a medium-sized, blackish bird apparently walking about on the surface of the water. This peculiar bird is the jaçana, a relative of the plovers. Unfortunately for anyone who would like to tell an excellent bird story, the jaçana does not actually walk on the water, although from a distance it appears to be doing just that. Actually, it is walking on lily pads and other aquatic vegetation, which, under its weight, sink out of sight below the water surface. This still rather remarkable feat is made possible by the bird's very long toes which have a span sufficient to stretch over parts of several leaves, thus distributing the bird's weight. Examining a specimen at close range, one's eyes are continually drawn to its absurdly large feet.

Aside from its feet, the jaçana at rest does not have an especially striking appearance. Its general color is a greenish black, but if it is disturbed there is a flutter of brilliant yellowish-green which was hidden when the wings were folded, and the bird is away with its long trailing toes clearly visible. A jaçana in flight should not be confused with any other species, since there is no other black bird in the American tropics with yellow wings. Most jaçanas are tropical in distribution, but one species extends as far north as southern Texas.

Do Any Birds Carry Their Young in Their Beak?

There are at least three kinds of birds that have been reported to move their young from one place to another. These are the wood duck, the hooded merganser (also a kind of duck), and the American woodcock, a relative of the sandpipers. The wood duck and the merganser, both of which build their nests some distance from the water in hollow trees, are said to move the newly hatched youngsters to the water. According to eyewitnesses, the young are sometimes carried in the beak, and sometimes on the back of the female. The woodcock is supposed to move its young when danger threatens by picking them up by the feet and legs.

I have seen several publications by biologists who claimed to have seen one or the other of these birds move their young, but most of these were published many years ago. Some present-day ornithologists state that they do not believe that this occurs; others simply ignore the problem.

Under the circumstances, I can see only two choices open to people looking for an answer to this question: to accept as true reported observations, until more evidence is forthcoming; or to consider that several reputable early biologists were unmitigated liars. I am not prepared to do the latter, and as a consequence, accept that these birds do occasionally move their young as reported.

I do not believe that moving the young is a routine procedure, however. There are many reports of eyewitnesses seeing the young ducks jump from the hollow tree nest and flutter to the ground. I suspect that this is the method usually used by young wood ducks and mergansers. When danger threatens her young, the female woodcock often puts on a great act of being injured, presumably to attract the danger away from her brood. This protective action may be taken much more often than the shuttle method of moving the youngsters.

TURKEYS AND OTHER FOWL-LIKE BIRDS

How Did the Turkey Get Its Name?

The rather incongruous name, turkey, now used for the birds both wild and domesticated, is closely connected with the history of the domestication of the fowls. When the Spaniards conquered the Aztecs in Mexico, they found that the Indians had domesticated an interesting bird; the males strutted about in pompous fashion and made peculiar gobbling noises. The Spaniards introduced these birds into Europe, where the people promptly confused them with guinea fowls. The guinea fowl, a native of Africa, was known as a turkey in some areas because some of the domesticated stock had been imported from Turkey. Out of this confusion, the American fowls were also called turkeys. Just why the North American bird should have completely usurped this title is not recorded. Whatever the reason, we today have a bird of New World origin with an inappropriate Old World name.

The domestic and the wild turkeys found in the United States are similar in general appearance, but in one way the two can be easily distinguished. The tips of the tail feathers of the domestic turkeys are white; in wild turkeys they are brown. Most domesticated turkeys came originally from the Mexican wild turkey, a variety different from the wild turkey of the United States. The Mexican variety has white-tipped tail feathers, a feature it passed on to its domestic descendants.

When the Pilgrims first came to North America, the wild turkey was a common species all over the eastern part of the country. However, our ancestors hunted the birds so enthusiastically that they were virtually exterminated in the New England states before 1850.

For a time it was feared that the wild turkey in the United States would go the way of the dodo and the passenger pigeon, but apparently the public woke up in time. Hunting regulations and conservation practices have caused a small increase in numbers of the birds. One phase of the assistance program for the wild turkey has apparently been a complete flop, not because of a lack of effort on the part of conservationists, but because of an idiotic reaction of the turkeys themselves. The idea was conceived of increasing the population of wild turkeys by rearing the birds in captivity and releasing them at appropriate times. Wild turkeys have been reared successfully in captivity; the difficulty arises at graduation. Most of them refuse to become wild. The birds often proceed to join the first flock of tame turkeys they contact.

This adoption of the "line of least resistance" is also a problem when certain other wild birds, such as ducks and geese, are reared in captivity. Perhaps this method of propagation has been more successful with the ring-necked pheasant, a bird imported from China, than with any other species of bird. Pheasants will usually readily accept their freedom, but many fall easy prey to predators before they learn to fend for themselves.

In addition to turkeys, geese, ducks, and chickens are the only domesticated birds of major commercial importance, and the probable origin of each of these goes far back in history. Geese are recorded in ancient Chinese, Indian, and Egyptian writings, and it is thought probable that the goose was the first bird domesticated by man. Most domestic geese were probably derived from the graylag goose, a wild species still fairly common in parts of Europe. Domestic ducks are thought to have been developed from the wild mallard of Europe, a species related to the mallard duck of North America.

There are probably more chickens than all other domestic fowls, and certainly the chicken is by far the most important. It is maintained on good authority that, except for dairy products, more food for man of animal origin is derived from poultry than from any other one source. All present-day chickens—from the massive 12-pound brahma to the less-than-a-pound bantam, from the pugnacious fighting game cock to the Japanese fowl with 12-foot tail feathers—came originally from the jungle fowls of Asia.

Can Any Bird Fly When Hatched?

Many kinds of birds when first hatched have practically no feathers, and it is several days or even weeks before they are able to fly. An outstanding exception is the brush turkey or mound bird of Australia and adjacent areas. The young birds when hatched have a complete coat of feathers and are able to fly almost immediately.

VULTURES, HAWKS, AND EAGLES

Are All Hawks Harmful?

Most people make no attempt to distinguish between the different species of hawks which have an evil reputation because some are confirmed eaters of chickens and small birds. As a result, perhaps no birds have been persecuted as much as these.

Studies of the stomachs of many kinds of hawks have shown that few do more harm than good. The exceptions include Cooper's hawk, a medium-sized species that kills game birds, songbirds, and chickens, and the smaller sharp-shinned hawk that feeds mainly on songbirds. Unfortunately these hawks are secretive in their habits and are such rapid fliers that they are seldom seen.

The majority of larger soaring hawks that are most often seen in the sky are either beneficial or at least compensate for any damage by their positive contributions. Large numbers of rats, mice, gophers, insects, and other animals that might otherwise eat the farmer out of house and home, are partially controlled by these birds of prey.

Today many enlightened states have laws protecting these hawks, but some years ago "scalp acts" in several states offered a bounty for every hawk and owl that was killed. One such law, in effect a year and a half, accounted for state payments of approximately $90,000 for more than 100,000 hawks and owls killed during the period. A biologist then made some interesting observations on the "savings" realized by the state from this law. He estimated a potential poultry loss during this period (attributable to hawks and owls) at about $1,875—an amount saved by a $90,000 expenditure. Then, estimating the damage done by rats, mice, and other rodents still alive because of the decimated hawk and owl population, our biologist assessed the losses at more than $3 million. These figures added up to the interesting if absurd total of more than $2,000 spent for each dollar saved. The scalp act was hastily repealed.

Are Eagles Harmful?

Eagles, which are related to hawks, have had their share of persecution. Of the two kinds of eagles in the United States—the golden eagle and the bald eagle—the latter today is most often seen only on dollar bills, coins, and on the seals of states and nations. At one time the bald or American eagle, the national emblem of the United States, was relatively common in this country as far north as Alaska. To paraphrase a statement of one biologist: the American eagle is common everywhere except where it should be—in the American skies. As a result of indiscriminate killing, bald eagles now occur in fair numbers only in Florida and Alaska. There was in Alaska for many years a $2 bounty on the bald eagle which resulted in the killing of more than 100,000, and the protective laws finally enacted in the United States may have been passed too late to prevent eventual extinction.

At one time it was thought that the bald eagle killed a significant number of fur-bearing animals and valuable game birds and that, in Alaska, it destroyed many salmon. Because of its regal bearing and appearance, the bald eagle has a reputation for aggressiveness. But detailed investigations of its habits have punctured this idea. The studies indicate that the birds feed primarily on fish. An eagle will sometimes pursue a fish hawk or osprey and force the smaller bird to drop a fish it has captured. Most of the eagle's alleged aggressiveness, however, seems to be directed against dead and often putrid fish which it finds washed up on shore. The birds do occasionally kill small mammals and game birds, but as often as not, the latter are birds that have been wounded by hunters.

The final blow comes when we learn that the bravery of the bald eagle is, to put it tactfully, open to question. Great horned owls, much smaller but more aggressive birds, have been known on more than one occasion

summarily to take over an eagle's nest and drive the rightful owners away. Those responsible for selecting the bald eagle as the national emblem of the United States apparently knew little of the bird's habits and reactions.

The golden eagle is found also in Europe and Asia. Much more deserving of its reputation for aggressiveness than its white-topped cousin, this species feeds upon various kinds of animals and occasionally attacks such large mammals as deer. A pair of golden eagles was once observed to keep a whole flock of much larger California condors at a distance until the former had finished their meal. For years Asiatic tribes have trained these truculent birds to help capture antelope and other game.

In this country the golden eagle is not protected by federal law, but it is by some state laws. Its food normally consists of small mammals—rats, gophers, ground squirrels, and rabbits. A few snakes and fish will be eaten, and the eagles, if hungry, may snatch an occasional turkey, deer, calf, or lamb.

In some regions where the golden eagle is unprotected by law, ranchers have pooled their resources and offered bounties for the birds. A recent innovation has been to hunt them from airplanes; one hunter has been reported to have killed, in this way, more than 500 golden eagles within recent years. Since they do occasionally kill stock, perhaps the number of birds in some areas needs to be kept within reasonable bounds, but their routine food habits hardly seem to justify methods aimed at total extermination.

Do Eagles Carry Off Young Children?

Most of the stories about attacks by eagles and other birds of prey upon human beings raise two separate though related questions. Do birds of prey carry off young children? Will they make unprovoked attacks upon human beings?

All the accounts that I have seen of young children who were carried away by these birds date back many years. Thus we read of a bearded vulture's attacking a three-year-old child in Switzerland in 1763 and carrying it for half a mile before the bird was discovered and driven away. Some years later, a white-tailed sea eagle was reported to have carried a child to its nest and killed it before the rescue party arrived. This happened in the Faroe Islands, north of the British Isles, and was supposed to have been well verified.

One of the most important factors to be considered in determining the truth of such stories is the maximum weight these birds are capable of carrying. One story states that two men in the Canadian Rockies saw a golden eagle flying at a low altitude with an animal in its claws. The men shouted and the eagle dropped its prey, a fawn mule deer said to have weighed nearly fifteen pounds. Experiments with golden eagles, however, have shown that for some birds seven to eight pounds is about the maximum weights they can carry, and it is not thought that even larger species or individuals can carry more than seventeen or eighteen pounds. The feet of condors, the largest birds of prey, and of most of the vultures, such as the bearded vulture, are relatively weak, so that they are not capable of carrying as heavy a load in their claws as are some of the eagles. It therefore seems impossible that any bird of prey could fly with any child except a very young infant. Despite many supposedly authentic stories, I do not believe that there is a single verified case. On the other hand, I see no reason why, in remote areas where the birds have not learned to fear man, they might not attack and carry off a very small unguarded baby just as they would attack a rabbit or other animal.

There have been several relatively recent reports of eagles making unprovoked attacks on human beings, and some of them at least appear to be well authenticated. In one case, reportedly investigated by Edward H. Forbush, an ornithologist, a golden eagle attacked a nine-year-old girl. Fortunately, her parents were near, rushed to the rescue, and killed the bird with some difficulty. The girl suffered lacerations and bruises. In another case reported from Scotland, a golden eagle, which earlier in the day had missed a meal when the bird it was pursuing fell exhausted at the feet of a hunter, some time later attacked the hunter. Before the man knew what was happening, the eagle had fastened its claws in his ankle. It hung on grimly, and the man would probably have been seriously injured had not his dog attacked the eagle. As it was, the bird was killed only after a considerable fight, and even then its talons had to be cut from the man's leg.

I see no reason to doubt these stories. Eagles, condors, and vultures have been known to kill even such large active animals as sheep, antelopes, and coyotes, eating them on the spot and making no attempt to carry them away. Bearded vultures have been seen to knock sheep and other animals from high cliffs and to feed on the fallen carcasses. Birds of prey that have not learned to fear man might as readily attack a human being as some other animal.

What Was the Thunderbird?

Many tribes of Indians relate tales of a gigantic eaglelike bird which many, many years ago was the scourge of the western plains. These enormous thunderbirds, as they were called, were supposed to carry off human beings and were even reported to feed upon bison. One story tells of the battle of a young Indian chief with a thunderbird that had recently seized and carried away his wife. Although a brave man, the Indian realized that a single human being armed only with bow and arrows would stand no chance against such an adversary as the thunderbird; so he decided to try to kill the bird by trickery. Consequently, he selected a group of his friends and had them conceal themselves near the thunderbird's nest. The warrior then strode forth and shouted his defiance to his enemy. The great bird swooped down to seize him and was promptly slain by a volley of arrows shot by the warrior's friends.

Such tales have been scoffed at by biologists for many years, but the discovery in California of the remains of an enormous eaglelike bird proves that birds of prey much larger than living species did exist in the past. The skull of this monster bird is twice the size of the bald eagle's, its other bones being also proportionately larger. It thus seems quite possible that the thunderbird legend of the western Indians was based upon a bird that actually did exist at one time and it may be that the bird also attacked human beings. However, it is doubtful that even these great birds could have carried anyone off, or that they would have been capable of killing a bison.

How Do American Buzzards Find Dead Animals?

There has been considerable argument over whether sight or smell is more important to American buzzards and vultures in locating dead animals, and even today the question is not entirely settled. A rather crude experiment which I tried when I was a boy may prove of interest. A friend and I had been hunting very unsuccessfully for several hours and we sat down to rest for a time. We had recently heard a discussion of this question, and we decided to try to attract some buzzards by using our bodies for bait. These birds were numerous in the general area, but since none was in sight at that time we lay down in an open field near some trees and remained motionless. Within a few minutes a turkey buzzard sailed into view, and it was very shortly joined by several others. After circling for a time, the birds settled in the nearby trees and peered hungrily at our bodies. After many more hopeful birds joined the waiting throng, we became tired of the experiment, got to our feet and resumed the hunt. There was a great beating of wings as the buzzards flapped off in disgust to look for more fertile fields. In this particular case, it is fervently hoped that the sense of sight was the most important in the locating of the bodies.

Other investigators have discovered, however, that the birds have found bodies of animals that were completely covered, and in a few cases buzzards have found animal carcasses within a short time after they had been placed out at night. These actions seem to show that the sense of smell was involved more than the sense of sight. It seems quite probable that both sight and smell may be used, and that the relative importance depends upon the situation. I personally believe that sight is the most important for the location of food at great distances, but that the sense of smell probably functions in finding putrefying carcasses that are concealed from view.

OWLS

Are Owls Beneficial?

Probably even more beneficial as a group than hawks are the owls; the number of pests they destroy is amazing. The great horned owl, considered the villain of the owl clan, sometimes destroys game birds and poultry; yet

even this slightly disreputable member of the group kills large numbers of pests. One study, in which more than 125 stomachs of the great horned owl were examined, found only 31 containing game birds and poultry. The remainder had eaten everything from insects to mice, a useful occupation for the species that is almost universally condemned.

Barn owls, which occur in Europe and other areas in addition to North America, are probably the most beneficial. They feed primarily on rats, mice, and other harmful rodents. A biologist recently examined the bones and other remains from one barn owl nest over a three-month period. He found that at least 240 different animals had been consumed during this period. Of these he was able to identify 89 field mice, 93 gophers, 27 kangaroo mice, 7 moles, 4 ground squirrels, and 3 rabbits. He was not able to identify the remaining 17 animals.

Owls are better mousers and ratters than the usual domestic cat. A man once had a severely rat-infested cellar; he procured several cats to rid the premises of the pests. Each morning when the cellar door was opened, the cats rushed out, spitting and hissing with fear. Since the felines seemed to be outclassed, there was no reduction in the rat population. By chance, the man got an owl and placed it in the cellar. The next morning nine partly-eaten rats were found, and for several weeks one or more rats were found daily. The owl literally ate itself out of house and home; rats became so scarce that the man had to feed the owl on raw meat to prevent starvation. Cat meat? This detail is unrecorded.

Screech owls, the medium-sized fellows with the unearthly cry, have been known to clean out an infestation of mice within a relatively short time. In nature they feed on insects, mice, and other small rodents—the main diet of most other kinds of owls in the United States and other parts of the world. Owls, actually, are among the most contributing members of the bird group.

PARROTS

What Bird Eats Living Sheep?

Before sheep were introduced into New Zealand, the kea parrot was content to feed upon berries, fruits, seeds, and similar food, and was thus a respected denizen of that country. But a short time after sheep appeared the feeding habits of many of the birds changed to include living sheep. It is said that they attack a live sheep, tear a hole in its body with their sharp beaks and eat the fat surrounding the kidneys. The sheep, of course, die as a result of such a wound. It is not definitely known why this sudden shift in diet took place, but it is thought probably that the birds first acquired a taste for flesh around slaughterhouses.

The New Zealand government has placed a bounty on the kea parrot which has resulted in the killing of large numbers of them, but they are still numerous in some areas. Fortunately for the sheep raisers, not all the parrots will attack living sheep; nevertheless, a sufficient number have acquired the habit to have caused the abandonment of sheep ranches in some districts.

CUCKOOS AND ROADRUNNERS

The Laziest Bird in the World

The cowbird, the European cuckoo, and its relatives are about equal contenders for the title of The World's Laziest Bird. None of them builds a nest in which to rear the young; each lays its eggs in the nests of other species. In many cases the owner of the nest does not notice anything amiss; it incubates the alien egg and raises the young cowbird or cuckoo as devotedly as though it were its own. The worst aspect of the situation is that the legitimate youngsters of the nest often do not survive the presence of the trespassers. The young cowbird is often larger and grows faster than the other young birds with the result that the others may be crowded out of the nest. The young of the European cuckoo is even more reprehensible; they deliberately push their nest mates from the nest, leaving them to die of starvation. Thus, for each cowbird or cuckoo that is reared, there is usually one legitimate brood of young birds that dies. There are a few species of birds, however, that discover the strange egg in their nests and appear to resent the intrusion. The yellow warbler uses a novel but difficult method of ridding itself of the cowbird egg. Instead of simply throwing the offending egg overboard, it usually builds a complete new nest over the old one containing the cowbird egg. As many as three yellow warbler nests, one above the other, have been found, the lower two holding a cowbird egg.

Cowbirds owe their name to their habit of gathering in flocks in the vicinity of cows. Depending even in their feeding upon the exertions of another animal, they catch and eat the grasshoppers and other insects that the cows flush from the grass as they graze. The male cowbird is the only black bird with a brown head in the United States; the female is a dull gray color. They are slightly larger than English sparrows.

What Bird Kills Rattlesnakes?

The roadrunner, one of the most familiar birds of southwestern and western United States, takes its name from its habit of running along the road in front of wagons or any other slow vehicle. Other names for this picturesque bird are chaparral bird, ground cuckoo, and snake eater.

Many stories have been told about the roadrunner's relations with rattlesnakes. Perhaps the most common is that it will build a corral of cactus or other spiny twigs about a sleeping rattlesnake, then attack the snake and kill it. Roadrunners have been seen to attack, kill, and even eat rattlesnakes, but no biologist has ever seen one build a corral about a rattlesnake, and until such confirmation is available this amusing notion cannot be accepted.

When a roadrunner fights a rattlesnake, it first fluffs its feathers, unfolds its wings, then attacks. The snake strikes at the bird repeatedly, but its bites fall harmlessly upon the bird's extended wing feathers. The fight usually ends when a well-aimed peck by the bird finds a vital spot on the snake's head. One roadrunner was seen to kill a rattlesnake 3½ feet long, after which it ate the snake's brain and nothing else. A snake over a foot or so in length is too large to be swallowed completely; the bird simply swallows as much as possible and waits until it has been digested before swallowing more. While waiting, the roadrunner walks about unconcernedly with part of the snake dangling from its mouth.

Certain other birds, such as hawks and eagles, will occasionally kill snakes, but by far the most famous snake killer among birds is the secretary bird of Africa. This bird owes its name to the long plumes or feathers extending from the back of the head. Someone with an active imagination apparently thought these feathers caused the bird to resemble secretaries of old who stuck the quill or feather pens behind their ears. Related to hawks and eagles, secretary birds are long-legged birds, up to 4 feet tall, that feed upon insects, lizards, birds, and rodents as well as upon snakes. In parts of South Africa these birds are protected by law, and ranchers sometimes tame them and keep them around their buildings to keep down the rat and snake populations. Such birds, however, cannot be completely neglected; if their normal food becomes scarce they are not at all adverse to a tasty domestic chicken now and then.

WHIP-POOR-WILLS AND NIGHTHAWKS

Do Any Birds Milk Goats?

In parts of Europe the belief that some birds milk goats used to be so firmly ingrained that the name of goatsuckers was given to the birds suspected of this practice. Even today, this common name is applied to the group of birds which includes the nighthawks, the chuck-will's-widows, and the whip-poor-wills.

Although they do not milk goats, the goatsucker group has other habits that are almost as interesting. Most of the birds feed chiefly on insects which they capture in flight. They have enormous mouths set with bristles, which make very efficient fly traps, and have been known to swallow even smaller birds with a single gulp. They also all have the unusual habit of perching lengthwise, rather than crosswise, on limbs.

Nighthawks, which may be found in large numbers in a limited area, are seen more often than the other species in this group. During the summer and fall these birds may fly at any hour of the day, but late afternoon is a favorite time. They can fly swiftly, but sometimes they are obviously not in a hurry. During the breeding season especially, a male nighthawk may frequently be seen fluttering along, gradually climbing higher and higher, its harsh cry intermittently breaking the silence. Suddenly it will partially fold its pointed wings and dive headfirst so swiftly that one wonders how it can keep from being dashed to death. Near the ground, however, it straightens its wings and zooms upward, the vibration of its wing feathers making a dull booming sound. Apparently some people think that the sound resembles the bellow of a bull, because the name of bullbat for this bird is much more common in some areas than is nighthawk.

SWIFTS AND HUMMINGBIRDS

What Birds' Nests Are Used for Soup?

In parts of Asia and certain islands of the Pacific are species of swifts (sometimes called swiftlets), related to the chimney swift of the United States, that nest in caves in large numbers. The nests are made primarily from the saliva which hardens into a whitish gelatinous mass. These are the nests that are used for making birds' nest soup.

There is a commonly held opinion in areas where birds' nest soup is rare or completely absent that the nests are collected after the youngsters have finished polluting the nest and have flown away. An English biologist, who has collected the nests and has investigated the situation, reports that this is not true. He states that the nests for commercial use are collected before the young are hatched, although second-hand nests may be eaten by the natives. This, of course, means that the problem of nest pollution is not as great as supposed, and that a gourmet would not have to strain out many feathers between his teeth.

Neither the price nor the taste (or lack thereof) seems to dim the demand for birds' nest soup, especially among Orientals. Collecting the nests is a dangerous occupation, since high, almost inaccessible cliffs seem to be favorite spots for nesting. According to reports, at least one collector falls to his death each year, and the average life expectancy of collectors is four to five years.

HORNBILLS

A Bird That Hatches Its Eggs in Prison

The nesting habits of some of the hornbills are about as remarkable as any to be found among birds. When a pair of hornbills have the urge to build a nest, they find a hollow tree with an opening large enough to admit the female. She builds a nest inside the hollow, while the male gathers mud and debris and cements up the entrance, leaving only a small opening through which he can feed his mate. One or more eggs are laid, depending upon the species of hornbill, and while the female is incubating the eggs and rearing the young the male brings her food regularly. He literally runs himself ragged: By the time the female and the young emerge from the hollow, the male is a skinny and bedraggled-looking specimen. If he should be killed during the nesting period, the female and her young probably would not starve in their prison, for it has been reported that other male hornbills in the vicinity come to the rescue and take over the duties of the unfortunate spouse.

This strange nesting habit is of considerable importance in the life of the hornbill family, not only because the eggs or young are thus protected from hungry enemies, but because during the nesting period the female is incapable of flight. While she is incubating the eggs and rearing the young, she sheds her feathers and grows a new coat. When she at last emerges from her prison, she is resplendent in brand new clothes, an extreme contrast indeed to the poor male who does not regain his former neat appearance for many days.

Hornbills are large birds found in India, the Malay Peninsula, and adjacent regions. They have big bills or beaks, and in some species a large crest rises from the base of the bill. Noticeable eyelashes are present, a feature not common among birds. The bills, despite their size, are not as heavy as they appear, since they are at least partially hollow and therefore relatively light in weight. One species, however, has a large, solid bill, which is so hard that it has been used for carvings in place of ivory. In some regions the bills of these birds are in such demand for love charms that the bird is exceedingly rare.

PERCHING BIRDS AND SONGBIRDS

The American Robin Is a Thrush

The American robin is not a true robin, although he will doubtless continue to be called one. The true robin is a smaller bird, occurring in Europe; it is this species that has figured so prominently in European folklore. This is the bird that was supposed to have covered the lost babes in the woods with leaves; it is also the species that was supposed to have got its red breast by scorching it while fanning the fire of a lost traveler. However, similar legends occur among the American Indians, who never saw the European robin. The American robin is really a kind of thrush, the spots on the breast of the young showing the relationship to this group.

Although they are often classified as fruit-eating birds, the American robins eat a variety of other food. Their fondness for cherries and berries is unfortunately not always confined to the wild fruit, and fruit growers in limited areas do sometimes suffer losses from robins and other birds.

The presence of the American robin early in the year does not necessarily mean that there will be an early spring. Some robins migrate south in winter, but many spend the winter in the United States, as far north as New England. During extremely cold weather these birds stay in dense woods and other protected places where they are not likely to be seen. If a warm spell occurs, some may venture out in search of food, to be hailed by an eager public as the first signs of spring. When cold weather comes again, the birds retire to secluded spots.

Where Did House Sparrows Originate?

The house or English sparrows have established themselves so well in the United States that it is hard to believe that they were introduced into this country a little over a hundred years ago.

First brought to New York state from Europe about 1850, the birds also came in during several later importations. Opinion differs as to whether the sparrows were first brought in because recent immigrants missed their chirps, or as a means of controlling caterpillars that were attacking shade trees in the east.

This sparrow is distributed over most of the United States, and there are few towns and cities that have not been invaded by the chattering throngs. Probably more domesticated than any other wild species of bird, they will eat almost any kind of food. Practically no one needs a description of the sparrow for identification; especially evident in the spring and summer is the black throat of the male.

Within the past few years there has been, in some areas, a noticeable reduction of English sparrows who apparently have fallen victim to the industrial revolution. The birds formerly depended upon the grain in horse droppings for much of their food, and as long as there were enough horses in use, the food supply could support a large population. The automobile, though useful, offers no edible by-products, a situation that apparently either has reduced the number of sparrows, or has caused them to scatter more widely in search of food.

The English sparrow, probably more studied than any other bird in the United States, has been found by consensus a primarily harmful group, despite an occasional local contribution to human welfare. The birds plug gutters and drain pipes with their nests, damage fruit, vegetables, and other crops, transmit poultry mites, rob other birds' nests, and, as a final effrontery, drive away more useful birds. The significance of the last, particularly, is pointed up by a study in which it was found that the stomach of a single cuckoo contained more insects than those of five hundred English sparrows.

The story of the English sparrow again demonstrates the unpredictable results of deliberately introducing into new territory a species of animal without proper scientific investigation of all the ecological factors involved.

The Crow Is Not All Villain

When I was a child, a common saying among farmers that it was necessary to plant four grains of corn in a hill to be sure that at least one grew to maturity, was explained by the following ditty, which I have never seen in print elsewhere:

> One for the blackbird.
> One for the crow,
> One for the cutworm.
> And one left to grow.

The crow's appetite for corn and other grain produces some losses, certainly. Hardy and clever birds, they can increase to astronomical numbers in some areas. This is especially noticeable in the fall and winter, when the birds congregate in tremendous flocks. Crows, when too numerous, are estimated to destroy millions of dollars worth of grain and other crops annually. They also destroy large numbers of eggs and young of other birds; according to some biologists, the crow deliberately hunts for birds' eggs during the nesting season, and seems to prefer eggs to other food.

On the positive side of the ledger, crows eat many insects and instances have been cited where the birds were of material aid in bringing grasshopper plagues under control. However, one unyielding opponent acidly remarked that the grasshoppers would not have been so numerous in the first place if the crows had not destroyed large numbers of the eggs and young of insectivorous birds.

Whatever the over-all comparative truths, it seems probable that crows do more harm than good when they are too numerous. The birds are not protected by federal law, and many systematic campaigns have been waged by state and private groups to reduce the crow populations. In one such foray dynamite bombs were planted in an area that was nightly occupied by thousands of roosting crows. The skirmish had eliminated 50,000 crows from the countryside by morning.

Readers may be appalled at such slaughter of even a greatly detested bird; however, there is no real danger of extermination. Crows are among the cleverest, hardiest, and most adaptable of birds. Unlike many species, they thrive in areas that have been cleared and placed in cultivation. No matter what measures are used against them, they are not likely to face extinction.

There are few absolutes in nature, and under special circumstances, even greatly beneficial birds may cause damage locally. There has been a peculiar development in this connection: Woodpeckers are reported to be chewing up telephone and power poles in various parts of the country. The industrious birds are doubtless searching for grubs, but in so doing they have reduced the poles to shadows of their former selves. One company is said to have replaced thirty-two poles within a year, and so far all strategy to frighten off the offending birds has failed. Most state and federal bird-protectionist laws recognize that even our best friends may occasionally get out of hand, and that for special situations it is usually possible to obtain permits for local control.

What Are the Most Useful Scavengers?

Scavengers are creatures that eat the bodies of dead animals, garbage, and other wàstes; a number of birds are so classified. They perform an important mission in nature, especially in warm climates where decaying animals rapidly become a health hazard.

The best-known bird scavengers in the New World are the species known as buzzards and carrion crows. Buzzards are types of vultures, and they belong to the same group as do the condors and other vultures of this region. Many Old World birds are also called vultures, but most of these birds are related more closely to hawks and eagles than to the New World vultures. In parts of Europe and in England, the term buzzard is often applied to hawks.

Buzzards may become quite tame. At one time it was a common sight to see groups of the repulsive-looking birds perched on buildings in cities of the southern United States, patiently waiting for someone to dump his garbage into an alley. With the introduction of sewage systems and the enforcement of sanitary regulations, alleys have become less attractive to buzzards in most towns in the United States, but the great birds are still common in the cities and towns of certain other countries.

Perhaps the inadequacy of their claws and beaks for offense and defense —unlike those of hawks and eagles—is the reason that the birds seldom attempt to kill living animals. Occasionally, however, when driven by excessive hunger, buzzards have been known to attack new-born pigs and other helpless animals.

Although the birds are relatively defenseless from the physical stand-point, they have an ace in the hole which they do not hesitate to use against an enemy that molests their nests or disturbs them at their ghoulish meals. This is the revolting habit of regurgitating with disconcerting accuracy as they flap, hissing, about an intruder. I do not know what effects such actions might have upon a hungry bird or animal, but I can say from sad experience that they effectively discourage human interference.

It was once thought that buzzards were of importance in the spread of cholera, a serious disease of hogs, but this has now been disproved. Under most conditions we must regard buzzards as useful if unesthetic members of our bird fauna.

Other scavengers of significance as "garbage collectors" are certain sea birds; gulls of one kind or another will eat anything from dead fish to small living birds. They do much good by eating dead fish, garbage, and other refuse that might otherwise become a menace to health. However, when gulls increase to tremendous numbers they do considerable harm— occasionally destroying crops, eating large quantities of fish waste before it can be manufactured into fish meal and other products, and consuming the eggs and young of ducks and other desirable birds. On parts of the New England coast of the United States, gulls are considered a serious menace to the lobster industry.

Although the birds are protected by law, authorities have sometimes made exceptions, and vigorous campaigns have been launched to reduce their numbers. Robbing the nests, and spraying the eggs with oil or other chemicals so that they will not hatch are common methods. Recently the same technique as that used on starlings—broadcasting the alarm calls of the birds themselves over a loudspeaker—seemed to clear an area of gulls. Again, how permanent this effect will be has not been determined.

Most birds of prey, such as hawks, eagles, and owls, occasionally scavenge; shore birds, including sandpipers and plovers, eat small dead water animals. Even the disreputable crow, general eater that he is, is not averse now and then to a touch of carrion in his diet.

A Bird That Hangs Its Food

Many people as they walk through woods or fields have been surprised to discover a grasshopper, lizard, or small bird hung on a thorn or barbed wire fence. The creatures responsible for this situation are called shrikes, butcher birds, and French mockingbirds. There are several species in the United States, and they are widely distributed in other parts of the world. The shrikes in the United States are about the same size as mockingbirds, and are similarly colored. However, shrikes have a noticeably larger head than mockingbirds, and a beak shaped like that of a hawk.

Shrikes feed on insects, small birds, lizards, and small mammals, such as mice. Once it captures its food, it often hangs it on a nearby thorn or barb of a fence. This habit is, of course, responsible for the common name of butcher bird. The claws and feet of butcher birds are not as strong as those of hawks which are able to tear their prey into bits with claws and beak. The habit of hanging the food on a thorn probably allows the bird to break up the food into pieces so that it can be more easily eaten. Apparently it often kills more than it can eat, and in this case the food is hung and forgotten.

What Songbird Flies under Water?

We accept the fact that such birds as ducks, penguins, grebes, and related birds are capable of swimming well and diving to considerable depths, for we know they are especially constructed for this type of activity. But it does seem strange that one of the totally unrelated songbirds—the water ouzel or dipper—should lead a similar existence. These birds, found in western United States and in other mountainous areas of the world, feed primarily upon water insects and seem to enjoy diving into the water in search of them. Not only do they stroll about on the bottom of a swiftly flowing stream, but they frequently fly under water, using their wings as though they were in the air. The feathers of the water ouzel are so thick and tightly fitting that its body does not get wet. This feather arrangement also probably explains why cold weather does not reduce the activities of these birds. For example, they have been seen to fly through holes in the ice and to emerge some time later none the worse for their chilly bath.

Dippers are grayish-colored birds about the size of a robin. They have

noticeably short tails and somewhat resemble the thrushes to which they are related. The name, dipper, probably derives from an interesting habit of the young birds. When they are hungry, apparently feeling that they must put on an act, either as persuasion for the parent birds to feed them or as advance payment for a meal, they execute a series of squats or dips, bending their knees, squatting down, and then straightening up again.

Three REPTILES

It is unfortunate that so many people are either afraid of reptiles or are repulsed by them, for within this group are to be found some of the most interesting of vertebrate animals. While it is true that some reptiles are dangerous, most of them do more good than harm.

The reptiles include snakes, lizards, crocodilians, turtles, and certain other creatures. The body temperature of reptiles, like that of amphibians, varies with the temperature of the surroundings, and they are therefore described as cold-blooded. In temperate regions in winter, reptiles hibernate in protected spots.

There are a wide variety of breeding habits exhibited among reptiles, but perhaps the greatest departure as compared with amphibians is the place of egg deposition. Reptile eggs must be laid on land. This applies even to the great sea turtles, which may remain in mid-ocean most of their lives except for a short excursion to shore for the purpose of laying eggs.

In addition to being able to deposit their eggs on land, reptiles have another characteristic which makes them more independent of water than the amphibians. Reptile skin is thick and, unlike that of amphibians, does not allow water to evaporate from the body. As a consequence, "reptile ramblings" are not necessarily limited to a moist environment, or to the coolness of afternoon and night. Some reptiles are quite sensitive to high as well as to low temperatures, and more than one snake collector has been made unhappy by finding his snakes dead after they were left in the sun too long.

Many people believe that reptiles are slimy, but actually the skin of all reptiles is very dry. The scales of some snakes and lizards shine when the sun strikes them, and it is this reflected light that sometimes makes the skin look wet.

Reptiles stand in the middle of vertebrate groups with respect to numbers of species. There are approximately 6,000 known species of reptiles, more than the known species of mammals and amphibians, but less than the number of fishes and birds. Millions of years ago, however, reptiles were the dominant form of animal life in the sea, on land, and even in the air. The reptiles still living today represent only a small remnant of the once mighty hosts which then ruled the earth.

SNAKES

As compared with most vertebrate animals, snakes have amazing capabilities. The absence of legs does not seem to handicap them to any extent since they can crawl rapidly, swim, and many can even climb trees. Most snakes can swallow objects several times the diameter of their head, and some can spit their venom for several feet with disconcerting accuracy.

Many species—for instance, rattlesnakes, copperheads, water snakes, and garter snakes—give birth to living young rather than laying eggs. Some of these are amazingly prolific, and have been known to have more than seventy-five youngsters at one time.

Those snakes that lay eggs usually deposit them in secluded spots: hollow stumps, in debris, or under a rock or log. The eggs are longer in relation to their diameter than hens' eggs, and are usually smaller; but the eggs of certain large species, such as the bull snake, are almost as large as those of a hen. The shell of snakes' eggs and those of many other reptiles are tough and somewhat leathery in consistency. Pythons are probably the most prolific of the egg layers; one female Indian python is known to have laid 107 eggs at one sitting.

Some snakes, such as the racers, coachwhips, and black mambas have the reputation of being able to run with tremendous speed. I have seen estimates as high as 20 miles per hour for the black mamba. If this speed were possible, the serpent would be able to overtake all human beings except trained sprinters. Careful experiments, using stop watches, have failed to confirm these excessive speeds. English biologist Colonel R.

Meinertzhagen found that about 7 miles per hour was the maximum speed attained by a black mamba, even when pressed. The allegedly speedy coachwhip or red racer of the southern United States has been timed at a disappointingly slow 3.6 miles per hour.

Most snakes are secretive in habit and are often more numerous in a given area than most people would suspect. At a meeting in Oklahoma of the International Association of Rattlesnake Hunters, almost a ton of rattlesnakes were captured within a few days. Most of the captives were sent to laboratories that manufacture snake-bite serum, although a few found their way into zoological parks and other places.

What Are the Most Dangerous Snakes in the World?

This question will draw about as many answers as there are authorities present. One difficulty with this situation is whether the snakes should be considered as individuals or as a species. And even if we decide how to consider the serpents, opinions will still differ.

From the standpoint of snakes as individuals, several would certainly rank high on any list. These include the king cobra of India, China, and adjacent areas; the tiger snake and taipan of Australia; and the common krait of India.

The late Dr. Raymond Ditmars, of the New York Zoological Park, considered the king cobra to be not only the world's most dangerous snake but also the most lethal wild animal in existence. This conclusion was based upon the large size of the snake (the longest venomous snake in the world), the potency of its venom, its relative intelligence, and the fact that these snakes are often extremely aggressive. People bitten by a king cobra have been known to die in less than an hour.

The tiger snake of Australia probably causes more fatalities in Australia than any other species. Drop for drop it has one of the most potent venoms known, and it has been estimated that if a tiger snake had poison glands as large as those of a diamondback rattler, it would have enough venom to kill 400 men. The tiger snake carries a relatively small amount of venom but, thanks to its potency, one snake has enough to kill many people.

Some biologists consider the taipan to be more lethal than the tiger snake. It contains more venom than any other Australian snake, is quite aggressive, and recent analysis has shown that its venom is almost as potent as that of the tiger snake. Its potential dangers to man can be recognized by the assertion of a biologist that a horse once died within five minutes following the bite of a taipan. In most areas, fortunately, the taipan is relatively rare.

The common krait of India is included in the list because of the high

mortality rate—up to 77 per cent—resulting from the bite, even when the patients are treated with antivenin. The Indian, or spectacled, cobra bites more people and actually causes more deaths than any other species but in one group treated with antivenin, less than 10 per cent died.

Several other snakes, such as the black mamba, could doubtless be included in this discussion; in fact, Europe is about the only continent without a serpent that could not conceivably be included in the list. Let us now consider venomous snakes on a world-wide basis. Several groups of snakes include species capable of killing human beings. These include the cobra group to which belong the cobras, the taipan and tiger snake, the kraits, mambas, coral snakes, and their relatives; the pit vipers, which include the rattlesnakes, moccasins, copperheads, the bushmaster and fer-de-lance; the true vipers, such as Russel's viper, the Gabon viper, and the common viper of Europe; the sea snakes, related to the cobras; and the rear-fanged snakes.

The rear-fanged snakes are so-called because their fangs are at the rear of the upper jaw rather than in front. The venom of many of these snakes is relatively mild, and until recently, many herpetologists were not inclined to consider these snakes as especially dangerous to human life. Now this attitude has changed. A short time ago a well-known herpetologist died after being bitten by a boomslang, a rear-fanged snake from South Africa.

All of the snakes that I have considered to be among the most dangerous species belong to the cobra group. Therefore I have expressed my opinion in answer to the frequently asked question of which is the more dangerous, a cobra or a rattlesnake. Rattlesnakes are certainly dangerous reptiles but drop for drop, their venom is considerably less potent than that of the cobras. And as a rule, cobras are more aggressive than rattlesnakes. Other dangerous snakes outside the cobra group were not included for these or other reasons. For example, the venom of some of the sea snakes is more potent than that of some of the cobras, but these serpents are timid and very few people come in contact with them. Unless provoked, these snakes are not considered to be especially dangerous to human life.

The dangerous snakes of the New World are the pit vipers, the coral snakes, and the sea snakes, although the latter are usually not a serious menace. The percentage of fatalities from coral snake bite is actually higher than that for rattlesnakes. Fortunately, coral snakes have very short fangs, they are not aggressive, and are seldom encountered. As a consequence, there are relatively few records of human beings being bitten by coral snakes.

Several rattlesnakes, the water or cottonmouth moccasin, the fer-de-lance, and the bushmaster are all deadly pit vipers. The fer-de-lance and bushmaster are Central and South American, but the water moccasin and many rattlesnakes are found in the United States. The western diamondback rattlesnake is considered to be the most important venomous snake in the United States. This is because it has a much greater distribution than any other deadly venomous snake in this country, and its habits are such that it comes in contact with people and domestic animals more often than other species.

The copperhead is also a pit viper, and probably accounts for more bites in the United States than any other species. It has a wide distribution and is often found around habitations. Fortunately, however, death seldom results from the bite of this serpent.

Most snakes will avoid people if given a chance, and this is a principle that should be kept constantly in mind. In country areas where venomous snakes are known to occur, always look before you step. If it is necessary to walk through high grass or brush which makes it impossible to see the ground, a long stick will be of considerable assistance. If you move slowly, and push the stick in front of you, this will give any snake that might be in the path a chance to get out of the way. Special precautions should be taken in stepping over large logs and in climbing cliffs. A snake might lie unseen on the opposite side of a log or be basking in a crevice that makes a good hand hold. If at all possible, such places should be examined before a person risks planting a hand or a foot on the spot. High-top boots offer considerable protection, and loose trouser legs are probably better than those stuffed in the tops of the boots. On more than one occasion people have been saved from snake bite when the striking reptile fastened its fangs in the flapping trousers instead of the person's leg.

How Many People Die of Snake Bite Each Year?

According to an estimate by the United Nations World Health Organization, approximately 40,000 people are killed in the world each year by snake bite. Burma is considered to have the highest rate compared with the number of inhabitants, but certain other countries have a greater total number of deaths.

Probably more people are killed by snakes in India than in any other country. One reason for this is that a large proportion of the inhabitants go barefooted and barelegged—an open opportunity for a snake. At one time it was estimated that approximately 20,000 people were killed every year in India by snakes, but within recent years the proper treatment of bites and precautions to avoid snakes have greatly reduced fatalities. The spectacled cobra, so called because of a pattern just behind the head resembling spectacles, is common in India, and some authorities would award this species first prize among snakes as a dealer of death to human beings.

It has been estimated that from 1,500 to 2,000 people are bitten by snakes in the United States per year, and that there are 100 to 150 deaths. Actual confirmed deaths, however, are somewhat less than this. According to one set of statistics, believed to be reasonably accurate, there were 71 confirmed deaths from snake bite in the United States from 1950 through 1954.

How Many Snakes Are Poisonous?

Not nearly as many snakes are poisonous as is commonly thought. There are about 2,400 different kinds of snakes known, and of this number only some 200 are dangerously poisonous to man. In most areas the kinds of poisonous snakes are a very small percentage of the snake population. Australia is the one outstanding exception; there the majority of snakes are venomous.

Venomous snakes are distributed generally over the temperate, subtropical, and tropical regions of the world, but there are a few large sections that are entirely free of them. These areas include Madagascar, Ireland, and New Zealand. There were no snakes of any kind in Hawaii until the recent accidental introduction of a harmless, wormlike, blind snake.

How Can You Tell a Poisonous Snake from a Nonpoisonous Snake?

The old belief that all venomous snakes have a large, triangularly shaped head and an elliptical pupil in the eye is far from correct. It is true that pit vipers, such as rattlesnakes, moccasins, and copperheads, do have

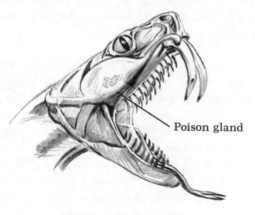

Poison gland

Pit Viper Without Skin

these features; this is also true of most of the true vipers such as the Gabon viper of Africa and the common viper of Europe. However, many nonpoisonous snakes have large trianguler-shaped heads, whereas cobras and coral snakes have slender heads and round pupils.

There is only one relatively simple feature that invariably distinguishes a poisonous from a nonpoisonous snake, and this is one that is not easily seen unless that snake is dead. Poisonous snakes have two long teeth or fangs, one on each side, in the upper jaw, the other teeth being much shorter. In most venomous snakes, these fangs are in the front part of the upper jaw; in the so-called rear-fang snakes, they are in the rear of the upper jaw, but these snakes are seldom encountered by the average person. In nonvenomous snakes, all the teeth are nearly the same length, none being greatly longer than the others. To examine a snake's teeth, it is, of course, necessary to open its mouth, a procedure to which a living snake will strenuously object. Great care should be taken in examining the mouth of a supposedly dead snake, since reflex muscular action may cause it to bite.

Is the American Puff Adder Poisonous?

The American spreading adder has many other common names, including hog-nosed snake, puff adder, blowing viper, and sand viper. The average person who is familiar with this serpent fears it more than any other snake in the United States. When it is disturbed, it puffs up its neck to twice the normal size, takes a deep breath and then expels the air with a noise that sounds like a steam engine and can be heard for some distance. Many people believe that venom is mixed with the expelled air and that the snake's breath is therefore deadly poisonous. I have even seen published statements that human beings have been killed or severely injured by this supposedly poisonous spray at a distance of 25 to 30 feet. If puffing and blowing does not discourage its antagonist, the snake may strike repeatedly.

Although an expanded, blowing puff adder is a fearsome sight to people who do not know its habits, it is really one of the most harmless snakes in the United States. The show it puts on is pure bluff. Not only is the puff adder not poisonous, but it is almost impossible to persuade it to bite. Slow-motion movies have shown that the snake strikes with its mouth closed, and men who have handled puff adders say that they have never been bitten, even though they have stuck a finger in the serpent's mouth.

The puff adder's bluff does not end with spreading, hissing and striking; it has one more trick in its repertory. If its show of aggressiveness does not frighten its attacker away, the snake goes to the opposite extreme and plays dead; or at least so its actions have been interpreted. It suddenly starts writhing, as though it were having convulsions, its mouth gapes, its tongue protrudes, and after considerable thrashing around it flops over on its back and remains quiet. It even allows itself to be picked up without showing any signs of life. However, it apparently has very definite ideas as to how a truly dead snake should lie, and if it is turned over on its belly it immediately flops over on its back again. This comical and highly entertaining snake frequently makes an excellent pet.

The name puff adder is also applied to another snake, a type of viper found in Africa, which is no relation of the American puff adder. It too has the ability to puff itself up, but this serpent is highly venomous.

Do Snakes Bite With Their Tongues?

Snakes have a forked flickering tongue with which—so the erroneous belief runs—they bite. Actually, a snake's tongue is quite soft and is incapable of inflicting injury of any kind. As the snake crawls about, its tongue darts in and out continuously, particularly when the snake's suspicion or interest is aroused. The tongue is a highly developed sense organ, used principally in touching and as an aid in smelling. At one time it was thought that it also helped to pick up sound vibrations, but this is now believed to be untrue.

Do Poisonous Snakes Bite or Strike?

One frequently hears that rattlesnakes and other poisonous snakes do not actually bite but rather strike, stabbing the victim with their teeth. Actually, venomous snakes both strike and bite, but the extent of biting varies with the kind of snake. The long-fanged snakes, like the rattlesnakes and related species, do not do much chewing. When the mouth is closed, the long, hollow, movable fangs are folded inward against the roof of the mouth. In striking, the snake opens its mouth, the folded fangs fall into biting position, and the snake launches itself forward. At the moment that the fangs penetrate the skin of the victim, the snake bites. The muscles used in this biting movement press the poison glands so that the poison flows out of the poison ducts, through the hollow teeth and into the wound. The strike, the bite, and the return to a coiled position are so rapid that one cannot follow the movements with the eye. Rattlesnakes and similar long-fanged serpents strike so hard that the fangs of a large specimen may penetrate even a leather boot.

Cobras and coral snakes have much shorter fangs than other poisonous snakes, and when they bite they hold on for a time and chew. The chewing movement contracts the muscles that force the poison into the wound. These snakes do not strike very hard, so rather thin canvas leggings are sufficient protection against them.

When angry, many of the cobras form what is sometimes called the hood. This is done by expanding the elongated, movable ribs which lie just behind the head. Not all cobras and their relatives are capable of forming a hood; in some, only a slight enlargement is possible; in others, none at all.

Are Poisonous Snakes Edible?

When I was a child there was a commonly held opinion that the flesh of venomous snakes was poisonous under some conditions. When a snake was at peace with the world it was thought, the venom was all concentrated in the head. When the snake became angry, the venom was carried by the blood all over the body, and if the snake was killed while in a rage the flesh would be poisonous. The way to kill a snake so that the flesh would not be poisonous, was to sneak up to a sleeping snake and cut off its head before it had a chance to become angry. If this was done, the flesh even of a venomous snake was quite safe to eat.

Actually, the flesh of venomous snakes is not poisonous. Even the venom itself is harmless in the digestive tract, unless there are breaks in the mouth, stomach, or intestine. Digestive juices destroy the venom. Only if the venom enters the bloodstream can it cause damage.

Snakes are eaten in practically all countries where the reptiles are large enough and numerous enough to make collecting worth while. In some areas certain snakes have a high market value and scientific expeditions that depend upon native collectors may find themselves bidding against appetites and local markets for choice specimens. In the United States canned rattlesnake meat has been on the market for years.

Can Snakes Bite under Water?

Some people believe that snakes must strike in order to bite and that consequently they will not bite under water. If snakes were not able to bite under water, a large number of water snakes would go hungry. Many of them feed on fish and frogs, and much of the prey is captured beneath the water surface. Thus, it is obvious that snakes can bite under water. It is also true, however, that they are less likely to bite human beings under water. The water certainly interferes with the striking power of the snake and, while a strike is not necessary for a bite, a more effective bite can be administered if the snake is free to strike.

Snakes That Spit Their Venom

One of the most striking and exasperating methods of defense that snakes have developed is found in a few cobras that actually spit or squirt their venom at their enemies. If the venom gets into the eyes it causes intense pain, and if it is not washed out, temporary or even permanent blindness may result. The venom does no damage on unbroken skin, however, and so far as is known, the eyes would not absorb enough to cause death. The snakes best known for this fiendish habit are called spitting cobras and are to be found in parts of Africa. These snakes apparently aim deliberately for the eyes and sometimes eject their venom as far as 10 or 12 feet with surprising accuracy. The special structure of their fangs is responsible for their spitting ability. The poison channel in each fang turns abruptly near the outside opening. When the poison glands are compressed, the venom passes down the channel, strikes the abrupt turn and squirts with considerable force from the channel opening in the front of the fang. In most poisonous snakes, the poison channel is straight; when venom is forced through it simply dribbles from the end of the fang.

What Are the Human Uses of Snake Venom?

Snake venom has been used for many things, but at the present time its most valuable use is in the manufacture of antivenin or serum against snake-bite itself.

In preparing this serum, the venom of the poisonous snakes is first collected by a process known as milking. The milker holds the head of a snake firmly and applies its fangs to the edge of a container. In some cases the fangs are pushed through a cloth or thin rubber sheet that covers the container. At the same time, the operator presses the poison glands to squeeze out as much venom as possible.

The preparation of antivenin is based upon the fact that living animals build up an immunity to venom if it is injected into their bodies in small amounts over a period of time. Horses are the animals most often used. The venom is dried, diluted, and injected into a horse. This is repeated every few days, the concentration of the dose being slightly increased at each injection. This procedure is continued until the horse has built up its immunity to such an extent that it can safely take a dose many times the strength necessary to kill an ordinary horse. Blood is then obtained from the immunized horse and the blood cells separated from the serum, or liquid part of the blood. This serum, after additional treatment, is the material used as antivenin.

In application, the antivenin is injected into the body of a person that has been bitten. Although antivenin has drastically reduced the number of deaths from snake bite, there is a certain danger in using the material, and it should be administered by a physician.

Many antivenins are made for a particular kind of snake, and the use of such a specific serum for the bite of another species may not be beneficial. However, there are antivenin preparations that contain the elements from several kinds of snakes. One such preparation may be used for all venomous snakes in the United States except the coral snake. But coral snake venom is of the same general type as that of cobras, and on a few occasions cobra antivenin has been given successfully to victims of coral snake bite. At the present time, fortunately, there is at least one antivenin preparation available for the most important venomous snakes of each continent. In some instances, as in the United States, the serum can be used for the bite of any one of several species.

Some time ago a newspaper report stated that a group of research workers of Miami, Florida, had developed a serum that would immunize dogs against the bites of rattlesnakes. According to the report, immunized experimental dogs had survived several times the lethal dose of rattlesnake venom. Since more than 300 dogs have been killed during one year in Florida from rattlesnake bites, and many more that had been bitten have never recovered fully, it is estimated that the hunters in Florida alone will be saved more than $150,000 if the serum is as successful as preliminary announcement suggest.

For hundreds of years various parts of snake anatomy have been used as medicine. Even today in the Orient almost any part of the snake, from the bile to the eyeballs, is in demand. While these ancient practices are not of any value, so far as is known, it has been discovered recently that snake venom does have medicinal properties. Greatly diluted venoms of one kind or another have been used in the treatment of epilepsy, asthma, arthritis, cancer, and other diseases. The venom of the cottonmouth moccasin of the United States has been used to control excessive bleeding, such as may occur after a tooth extraction.

Recently it has been claimed that snake venom is useful in the treatment of polio. So far, this medication has been used primarily on monkeys, but has been tested successfully also in a few human cases.

Is There a Snake that Stings with Its Tail?

The hoop snake and stinging snake are local names for two kinds of snakes, commonly called mudsnakes. Both these snakes sometimes rest with their bodies in a partial circle, and even such a snake expert as the late Dr. Raymond Ditmars admitted that he had occasionally mistaken them for bicycle tires. Some people with a very good imagination have decided that any snake that rests in this way could undoubtedly take its tail in its mouth and roll from one place to another. However, no snake is capable of performing such an acrobatic feat. The mudsnakes have a small, hard spine at the tip of the tail, which they probably use in burrowing. Despite the fact that it is generally believed to be deadly poisonous, this spine is completely harmless.

What Do Snakes Eat?

Snakes of one variety or another will eat almost anything from insects to people. One rule so far as known is never broken: All snakes feed upon food of animal origin; there are no snake vegetarians.

Aside from venomous species that occasionally bite man or his domestic animals, the status of snakes is largely dependent upon their food habits. For this reason their tastes are of more than passing interest. Snakes that probably do more harm than good are those that feed upon beneficial animals, or upon those that man himself likes to eat. In this category are the hog-nosed snakes or spreading adders, the garter snakes, and several species of water snakes. The hog-nosed snake of the United States feeds principally upon toads, but will also eat frogs, insects, and other tidbits.

A toad captured by a hog-nosed snake gulps in air, thereby causing the body to swell. However, the hog-nosed snake has a sharp extra tooth near the rear of its mouth, and as the inflated toad is laboriously drawn into the mouth of the snake, it comes in contact with the sharp tooth. The hapless amphibian is then punctured and the swallowing process proceeds more rapidly.

Many fishermen maintain that water snakes destroy large numbers of game and food fish, and this is probably true in some areas. They are sometimes destructive around fish hatcheries, and under such circumstances the reptiles must be checked. These snakes also eat frogs and toads.

Yet, even these serpents that destroy animals beneficial to man in one capacity or another contribute something to man's well being. For instance, water snakes in addition to eating fish also eat turtles and large water insects many of which destroy young game fish. Hog-nosed snakes and garter snakes consume grubs and other harmful insects in addition to the beneficial amphibians that they eat. The bull snake feeds primarily upon mice, gophers, rats, and other destructive rodents, although its appetite occasionally turns to the eggs of birds and chickens. One 5-foot specimen was found to contain thirty-five field mice, which indicates how valuable these serpents may be. Other snakes that destroy harmful rodents include the indigo snake and pilot black snake, various so-called chicken snakes, and even several kinds of rattlesnakes, as well as other venomous snakes in different parts of the world.

A few species of snakes occasionally eat other serpents, but certain ones concentrate upon a snake diet more than others. It is well known that in the United States several kinds of king snakes often kill and eat other species. King snakes are immune to the venom of copperheads, moccasins, and rattlesnakes, and for their size they are probably the most efficient fighters among the snake clan. They unhesitatingly attack snakes larger than themselves, and will often succeed in swallowing the larger reptile.

One species of serpent, the mussurana, apparently eats snakes almost exclusively. According to the late Dr. Raymond Ditmars, of the New York Zoological Park, this serpent seems to hunt for the venomous species. The mussurana is widely distributed in Central and South America; it is blue-black in color and attains a length of 8 feet. One authority states that he has never known a mussurana to try to bite a person, even when it was being handled. This trustfulness toward people, plus the fact that many natives know the eating habits of the mussurana, have caused it to be protected in many areas.

Snakes Walk with Their Ribs

Snakes have overcome the handicap of being legless and armless and can crawl and swim. Some species can even climb. On the snake's belly is a series of plates, each of which is free at the rear edge and attached at the front edge to a movable rib. In leisurely crawling, the ribs and plates are moved forward and then back, progress being aided as the free edge of the plates catch on rocks, sticks, and other obstructions. Snakes are the only animals that actually walk with their ribs.

When a snake is really in a hurry, it wiggles its body from side to side, using rocks and uneven places in the ground to help push its body forward. Most snakes are quite helpless if placed on a slick surface, such as a large piece of glass. Neither the plates nor the sides of the body are able to find purchase, and the snake flounders about helplessly. Exceptions are the rattlesnake of the western United States and Mexico known as the sidewinder, and certain other desert snakes in other parts of the world. These serpents have developed a special type of locomotion for traveling through sand that works equally well on slick surfaces.

Does the Coachwhip Snake Whip Human Beings?

In some parts of the United States there is a popular belief that the coachwhip snake will attack a person by wrapping its body about him and administering a sound thrashing with the end of its tail. To add fuel to the story the color pattern of its tail does resemble a plaited whip. However, I have never talked to anyone who claimed to have seen this happen and, needless to say, biologists give no credence to the story.

The common name of coachwhip snake is applied to several varieties of snakes called racers, or whipsnakes.

Do Snakes Swallow Their Young for Protection?

This story has probably won wider acceptance than any other fact or fancy concerning snakes. Biologists who deny it are almost sure to be bombarded wih uncomplimentary letters. No biologist, no matter how many snakes he has observed and studied, has ever seen a mother snake swallow its young.

It is unquestionably true, however, that many people have seen what they thought was a mother snake swallowing her young for protection; but they simply misinterpreted the snake's actions. Many snakes eat other snakes and lizards, and an inexperienced person, seeing a snake swallow the brood of another female snake, might well think he was seeing young snakes going into their mother's mouth for protection. Unfortunately, most untrained observers make no attempt to prove or disprove this obvious interpretation, although I have read of at least one man who did. While walking in the woods one day, he surprised a female snake with several young. The young snakes crawled rapidly to the female and disappeared, apparently down her throat. If the man had not investigated further, he would have believed to his dying day that he had seen a female snake swallowing her young. He captured the adult snake, but when she did not release the young after several hours he returned to the woods and examined the spot where he had found them. A brief search revealed the young snakes snugly reposing at the bottom of a hole in the ground. When he had first come upon the snakes the mother snake, while watching him, had placed her head over this hole, and all the young ones had crawled under her head into it. From a distance it had looked as though they were disappearing down her throat.

Is the Rattlesnake a Gentleman?

Two beliefs are current regarding the rattles of rattlesnakes. One is that the age of the snake can be determined by the number of rattles it has, since one and only one rattle is supposed to be added each year. The other belief is that the snakes have a code of honor much higher than that of human beings and always rattle before they strike.

Although a rattle is usually added each time the snake sheds its skin, this does not always happen. In any case, it is not much help in determining the age of a snake, because the number of times a snake sheds its skin depends upon the amount of food it gets to eat. It may not shed its skin at all, or it may shed it several times; two or three times a year is probably

average. Also, rattles frequently break off, so that a large snake, several years old, might have only one or two.

Unfortunately for the romanticists, all rattlesnakes are not gentlemen (or ladies) and they do not always rattle before striking. When rattlesnakes become frightened or angry, they usually vibrate their tails rapidly, which causes the rattles to strike together and make a distinctive buzzing sound. During warm weather, when the snakes are not sluggish, the majority will probably rattle if given half a chance, but the practice is far from invariable. The late Dr. A. I. Ortenburger of the University of Oklahoma studied this habit among rattlesnakes in Arizona and found that only 4 per cent of those he collected rattled before they struck. While this high percentage of villains among the rattlesnake clan would probably not hold under all conditions, his experience does emphasize that a warning rattle cannot always be expected.

Do Snakes Charm Their Prey?

Snakes are not capable of charming human beings; if they were, snake collectors would very shortly become extinct. It is true that some people are so frightened when they see a snake that they are frozen motionless, but this reaction is not the same as being charmed or hypnotized. Most biologists do not believe that snakes can charm smaller animals any more than they can charm people, but it seems possible that some of the smaller creatures may likewise become so frightened that they do not move until it is too late. Birds are most commonly associated with the snake-charming story, but their occasionally peculiar behavior around snakes probably has another cause. Observers have frequently seen a mother bird fluttering dangerously near a snake's head, giving an impression of easy capture, until it has drawn the snake a safe distance from the nest. Then it miraculously recovers and flies safely away, doubtless to the chagrin of the hungry snake. Occasionally, however, a bird becomes too brave while trying to attract a snake's attention and is captured. Anyone seeing this happen might get the impression that the bird had actually been charmed.

Do Snakes Commit Suicide?

When biologists collect snakes, they sometimes jam several of the reptiles unceremoniously into a collecting bag to save space. Snakes handled in this way frequently become angry and strike blindly in all directions. Occasionally one will bite itself or one of its fellows, instead of the object of its wrath, and often the bitten individual will suffer no ill effects. Some snakes are thus apparently immune, to some extent, to their own venom and to that of other individuals of the same species. There have been reports, however, of some snakes dying after biting themselves, and after the injection into their bodies of venom from the same species. It is also true that if the fangs of an irate snake should penetrate its own heart, or that of one of its kin, that death will occur.

Now and then a snake does kill itself, but whether or not this should be called suicide is difficult to say. Death by suicide is defined as death voluntarily self-inflicted, and until better methods of reading snakes' minds are developed we cannot say positively whether they kill themselves on purpose or by accident.

Do Sea Serpents Exist?

Sea serpents do exist. They are not, however, the sea serpents of fable that bellow like a bull and spend most of their time hunting for a ship to attack. The true sea serpents are snakes that live along the coasts of Asia, some of the Pacific islands, Central America, and other areas. There are a number of different kinds of sea snakes, and in all of them the tail is compressed from side to side, forming an efficient swimming organ. Most of these serpents are relatively small to medium size, being 3 or 4 feet in length, but a few species may attain a length of 9 to 12 feet. They are related to the cobras and are highly venomous. The venom of some species is so potent that fish upon which they feed die almost instantly when bitten. Yet the snakes are not aggressive and most are loath to bite. Natives sometimes catch them accidentally in their nets and remove them with their bare hands, but this is a procedure that is definitely not recommended. Many natives have died from the bites of sea serpents that were handled too roughly and carelessly.

These real sea serpents, however, are too small to have given rise to all the sea serpent stories that even today make headlines in newspapers. About 1840, considerable interest was shown in an enormous skeleton that was exhibited in Europe as the skeleton of an authentic sea serpent. It was 114 feet long and weighed over 3½ tons. The European tour was so successful that the owner brought his exhibit to the United States. When the novelty wore off and gate receipts started dropping, the man sold the skeleton to a museum in Europe, where it was soon discovered that the skeleton was made from the bones of five different whales.

Although no true sea serpent of the size described in the usual story has ever been found, there are some animals in the ocean that untrained or inebriated persons might mistake for a sea serpent if only part of it were seen at a distance. The oar or ribbon fish, for example, is an elongated extremely compressed fish, believed by some to attain a length of over 50 feet (although about 21 feet is the greatest length actually measured), and it has several frill-like structures growing just behind the head. This frill could easily be taken for the "mane" of a sea serpent; for that matter, many people would assume that any 50-foot undulating body could belong only to an enormous sea serpent. Some of the large squids, animals related to the octopus, have arms or tentacles 30 feet long, the end of each tentacle being enlarged and greatly resembling the head of a snake. Two of these tentacles writhing on the surface could also easily be taken for a sea serpent.

No sea serpent of the conventional hair-raising variety has yet been recovered, and the chances are good that none ever will be. But most open-minded biologists are willing to admit the possibility that there may be peculiar unknown creatures lurking in inaccessible parts of the ocean. That the discovery of large previously unknown creatures is not impossible is well illustrated by the coelacanth fish that was widely publicized some years ago. This fish was thought to have been extinct for 60 million years, when a 5-foot, 125 pound specimen was caught in 1938 off the coast of South Africa. One day a real flesh-and-blood sea serpent may be collected, thus confounding the skeptics.

What Is the Largest Snake?

A short time ago a youngster came into my office and asked if I knew that some boa constrictors grew to be as long as a building across the street, to which he pointed. I looked at the building and saw that it was at least 75 feet long. I then assured my questioner that I did not know that the boa constrictors grew this large and asked him where he received this interesting information. He said that an older boy had given him the figures and loyally maintained that his friend was an expert on snakes. He was quite disappointed when I showed him several books which stated that the true boa constrictor is not a very large snake, and that the largest known measurement for any snake was considerably less than he had thought. This story illustrates two ideas that many people have. One is that the name boa constrictor can be properly applied to all large snakes; the other—if they know that there are several large species—is that the boa constrictor is by far the largest. Another common belief is that many of the large snakes routinely grow to lengths of 60 to 70 feet.

The term boa constrictor should be applied to only one kind of snake, and reference to the table on page 183 will show that several snakes are larger. We must become resigned to the fact that no living snake attains a length of 60 or 70 feet, although an extinct snake, remains of which have been found in Egypt, is estimated to have attained a length of 50 feet or more.

The two chief competitors for the title of the world's largest snake are the anaconda of South America and the reticulated python of the Far East. Some years ago essentially all herpetologists (except possibly for those in South America) accepted the python as the champion without reservation. There is one authentic measurement of 33 feet for this serpent. Now the sentiment is swinging toward the anaconda. Some biologists now accept, tentatively, a 37½-foot anaconda measured by an engineer in Colombia, and a man wrote me from Canada that he killed one in Brazil some years ago that was 42 feet in length. One difficulty so far as the anaconda is concerned is that the largest specimens occur in areas so inaccessible that it is almost impossible to transport really big snakes either alive or dead.

Very little information is available about the weight of anacondas over 20 feet in length, but most herpetologists are agreed that these snakes are considerably heavier than pythons of the same length. A 19-foot anaconda was found to weigh 236 pounds, but it was later found that this particular snake had "cheated"; she later gave birth to 72 youngsters! A. Hyatt Verrill gives a weight of 360 pounds for an anaconda slightly longer than the above. Based upon the weights of smaller serpents of known lengths, biologists have estimated that a 30-foot anaconda would weigh about 600 pounds, and that a 40-foot giant would tip the scales at 1,000 pounds.

Pythons cannot do nearly as well in the weight department as anacondas, although this could be because more information is available relative to longer specimens. A 28-foot reticulated python, exhibited by Hagenbeck, weighed 250 pounds, and another just over 27 feet weighed 191 pounds. It has been estimated that a healthy reticulated python of 30 feet would weigh about 350 pounds.

Incidentally, at this writing, the largest snake on exhibition in the United States and probably in the world, is in the Pittsburgh Zoo. Appropriately named Colossus, this reticulated python measured 28½ feet in 1956. It is now believed that this snake is at least 30 feet in length.

The king cobra, with no close competitors, is the longest venomous snake in the world. There is one authentic measurement of 18 feet 4 inches, while another specimen over 19 feet long has been reported. The eastern diamondback rattlesnake of the United States has the distinction of being the heaviest poisonous snake in the world. It is very heavy-bodied as contrasted to the slender king cobra.

I feel quite sure that both the eastern and western diamondback rattlesnakes occasionally exceed 8 feet in length if the rattle is included in the measurement. The late Dr. Raymond Ditmars stated that he had measured two eastern diamondbacks over 8 feet long, the longest of which was 8 feet 6 inches. And in the summer of 1962, a friend of mine, who does not

LARGE SERPENTS OF THE BOA AND PYTHON GROUP

Species	Probable Maximum Length	General Distribution and Remarks
Anaconda	35 to 40 feet	South America. There is one specimen of 37½ feet, "partially authenticated."
Regal or reticulated python	33 to 35 feet	Malay peninsula, Burma, Indochina, China, Philippine Islands, and adjacent regions. One 33-foot specimen has been measured.
African rock python	20 to 25 feet	Africa.
Diamond python	20 to 21 feet	Australia and New Guinea.
Boa constrictor	17 to 19 feet	Southern Mexico, Central and South America. One specimen of 18 feet 6 inches is on record.

OTHER LARGE SNAKES

Species	Probable Maximum Length	General Distribution and Remarks
King cobra	18 to 19 feet	China, India, Malay Archipelago, Philippine Islands and adjacent areas. The largest verified record for this species is 18 feet 4 inches. The head of this specimen is in the Museum of Comparative Zoology at Harvard.
Black mamba	14 to 15 feet	Central and South Africa. The longest venomous snake except for the king cobra.
Bushmaster	11 to 12 feet	From Nicaragua southward throughout tropical South America.
Taipan	10 to 11 feet	Australia. This species and the giant brown snake are the longest venomous snakes in Australia.
Giant brown snake	9 to 10 feet	Australia. An Australian biologist states that he measured one over 9 feet in length.
Indigo or gopher snake	9 to 10 feet	Southern United States and Mexico. One measurement of 8 feet 7½ inches has been made, and there is one 13-foot skin (stretched?) on record. Probably the longest snake in the United States.
Black chicken snake; pilot black snake	8 to 9 feet	Eastern United States. One specimen of 8 feet 5 inches is known.
Bull snake	8 to 9 feet	Middle United States. One of 7 feet 8 inches is known, and another of 9 feet has been reported. The 9-foot specimen is doubted by biologists.
Coachwhip	8 to 9 feet	There is one record of 8 feet 2 inches.
Eastern and western diamondback rattle-snakes	7 to 8 feet	Without rattle. Central, southern and western United States.

exaggerate any more than you or me, told me of a western diamondback just over 8 feet that was killed on his ranch near Hebbronville, Texas. Present-day herpetologists, however, do not recognize lengths of rattlesnakes that include the rattle, presumably because the rattle is often broken. Thus the probable maximum lengths for rattlesnakes in the accompanying table is somewhat less than the above figures.

Do Big Snakes Eat Human Beings?

All who have investigated this matter agree that the big snakes do not attack human beings as frequently as they are reported to; nevertheless, it seems well established that a few such attacks have occurred. Several writers cite cases which they are convinced are authentic. In one instance in the East Indies, a boy of fourteen was swallowed by a python. The snake was discovered a short time later, killed, and the boy's body extracted. The size of the snake is not mentioned. Another incident occurred on the island of Ukerawe in Lake Victoria, Africa. Here, according to the story, a woman was killed by a python that measured only slightly over 14 feet. The snake was discovered coiled about the woman's body and was killed before it had had a chance to try to swallow it, although it is most improbable that such a small snake could have swallowed an adult human being.

One instance is of particular interest, since Frank Buck, an experienced person, was at hand when it occurred. The headsman of a tribe in the Philippine Islands kept in a cage a 25-foot python which was looked upon with reverence by the natives. One day the snake escaped and, when it was found, there was a large bulge in its body, indicating that it had recently fed. Buck himself felt the outline of a human body within the snake, and several counts of the headsman's numerous children revealed that one was missing. This incident disturbed the headsman not one whit: He apparently felt that he could afford to lose additional children rather than part with his precious python. At any rate, the python was returned to its cage and allowed to digest its meal in peace.

Recently the anaconda of South America has come in for its share of attention with respect to killing human beings. Biologist Rolf Blomberg, who captured a 23-foot anaconda in South America some years ago, investigated many stories and found two that he considered authentic. In both cases the victims were attacked in the water, while swimming. One was an adult, and apparently he was too large for the snake to swallow. In the other case, which involved a 13-year-old boy, the body was swallowed, but some 24 hours later, the father of the boy discovered the snake partially out of the water where it had regurgitated the body. The snake was killed, but unfortunately no record was made as to the size of the serpent.

How Big an Animal Can a Snake Swallow?

This is a subject on which the fiction writers exercise their imagination freely. And so we read with horror of the terrifying experiences of some explorer who reports that several of his men have been killed and eaten by a single huge serpent, or who has seen an enormous serpent attacking and swallowing a large buffalo or crocodile. The trouble with such stories is that there are no known instances of a snake's swallowing an animal as large as a buffalo, a mature crocodile, or even a lion, nor is there any evidence that snakes exist that are large enough to swallow several adult human beings in succession.

The largest animal that a captive snake has been known to swallow was an 84-pound goat; another snake, 20 feet in length, swallowed a hog weighing 80 pounds. A wild boar reportedly weighing 130 pounds, was taken from the stomach of a python, but I do not know the size of the snake. It is believed that an animal weighing 150 to 175 pounds is about all that even the largest snake can swallow—which is certainly far less than the weight of a buffalo or of some of the other large animals supposedly eaten by these serpents.

Such feats might be possible if, as many people believe, the snake squeezed its prey into a pulp. However, the prey is killed not by the application of bone-crushing pressure, but of pressure only strong enough to prevent breathing and to interfere with blood circulation. The victim is not crushed out of shape at all. In fact, it is not believed that snakes are capable of exerting such enormous pressure, and it is certainly not necessary for them to do so.

How Do Snakes Swallow?

Although the capacity of snakes has been considerably exaggerated, small snakes can swallow objects large enough to make a remarkably true snake story. Many of them regularly swallow prey two or three times as big around as they are themselves. The secret of how this is done lies in the loose construction of a snake's head and in the fact that the various parts can be moved independently. In eating, the snake unhinges its jaws and advances the upper and lower jaw alternately over the body of its prey. As the size and shape of the prey make it necessary, the bones of the snake's head stretch so far out of their normal positions that one wonders if snakes actually enjoy eating. After the first part of the meal gets past the rear teeth, the muscles of the throat begin to exert pressure; this, plus wiggling movements of the body, carries the food to its final destination, the stomach.

The time required for the complete process varies considerably, depending upon the size and shape of the prey. A 10-foot python has been known to swallow a 7-foot snake of the same species in the astonishingly short time of 10 minutes. Large or awkwardly shaped objects may take several hours. As the food enters the mouth it is liberally lubricated by the salivary glands, but the snake does not moisten its prey with saliva before it starts to swallow it, as has sometimes been stated.

If the swallowing process takes a long time, the snake may rest between efforts. With a large object blocking its breathing passage, it would suffocate if it did not have a special way of breathing during this time. However, it can push the end of its windpipe out between the floor of its mouth and the object which is preventing the air from reaching its lungs. After breathing for a time, the snake withdraws the tube and gets down to the business of eating again. Once the food is downed, the bones of the head return to their normal position within a surprisingly short time. Occasionally the snake yawns a few times, which helps to restore the shape of the head.

Must Snakes Coil in Order to Strike?

It is not necessary for a snake to coil its body in order to strike. Some species, such as cobras, seldom coil at all, but rear up and strike in a downward direction. Even rattlesnakes and other species that have the reputation of always coiling before striking will certainly not take the time to arrange themselves carefully into a neat coil if they are surprised. These snakes can strike quite rapidly and effectively by drawing the body into an S-shaped loop and then throwing it forward.

The striking distance of most snakes is much shorter than is commonly believed. Snakes that are violently angry and excited may strike out in all directions and from almost any position, thus giving the impression that their striking distance is much greater than it actually is. One-half to three-fourths of their body length is the striking distance of most species. The strike of a snake is not very accurate at a distance, and many of them seem to realize this, for they seldom attempt to strike at an object the maximum distance away.

Most snakes are as earthbound as the proverbial stone and do not jump from the ground when they strike. There are, however, a few species that actually can jump a short distance, although their ability in this respect has been exaggerated. The jumping viper of Mexico and Central America, a relative of the fer-de-lance, is probably the most famous of these jumping serpents. It is venomous, and attains a length of about 3 feet. When it strikes, it may jump and slide forward as much as 2 feet; and if it strikes from a log or other elevated position it can propel its body forward for 3 feet or so.

Will Snakes Cross a Horsehair Rope?

A horsehair rope is frequently supposed to be a complete protection against snakes. Men have told me that they have slept on the ground perfectly content because they had encircled their sleeping bags with a horsehair rope.

If a rope of horsehair were a sleeping man's only protection against snakes, it would not be at all surprising if he were to wake up with one as a bedfellow. Rope of any type will not discourage a snake any more than will some other object of similar size. This has been demonstrated with live snakes and horsehair ropes, the proof being good photographs of serpents halfway across the rope.

However, snakes have a tendency to avoid human beings and any object to which the human odor adheres; thus a horsehair rope or any other object that had been handled sufficiently to give it human odor would probably be avoided by most snakes.

Do Fakirs Really Charm Their Snakes?

A snake charmer or fakir at work may be interesting to watch, but he does not actually charm the snakes, and many of his actions are for the benefit of his audience rather than the snakes. The eerie squeaky music he produces is a total loss as far as the snakes are concerned, for they are stone deaf. They are, however, very sensitive to any vibrations which pass through the ground or the basket in which they are kept. By surreptitiously tapping the basket or stamping on the ground, supposedly keeping time to the music, the fakir can induce the snakes to rear. As he plays his instrument, he keeps his body in constant motion, and the "dancing" or swaying of the snakes is the result of his movements. A cobra whose body is raised in striking position follows the object of its attention; as the fakir moves about, the snake also moves its body to keep its eyes continuously fixed upon the snake charmer.

What Is the Jointed Snake?

One of the most vivid impressions of my childhood is of a man vigorously lambasting what he said was a jointed snake. It seemed to me that there were at least a dozen pieces, each trying to outdo the other in the vigor with which it wiggled. The poor man seemed almost surrounded by writhing pieces of snake, and he became almost frantic trying to decide which piece he should beat. He at last compromised by beating each piece in turn until he had succeeded in drubbing them all into unrecognizable masses. Two things about this incident impressed me greatly. One was the liveliness with which the pieces of the snake wriggled, and the other was the great fear with which the man regarded it. It is small wonder that many children grow up with a deep fear of jointed snakes.

According to the usual jointed-snake story, this fabulous reptile can break its body into several pieces when it is attacked. These pieces will later assemble at a previously determined place where they reunite to form again a complete snake. The only sure way to kill this dangerous creature, so the story goes, is to bury each piece separately. The snake is, of course, supposed to be deadly poisonous.

Several things are wrong with this story. The jointed snake is not a snake at all, but a legless lizard. However, it is so snake-like that people are to some extent justified in mistaking it for one. The body does not break into pieces, but the slender tail may be broken by a light blow, and the tail may break again. These detached pieces do wriggle about in quite lively fashion. While the attacker is busy subduing or beating the fiercely struggling tail into submission, the front and most important part of the lizard escapes safely into the bushes. The lizard eventually grows a new but shorter tail. The pieces of the tail that have broken off never reunite, and if the body of the lizard is injured it dies.

There are several species of jointed or glass-snake lizards in various parts of the world, but only one in the United States. These reptiles are definitely not venomous and, even if the species in this country were to bite, it could give only a slight nip. Some specimens, after they have been in captivity for a while, become quite tame, and frequently develop into interesting pets.

Snakes and legless lizards can usually be easily distinguished. A legless lizard has movable eyelids, and just behind the eye there is a rather large hole, the opening into the ear. Snakes do not have either eyelids or ear openings.

LIZARDS

Lizards are closely related to snakes, but because of the well-developed legs of most lizards the two are usually easily distinguished. There are some lizards without legs, however, and these legless reptiles are called snakes by most people.

Lizards vary in size from small skinny worm-like creatures to the monitors of Komodo, the largest of the lizard family.

There is such a variety of forms and shapes among the lizards that it is only natural that many common names should have been used for the different groups. In addition to the monitors, other kinds of lizards include the iguanas, skinks, geckos, and chameleons. Of these, the iguanas are among the most striking in appearance. The body is somewhat compressed from side to side, and there is a row of long spines extending down the middle of the back. Iguanas, common in tropical America, may attain a length of 6 feet.

Most lizards lay eggs which the females bury in the soil. The shells in most cases are similar to those of snakes, being of a leathery consistency rather than hard like crocodilian eggs. The period of incubation is usually only a few weeks, but that of the tuatara of New Zealand is reported to be more than a year. The tuatara, which is lizard-like in appearance and is often called the tuatara lizard, is not a true lizard at all. The reptile has many peculiar features, and it is classified into a group entirely apart from all other living reptiles. It has been called a "living fossil" because it has so many characteristics found in long extinct reptiles.

A few lizards give birth to living young rather than lay eggs, and excellent examples are many of the so-called horned toads, which are actually lizards. They are widely distributed in the southwestern United States and Mexico. These little fellows are more easily caught than the average lizard and they are popular with tourists.

Most horned toads taken home by their captors are allowed to die, but the reptiles actually make excellent pets if they are given proper attention. A large cage should be provided with plenty of dry sand, and the cage should daily be placed in the sun for several hours. While it is in the sun, living insects such as flies, mealworms, and ants should be put in the cage. Horned toads will eat almost any kind of small insect, but they do not like earthworms which many people apparently try to stuff down their throats. Water should be supplied by occasionally sprinkling the cage so that drops of water, resembling dew, will stand for a time where the reptiles can reach it. Horned toads will seldom drink water from a filled container, but will eagerly lap up drops from the sides or floor of the cage.

Lizard's Prey

Many lizards eat living animals of one kind or another, but the particular kind of prey is often dependent upon the size of the lizard. For instance, the young of some large lizards eat insects and other small animals while they are small, but turn to larger game as they get older. The menus of the monitors, the group which includes the largest of the lizards, consist of almost any type of animal that they can overcome.

In tropical America there occur some large lizards known as tegus. These swift, voracious creatures are largely carnivorous. In some areas they develop appetites for chickens, and sometimes become such pests that the natives use dogs to hunt them down.

The food of small lizards is made up primarily of insects. Biologists from time to time have killed various kinds of lizards and peered into them to find out what the animals had been eating. One study made in Utah is especially enlightening. Over a period of several months 2,659 lizards were killed and examined. A few beneficial insects, such as ladybird beetles, were found, but by far the majority of insects in the lizards were harmful. Approximately 1,500 of these lizards were a small species called the brown shouldered *Uta*, and of this number more than half had been eating beet leafhoppers. This insect attacks several kinds of vegetables in addition to sugar beets, and it has been estimated to cause annual damage to the extent of several million dollars. More than 9,000 beet leafhoppers were found in the lizards, and some individuals were each literally stuffed with more than 100 of the insects.

Lizards are considered to be especially valuable as insect destroyers in the tropics where, some biologists believe, they are almost as efficient as birds in this respect. There are few houses in these areas where one does not encounter several lizards scurrying about, feeding on cockroaches or other insects that have been attracted to lights at night.

It is not always possible to analyze accurately all factors relative to outbreaks of insects, but many biologists believe that Puerto Rico furnishes an excellent example of the value of lizards in insect control. Cane growers on the island did not have too much trouble with white grubs until the introduction of mongooses to help destroy the rats that had developed a taste for sugar cane. The mongooses probably did kill some rats, but unfortunately their menus also included a burrowing lizard with a well known taste for white grubs. As the lizards grew scarcer, the grubs increased in numbers, and sugar cane production was drastically reduced. The situation became so critical, that giant South American toads were imported to help stem the grubworm tide. The toads did well for a time, then suddenly decreased in numbers, which again exposed the cane fields to the voracious appetites of the grubs.

A recent war on mongooses in Puerto Rico, using poison bait as the weapon, has greatly reduced the number of mongooses. If this reduction can be maintained, perhaps the burrowing lizard will increase in numbers sufficiently to reduce the grub population to respectable size.

There is a commonly held opinion that as a group the iguanas are vegetarians, but this is not the case. Many iguanas eat fruits and leaves to some extent, but they are not averse to eating living animals or their products, such as bird eggs. The so-called marine iguana, an inhabitant of the Galápagos Islands off the west coast of South America, and a few other species are the only iguanas that are primarily vegetarians. Their food consists almost entirely of sea weed which occurs in quantity around the rocky islands upon which the lizards live.

The prize for a strong digestive system should go to another iguana that also lives on the Galápagos Islands. This lizard, sometimes called the land iguana, is primarily a vegetarian and it eats quantities of cactus plants. Not only does it eat the flowers and fruit but also the cactus pads which are studded with long sharp spines.

Are Brightly Colored Lizards Poisonous?

In some parts of the United States the brilliantly colored lizards have the reputation of being deadly venomous. This is especially true of the blue-tailed skinks, some of which develop a brilliant red head. These lizards, as well as other brightly colored ones, are called scorpions, and children are taught to fear them. Although some of these highly colored lizards might bite if they were caught with the naked hands, none of them is poisonous. There are almost 3,000 different kinds of lizards known, and of this number only two—neither of them brilliantly colored—are venomous: the gila monster and one of its relatives, the Mexican poisonous lizard. These lizards are black with orange or yellow splotches and attain a length of about 2 feet. Their pebbly scales and their coloring have earned them the popular name of beaded lizards. The gila monster is found in the southwestern United States and in Mexico; its relative, in Mexico and Central America.

There is still considerable disagreement as to the dangers of the bite of the gila monster. A number of cases of death have been reported, and one study gives a mortality rate of about 20 per cent. Some biologists believe that this figure is much too high, but it is certain that the gila monster is venomous and thus potentially dangerous to human beings.

Are there True Chameleons in the United States?

There are no true chameleons in the United States, although lizards, incorrectly called chameleons, are often sold here in carnivals and circuses. The reptiles usually sold are true lizards known as Carolina anoles, even though they are referred to as American chameleons.

True chameleons occur in Africa, India, Ceylon, and adjacent regions with one species being found in Spain. They are among the weirdest appearing of reptiles. The body is flattened from side to side, the head is rather short and blunt, and the protruding eyes can be moved independently. It can grasp limbs with its feet and tail, and the tongue with which it captures insects is longer than the body. Its movements are slow

and deliberate, and some biologist has remarked that no reptile has the right to look so ridiculous.

In the mind of the average person the chameleon is probably most associated with quick color change, and the idea that the reptiles always match the color of their background. As a matter of fact, several lizards, including the Carolina anole can do about as well with respect to color change. And carefully controlled experiments have shown that none of these reptiles always matches the color of its background.

There are several reasons for this. One is that the creatures are not capable of matching some backgrounds upon which they might be placed. For example, I have seen "pet" Carolina anoles placed on a white shirt, and they remained a glaring green color. Another reason they do not always match their backgrounds is that factors other than background affect their color. These include light, temperature, and the health and emotions of the animal. This situation is well illustrated by the experiments a biologist performed some years ago. He changed lights and backgrounds and got some reactions from some of his specimens, but twenty specimens from Florida were completely uncooperative; they remained the same color throughout the experiments.

We must therefore regard with suspicion the story of the man who claimed to have driven a chameleon insane by placing it on a plaid background.

Can Horned Toads Squirt Blood from Their Eyes?

One of the most interesting little creatures of the southwestern part of the United States is the so-called horned toad. A more correct name for these reptiles is horned lizards, since they are not toads at all, but true lizards. Perhaps the most improbable story connected with the horned lizards is that they squirt blood from their eyes when they become excited or angry; yet it is true. I had one of these little reptiles in a jar one day when a student who was interested in reptiles came into the laboratory. He answered affirmatively when I asked him if he wanted the lizard for his collection. As I turned back to my work, he reached into the jar to get it, and almost immediately let out a surprised shout.

"Hey, look what happened!"

I looked, to find him grinning from ear to ear, holding the lizard with one hand, and pointing to his red-spattered shirt front with the other. To this student, the soiling of a white shirt was a small price to pay for seeing a horned lizard squirt blood from the corners of its eyes. I immediately collected some of the discharged material, and an examination under a microscope showed that it was unquestionably blood.

This occurrence is thought to be the result of a rise in blood pressure which may take place during fright or anger, and which causes the capillaries near the corners of the eye socket to rupture, squirting blood for some distance.

Lizards That Fly

In Indonesia, the Malay Archipelago, and adjacent areas are several species of brilliantly colored lizards to which the name of flying dragons has been applied, although they do not look particularly like dragons. As a matter of fact, with their bright spots or splotches of red, yellow and black, which are especially noticeable when the lizards are in the air, they greatly resemble gigantic butterflies, and are sometimes called butterfly lizards. Although they are able to glide through the air for some distance, they do not actually fly. Their "wings" are folds of loose skin which are attached to and supported by moveable ribs, five on each side. When the little creatures are scurrying about on the ground looking for insects, the ribs are kept folded against the body, but when one of them decides to extend its hunting ground to a nearby tree it spreads its wings and launches itself into the air. The wings do not move, but are kept rigid, so that the lizard actually glides or sails rather than flies. The lizard's confidence in this method of travel is well founded, for it may glide safely across a space of 60 feet or even more. Despite their name, these lizards are harmless and relatively small. Their length varies from about 8 to 12 inches, which includes the long slender tail.

Dragons Do Exist

About forty years ago, the civilized world was startled by reports of the discovery of enormous man-eating lizards on some of the islands of the then Dutch East Indies (Indonesia). Immediately the Sunday supplements of various newspapers ran accounts of many supposedly firsthand experiences, some of which told of men who had been killed and eaten by the ferocious monsters, and even described the way that steam and vapor issued from their mouths as they breathed. Biologists at that time accepted the existence of these gigantic lizards and even thought that they attained a length of over 20 feet. Because the lizards had been discovered on the island of Komodo, and because they were large and allegedly ferocious, they were called dragons of Komodo.

It is now known that many of these first stories were pure fiction. Smoke and steam of course do not issue from the lizards' mouths, and their maxi-

mum size is between 10 and 12 feet rather than 20. Several years ago I
saw on exhibition a dragon of Komodo that was 10 feet 2 inches long and
weighed 365 pounds; these are the greatest actual measurements for one
of the creatures of which I have any knowledge. The dragons of Komodo,
however, are by far the largest of the lizards. A few other species are
almost as long, but no other species is so massively built.

Stories about their ferocious nature may also be considerably discounted.
Persons who have studied the reptiles in their native haunts and who have
handled them in zoological parks are unanimous in saying that they are
relatively mild or even timid unless cornered. A Lady Broughton went to
Komodo some years ago and spent a number of days studying them, and
although she was several times within a few feet of these supposedly
ferocious reptiles they did not show any sign of attacking her. However,
any animal of this size should be handled with caution, especially in the
wild state or if newly captured. Because their natural food includes such
fairly large and active animals as goats and wild pigs, they are doubtless
as ferocious as they seem when in pursuit of their prey; if one were disturbed while feeding, or were brought to bay, the chances are that it would
attack. The dragons of Komodo are greatly feared by the natives, but I
have never heard that one of the reptiles attacked a man unless provoked.

Some Lizards Have Three Tails

Now and then a collector finds a lizard with as many as three tails, and
a forked-tailed lizard is not too uncommon. The reason for this peculiar
development is that the regenerative process by which a lizard replaces a
lost tail sometimes works abnormally. When a lizard loses its tail, the
injury stimulates cells within the stub to start growing, and growth continues until the tail is replaced, although the new tail, as a rule, is shorter
than the original. Usually this stimulation occurs in only one part of the
stub, but in some cases cells in two or more parts begin to grow independently, with two or more tails resulting. Occasionally a lizard may
receive a slight injury to the tail, not sufficient to cause it to break off
completely, yet sufficient to stimulate growth in the tail-producing cells.
Once started, the cells continue to grow until one or more new tails have
developed, although the lizard still has its original tail.

Lizards That Can Run on Water

Basilisks are peculiar lizards that live in South and Central America.
When a basilisk wants to cover ground in a hurry, it rises on its hind legs,
which are better developed than the front pair, and runs with its long

trailing tail functioning as a balancing organ. As if this habit were not remarkable enough, the basilisk also has the ability to run on the surface of the water. Eyewitnesses say that it is able to run successfully across as much as a quarter of a mile of water surface. These lizards have large feet, and their bodies are not very heavy. As long as they continue to run, their speed is such that they do not sink, but if they slow up or stop, they sink as quickly as any other animal of similar size. They are good swimmers, however, and a dunking does not injure them.

Some of them grow to about 3 feet, but much of this length includes a very long tail. Most of them have an erectile crest on the head, and some have, in addition, finlike ridges along the back and tail. When they are angry or excited, the crest or hood is raised and the loose skin or dewlap under the lower jaw is greatly expanded.

According to mythology, a basilisk is a ferocious creature capable of killing a person with its breath or simply by looking at him. Apparently the men who first saw and named these crested lizards thought that they were comparably dangerous. The name they gave them is still used, although it is now known that they are harmless.

CROCODILIANS

The term crocodilian is used to include alligators, gavials, caimans, and their relatives as well as the true crocodiles. All of these creatures have the same general appearance and, aside from a few large lizards, crocodilians are not likely to be confused with any other reptile.

Gavials have long slender snouts and, although some grow to be quite large, most of them have a timid disposition. Gavials feed mostly on fish and carrion. They are common in parts of India, and, according to one report, were once considered sacred by certain religious sects.

Crocodiles can easily be distinguished from alligators. A crocodile's head narrows sharply from the level of the eyes toward the tip of the snout and, when the jaws are closed, a large tooth in the lower jaw near the front of the head is completely exposed. An alligator's head is almost as broad at the end of the snout as at the eyes, and when its jaws are closed, the tooth in the lower jaw is not visible. Only two kinds of alligators occur in the world: one in the southeastern United States and the other in China. Crocodiles are widely distributed over the world. One kind is found in the United States, confined to the southern part of Florida.

American Crocodile

Alligator

Caimans (also spelled caymans), which occur in Central and South America, have broad snouts like alligators but the two need not be confused in nature since they never occur in the same area.

All crocodilians are considered to be amphibious, since both youngsters and adults spend part of their time in the water and part on land. They are relatively awkward on land, but if necessity demands most of them can raise the body on their stumpy legs and run with surprising speed for short distances. A crocodilian sunning itself on shore should not be approached incautiously. Most of them will slither into the water at one's approach, but hungry individuals of certain species may occasionally rush toward the intruder. The long powerful tail, often used as a weapon, is capable of knocking a man flat on his face and within reach of the tooth-studded jaws.

Once in the water the crocodilian really comes into its own and no one considers the reptiles awkward in this element. Powerful strokes from the tail propel the body so rapidly that there are few land animals that have a chance of escaping if pursued by one of the hungry reptiles.

Although crocodilians can stay submerged for long periods they, like all reptiles, are lung-breathers and must ultimately stick their noses above the water surface in order to get air. Their nostrils are on the top side of the snout so that it is possible for them to breathe with only the tip of the nose exposed. Many crocodilians construct dens in the banks of streams, which may extend inward for fifteen to twenty feet. The entrance may be under water, but at the opposite end is a relatively large room above the water. Here the crocodilian comes to rest or for safety, and it may even carry the body of a victim to the den to be devoured at leisure.

All crocodilians lay eggs and, as with other reptiles, the eggs must be deposited on land. Female crocodilians vary somewhat in the kind of nests they construct. Some dig a hole in the sand, deposit the eggs, and cover them. Others, such as the American alligator, gather together a large mound of decaying vegetation and lay the eggs in the midst of the material. Several dozen eggs, somewhat larger than those of a hen, may be deposited in one sitting. When hatched young crocodilians are 9 or 10 inches in length.

Crocodilians shed their teeth frequently. The discarded teeth are replaced by new teeth which have grown into the hollow bases of the old ones, the old tooth not normally being shed until the replacement tooth is quite large.

How Crocodilians Dine

All crocodilians are carnivorous, which means, broadly speaking, that they eat meat or flesh. As a group they will feed on anything from a crawfish to a man. Under most conditions fish, turtles, frogs, and other aquatic animals make up much of the creatures' diets, but any land animal, as it drinks, might be attacked by a hungry crocodilian.

When a crocodilian seizes a large land animal, the reptile immediately tries to drag it into the water. If this maneuver is successful, the crocodile holds its victim under the water until it is drowned. The crocodile can stay under water longer than most land animals, and a fold of skin prevents any water that might enter the mouth from getting into the respiratory passages.

Once its victim is dead, or even before, the crocodile proceeds to dismember the body with dispatch and efficiency. The reptile seizes a leg and, folding its own legs against its body, rotates rapidly in the water by means of the powerful tail. If anything is left of the victim after the reptile's appetite is satisfied, the crocodile may carry its remains to a den in a nearby bank.

One would think that an animal as much at home in the water as a crocodilian would have little trouble overcoming a swimming land animal, even though the latter might be quite large. Eyewitnesses state, however, that even these giant reptiles sometimes bite off more than they can chew, so to speak. An alligator hunter was once fishing in a lake in Okefenokee Swamp, Florida, when he saw a black bear enter the water and start swimming across the lake. About half-way across, a large alligator seized the bear and dragged it under the surface. As the bear went down it turned and slashed at the alligator's head with it claws. The water boiled furiously for some time as the combatants struggled, but at last the bear appeared at the surface and continued its interrupted journey. Another man said that he once killed an alligator that had long claw marks on its belly and so much flesh torn from one side of its head that the jaw bone was exposed. Apparently this alligator had also made the mistake of tangling with a bear.

Crocodilians have voracious appetites, and when they are numerous they may have a profound effect on the wild animal life in the vicinity. At one time alligators were common in many streams and swamps of the southern United States and they doubtless destroyed many game birds and fish. They are now so reduced in numbers, however, that the reptiles probably have little effect in most areas in this country. In fact the alarming increase in muskrats in the South, and the consequent damage to crops and levees in some regions, has been blamed upon the wholesale destruction of alligators.

The situation is different in other areas of the world. In parts of India the natives are dependent upon fish for much of their food, and sometimes marsh crocodiles or muggers become so numerous that they enter into direct competition for the fish in the rivers.

In certain ranching areas of South America, crocodilians sometimes become so numerous that they chew up large numbers of cattle and sheep. Crocodile hunts are then organized to reduce the numbers of the marauders. According to reports, the cowboys often capture the reptiles by lassoing or harpooning them, after which they are pulled on shore and eventually dispatched.

Even if we omit man-eating crocodiles from consideration, the eating habits of some crocodilians are sometimes definitely harmful to man. On the other hand, we must not overlook the possibility that the reptiles may occasionally contribute some good to man's well being. We have mentioned that muskrat damage may be partly due to the destruction of alligators, which can help keep the rodents in check, and crocodilians as a group probably eat certain fish that might crowd out more desirable species. Probably the crocodilians' greatest contributions, however, are as scavengers. Dead fish or other animals in the water are devoured by the hungry reptiles, thereby preventing pollution of the rivers and streams.

What Are the Most Dangerous Crocodilians?

It is a wise man who regards any large crocodilian as potentially dangerous, for even species that are normally shy and mild-mannered might on occasion attack a person. Gavials and alligators are usually not as danger-

ous as are the caimans and certain crocodiles, but all these reptiles should
be looked upon with suspicion.

There are several kinds of crocodilians that occasionally attack people,
but the African or Nile crocodile and the salt water species are by far the
most notorious man-eaters. The African crocodile occurs in the Nile and
many other large rivers over an extensive area of Africa. The salt water
crocodile is widely distributed in India and other parts of Asia, Australia,
and many islands of the Pacific, including the Philippines.

It is difficult to obtain accurate statistics of death caused by crocodiles
because of the remoteness of the many native villages affected. But according to one report, almost 250 people were killed in India during a single
year by the salt water species. Many authorities agree that crocodiles kill
more people in Africa than does any other animal, with the possible exception of venomous snakes, and that hundreds of natives are devoured by the
monster reptiles yearly. Native children frolicking in shallow water are the
most frequent victims, but many careless adults are attacked as they wash
clothes or dangle an arm over the side of a boat.

The reptiles have been known to rush out on shore and seize a victim,
and they may even attack people in boats. The following incident was
related by an eyewitness: An African native was fishing from a small boat
when a companion on shore noticed a small current approaching the
fisherman. Looking more closely he saw that the current was made by an
enormous crocodile that had been attracted by the fishing activities. The
observer yelled and the fisherman jerked up his arms just as the reptile
leaped partly from the water and missed his target by inches. The crocodile quickly reversed itself and with a terrific swing of its tail knocked the
fisherman from the boat. Although the man was only a short distance from
shore, the reptile overhauled him and fastened its jaws on his leg. During the tug of war that followed, the native managed to pull loose, but
he left a large chunk of leg muscle in the crocodile's mouth. The man's life
was saved, but he had a permanent limp as a reminder of his narrow
escape from death.

The American alligator is not normally a danger to human beings, but
the late E. A. McIlhenny, well-known authority on the reptiles, gives the
following account of being the object of an unprovoked attack. He was
rowing through a bayou when suddenly a large alligator came to the surface and gave his canoe a resounding smack with its tail. The canoe was
upset, but the water was shallow and McIlhenny scrambled to his feet to
see the alligator preparing to rush him. Fortunately, he still had his gun,
and a quick shot ended the alligator's desire for food. This reptile was
approximately 12 feet long.

Another biologist had an experience with an American crocodile which
well illustrates the difference in temperament between this species and

the American alligator. He received a crated crocodile, and after it was released, he decided to drive it into a prepared enclosure. Having had no previous experience with crocodiles, but being familiar with the reactions of alligators, the biologist strolled up to the animal and carelessly poked it in the side with a stick. The crocodile gave an angry hiss and quick as a flash swung its tail and knocked the biologist off his feet. Only wild scrambling saved the man from serious injury, for the crocodile actually pursued him.

Do Crocodilians Guard Their Nests?

The American alligator probably has the greatest reputation for guarding the nest than any other species. After the female has deposited the eggs, she supposedly stays in the general vicinity of the nest and occasionally scratches around it with her wet body which helps to keep the eggs moist. At the time of hatching, the young give vent to a series of raucous squeaks, whereupon the mother rushes to the nest, opens it, and sometimes escorts the nightmarish infants to the water and swims with them for a while. That the males of some species are not prompted by any such feeling of devotion is indicated by the report that the male South American caiman sometimes eats its own offspring if the opportunity presents itself. The female frequently comes to the rescue, fights off the male, and, so the story goes, takes some of the young in her mouth and hides them in a secluded spot.

Some naturalists report that they have scratched into numerous crocodiles' nests and have never been caught in the act by an outraged female; consequently, they do not believe that any crocodilians guard their nests. Probably some species are not particularly vigilant; and in areas where the alligator has learned to fear man—and also if the female has been killed— one could probably rob the nest undisturbed. I believe, however, it has been well established that the American alligator, at least, does keep a careful watch on the nest. I also believe that female alligators help their young from the nest, and frequently swim with them for a time. However, I must have more proof before I can swallow the story that female caimans move their offspring from one place to another like a loving mother cat.

Do Crocodiles Have Any Enemies?

Adult crocodiles have few enemies other than each other, man, and perhaps the hippopotamus. During the breeding season males often fight among themselves for the attentions of a female, and these battles may result in the death of the defeated suitor. Human beings, of course, kill many crocodiles and, although hippopotamuses are not especially pugnacious, they will not tolerate a crocodile making a meal of one of their youngsters. The hippo has a tremendous mouth studded with enormous teeth. Even the tough armor of a large crocodile cannot withstand the full power of the jaws and teeth of a four-ton hippo.

The nests and youngsters of crocodiles are the targets of many enemies, just as are the nests and young of most wild animals. The natives of many areas relish the eggs and even male crocodiles are not averse to chewing up a nestful if they stumble upon one unguarded. On a world-wide basis, the greatest natural enemy of crocodile eggs, and by far the most famous, is the Nile monitor. This lizard grows to about 5 feet in length, and in some regions it feeds largely on the eggs of the African crocodile. Unfortunately, the skin of the Nile monitor makes excellent leather. It has been hunted so persistently that it is now rare in parts of Africa.

Young crocodiles are also the targets of monitor lizards and hungry adult male crocodiles. The youngsters normally stay in shallow water where they are usually relatively safe from their voracious fathers. During drought, however, when the rivers start drying up and fish become scarce, adult crocodiles often do not get enough to eat. They then invade the shallow water, and may even get some distance from water in search of food. During this time the population of young crocodiles is drastically reduced, because the adults will eat all they can catch.

As one might expect, man is by far the most important enemy of crocodilians. The principal reason for this is the demand for crocodilian skins for the manufacture of handbags, wallets, watch bands, shoes, and a variety of other items. The reptiles have been hunted so extensively that they have been eliminated from many areas. At one time, most of the skins processed in the United States came from the American alligator, but now a large percentage of crocodilian leather comes from crocodiles and probably caimans. They are all labeled "alligator" in the market place.

Can You Eat an Alligator?

Crocodilians are hunted regularly for food in many parts of the world, but they are seldom eaten in the United States. Almost everyone who has eaten crocodile or alligator meat has agreed that it has a pleasant flavor. But there has been considerable disagreement as to what other meat it resembles most. A zoologist has described the reactions of members of a large boardinghouse, which included both men and women, to a meal that consisted of two 3-foot alligators: Some guests stated that it tasted like pork, others said it reminded them of fish, and so on.

During World War II the armed forces emphasized the possibilities of men surviving under adverse conditions, and soldiers were instructed on weird sources of food. During a demonstration, pieces of crocodile meat, along with other odd tidbits, were served to a class of which I was a member. This was my first experience with crocodile meat, and I tasted it somewhat gingerly. But I was pleasantly surprised to find that it reminded me of an appetizing fish.

How Large Are Crocodilians?

Anyone who reads very much about crocodiles is almost certain to find record of two enormous salt water crocodiles which were reported many years ago. One of these was a 33 foot crocodile killed in Bengal, and the other a 29 foot specimen shot in the Philippines about 100 years ago. The average crocodile or alligator was much larger many years ago than it is today, because now many more of them are killed before they attain their maximum size; even so, there is great doubt as to the accuracy of these two measurements. Fortunately—or perhaps unfortunately for the sensationalists—the skull of the reported 29-foot specimen is still in existence. The late Karl Schmidt, of the Chicago Natural History Museum, examined it, and estimated that the crocodile would have had a maximum length of 22½ feet if it had been measured by a hard-boiled scientist. He believed that the largest crocodilian ever measured by a biologist was an Orinoco crocodile of 22 feet 4 inches, and he did not think that any grow to be over 23 feet. In former times, the American alligator also grew to a large size; E. A. McIlhenny reports one of 19 feet 2 inches and two others of over 18 feet. For a long time it was said that the British Museum had a mounted gavial 30 feet long, but recent investigation has revealed that this specimen had apparently mysteriously shrunk in size. The largest mounted gavial in this institution is only about 15 feet in length.

There is certainly no argument about the fact that present-day crocodilians are mere pygmies compared with some of their extinct relatives. Those gigantic reptiles may sometimes have attained a length of 50 to 60 feet, although this exceeds estimates based upon a fossilized skull. A reconstructed skull of one of these monsters, fragments of which were discovered in the Big Bend area of western Texas, is carefully mounted in the American Museum of Natural History. It is approximately 6 feet in length and has teeth 5 to 6 inches long with a diameter of 2 inches. It has been estimated that the owner of this skull would have been over 45 feet long, and it is quite possible that larger specimens were alive at that time.

TURTLES

One of the first questions that usually arises about turtles is how the names turtle, tortoise, and terrapin should be used. Not even the experts are in agreement regarding the limitations of these names. Many people use the term tortoise for those that live on land all the time. Such a reptile is the common box tortoise that one sometimes sees lumbering across highways or scratching around in flower gardens. To some, only the fresh-water species with a market value, such as the diamondback, are terrapins. All other species, both marine and fresh-water, are turtles. About the only point agreed upon is that any and all of these reptiles can be spoken of as turtles in a general sense.

Turtles are entirely toothless, but this does not seem to handicap them in the least. They have sharp bony jaws which they use efficiently, as many a careless person has discovered. These jaws are well adapted to the diet and eating habits of the animals, since they do not chew, but merely seize and bite off chunks of food which they swallow whole.

Many turtles will eat material of either animal or plant origin; some have developed a taste for carrion. The leaves and flowers of plants are often eaten, and slugs, snails, crawfish, and insects make up a majority of the animal food of the smaller species. Some of the larger turtles will eat almost any kind of animal that they can capture and overcome.

Many turtles are at least partially aquatic. Some, such as the larger marine species, probably seldom see land except for brief periods during the breeding season. But there are some strictly land-inhabiting species, such as the box tortoises previously mentioned. Some of these will enter water only if forced to do so, and will scramble back on land at the first opportunity.

All turtles lay eggs and, as is true for other reptiles, the eggs must be deposited on land rather than in the water if they are to hatch. A female turtle usually constructs a nest of some kind, which normally consists of a hole dug in the sand, soil, or decaying vegetation. The hole is dug by the hind legs and, after a batch of eggs is deposited, they are covered and left to their fate by the female.

The number of eggs laid by a single turtle at one time varies with the kinds of turtles and even with individuals of the same species. The young and eggs of sea turtles probably have fewer chances of survival than those of most turtles and it is not surprising to find that they often lay large numbers of eggs. Nests with more than 100 eggs have been discovered, and some authorities believe that large specimens are capable of laying between 200 and 300 eggs at one sitting.

Hawksbill sea turtle

Diamondback terrapin

Galápagos tortoise

The so-called tortoise shell of commerce, known as *Carey* in Central and South America, is probably the most famous product derived from turtles. It is obtained from a marine species known as the tortoise shell turtle, and has been used for centuries for inlaid work, knife handles, toilet articles, the well-known "high combs" of Spanish senoritas, and many other ornamental objects. It is still used extensively in India, China, Spain, and Japan, but plastic imitations are more common in the United States.

How Is Tortoise Shell Obtained?

True tortoise shell—as previously mentioned—is obtained from a sea turtle called the tortoise shell turtle. It is also called the hawksbill, because the shape of its upper jaw greatly resembles the beak of a hawk.

Tortoise shell consists of the large transparent plates or shields that cover the bony part of the shell and is usually obtained by the application of heat, which causes the shields to come loose from the underlying bone. One of several methods may be used, varying considerably in unpleasantness as far as the turtle is concerned. One of the cruelest methods, which has been practiced by natives in some areas, is to capture a female turtle when she comes ashore to lay eggs, bind her to a pole, lower her back downward close to a bed of embers, and leave her there until the shields peel away from the bony base. Then she is released in the hope that she will grow new plates so that she may be recaptured and repeeled. Regeneration of the plates does take place in some cases, but the new plates are usually abnormal and have little value.

While this method of peeling a living turtle doubtless shocks many readers, one possible advantage to the turtle should not be overlooked. Peeled turtles, so far as is known, can still reproduce, so that the practice of releasing them may have prevented their becoming extinct in many areas. In some regions, the turtles are killed and then placed in boiling water until the tortoise shell is loosened. Although this practice is more humane as far as the individual turtle is concerned, it does not contribute to the preservation of the species.

Is the Turtle Egg Edible?

Not only are turtle eggs good to eat, but in some areas the nests of the reptiles are so numerous that turtle eggs are a staple food for the natives. The eggs of some species are supposed to be more nutritious than hens' eggs, and one enthusiast states that a dozen eggs of the green turtle may be consumed at one time.

On a world-wide basis the eggs of sea turtles, including those of the green turtle, the loggerhead, the hawksbill, and the leathery turtle, are doubtless eaten more than those of any other group. These reptiles are widely distributed, and consequently they deposit their eggs on the shores of many islands and continents. Some years ago, and perhaps even now, turtle eggs were peddled successfully in the coastal cities of the southeastern United States where they often substituted for hens' eggs. Various kinds of allegedly edible concoctions may be made from the eggs, including candy, pickled eggs, and so-called egg butter.

Turtle eggs are hunted enthusiastically by both man and beast, and in view of this it is incredible that some of the larger species have not been exterminated long ago. During one year more than 16,000 nests of the green turtle were rifled on some islands off the west coast of Borneo, and the yearly haul from the Burma coast is reported to be approximately 1.6

million eggs. It is fortunate from the standpoint of the turtle clan that large female marine turtles are capable of shelling out several hundred eggs annually.

From the commercial standpoint, females containing eggs are especially valuable, since the "turtlers" can expect remuneration from the turtle itself and from the eggs. The turtle is sold for making soup, and the eggs, often left in the egg tubes, are smoked and sold by the foot.

The eggs of fresh-water turtles are not eaten by people as extensively as are those of marine species. However, many animals plunder the nests for food, and now man has discovered that the eggs make excellent fish bait. On Reelfoot Lake in Tennessee the eggs are collected and sold by the thousands to fishermen for use on their trotlines. Many enthusiastic egg hunters are not content simply to rob the nests, but search for female turtles getting ready to lay their eggs. When found the turtles are pounced upon, their shells cracked with a hammer, and the unlaid eggs unceremoniously yanked out. This wholesale nest robbing and slaughter of female turtles contributes nothing toward the well-being of future generations of the reptiles.

How Dangerous Are Turtles?

It is thought by many persons that turtles in the water are dangerous, but this is not borne out by the facts. On land some turtles, such as the snappers and the soft-shelled turtles, are distrustful of human beings; one is quite likely to test its biting ability upon any portion of human anatomy that comes within reach. Special care should be taken in removing hooks from a turtle you catch while fishing, but in the water the reactions of most turtles apparently undergo a drastic change, as though they feel protected. Outside of juvenile fiction, I have never heard of an unprovoked turtle attacking a person in the water.

Some sea turtles, such as the loggerheads and leatherbacks, have a reputation for being pugnacious, but so far as I can determine these stories are based primarily upon the actions of individuals that were being attacked or were in captivity.

In some regions a native ties a rope about his waist, locates a turtle, attaches himself leech-fashion to its back, and hangs on for dear life while his companions haul him and his catch into the boat. If the turtle is in shallow water, the rider may wrestle it into the boat, although I have an idea that this method is used primarily for movie shorts. In some places, the turtles are harpooned or caught in nets.

Perhaps the most common practice in collecting turtles is to take advantage of the female turtle when she comes ashore to deposit her eggs. Sometimes many of them come to the same place at the same time, so that if the "turtlers" are lucky, they may catch a large number in a single night. When the hunter locates a turtle, he turns it on its back, in which position it is helpless, then continues his search, treating all he finds in similar fashion. When he is ready, he returns and collects the catch at his leisure. Some people say that the turtle catchers allow the female turtles to deposit their eggs before capturing them; if this were the case, the practice would not be so bad. However, it is hard for me to believe that hard-boiled turtle catchers squat patiently on their haunches waiting for the female turtles to deposit their eggs when they could catch many more by collecting them at once.

Some of the sea turtles if attacked can give a good account of themselves, as the following incident illustrates. Some years ago a loggerhead turtle reported to have weighed 610 pounds escaped from an east coast market, and the irate owner offered a $50-reward for its return. Five men armed with nets, harpoons, and ropes set out in a small boat to collect the easy money. The turtle apparently liked his surroundings because instead of heading far out to sea he was discovered contentedly sleeping at the surface within the harbor. One of the men tried to spear the sleeping monster but the spear failed to penetrate the thick shell. The resentful turtle rushed the boat and almost upset it with its flippers. The startled men beat him over the head with the oars, but discovered that their choice of weapons was poor: The ends of the oars, one after the other, were seized in the reptile's mouth and broken off or crushed into small bits. During the fracas one of the men received a long gash in his arm, either from the turtle's beak or flippers. The fight lasted almost an hour, after which the turtle, tiring of the sport, retired from the scene. Two hours later the battered men, paddling with their oar stumps, managed to make the shore with the boat barely afloat.

Sea Turtles Are More Comfortable on Their Backs

Feminine shoppers with humanitarian ideals are sometimes horrified at the supposedly cruel way in which sea turtles are displayed in the fish markets: The reptiles are simply turned on their backs, and left with their flippers waving helplessly. Actually, they are far more comfortable in this position than if they were turned right side up. The under-shell of the sea turtle is so weak that it is not capable of supporting the animal for any great length of time; if a turtle were to remain out of water on its stomach very long, its weight would press the lower shell upward, crushing the heart and lungs and causing death within a short time. In the natural state, this problem seldom arises, since the turtle's weight is supported by the water; they seldom venture on land except to lay their eggs.

Can a Turtle Crawl from Its Shell?

There is a widespread belief in some areas that the shell of a turtle is not attached to the reptile's body. It is thus thought that the turtle can easily come from its shell if properly persuaded. One method that has been recommended to me is placing the turtle on a hot stove.

A turtle on a hot stove would certainly crawl out of its shell if this were possible, and if by so doing the creature could escape the "hot tummy" it was getting. However, it would be just about as easy for a human being to pull off his skin and dance around in his bones as for a turtle to crawl from its shell. Part of the shell is composed of greatly flattened ribs which are fused to the remainder of the shell, and various other parts of the body such as the backbone are firmly attached to the shell. The only way a turtle can be removed from the shell is to cut him out, and even this is frequently a very difficult procedure.

Because of the shell that surrounds much of a turtle's body, the arrangement of certain body parts is different from that of other animals. One of the most interesting of these modifications is the position of the shoulder blades, the large flat bones in human beings that occur on the back just behind the attachment of the arms to the body. In animals other than turtles, these shoulder blades are outside the ribs, but in turtles the bones are inside. The attachment of the front limbs to the skeleton in turtles also occurs inside the ribs, a condition that is not found in any other animal.

Can Alligators and Turtles Mate?

Lurking in the muddy waters of the Mississippi River and other large streams of the southeastern United States are enormous turtles that may weigh over 100 pounds. They are the largest fresh-water turtles in the world and are certainly among the ugliest of the turtle clan. These turtles are called alligator turtles, a name which it is said was given to them by the early settlers, who thought they were the result of a cross between an alligator and a common snapping turtle. It is biologically impossible for an alligator and a turtle to mate, the belief of the early settlers to the contrary.

The size of these turtles is certainly impressive, but biologists maintain that their ferocity and the strength of their jaws have been considerably exaggerated. They are considerably less pugnacious than their smaller cousin, the common snapper, and although I have no intention of testing them, it is almost certain that even the largest specimen could not take off a man's arm at a single snap. However, such a large turtle should not be handled carelessly; if aroused, it is surely capable of inflicting deep lacerations upon any part of human anatomy within reach.

Despite the fact that the alligator snapper is probably not as dangerous as commonly thought, a 100-pound specimen swimming in a clear water aquarium is something to compel attention. The enormous head, the bright beady eyes, the tremendous slash of a mouth which makes the creature seem to be perpetually grinning—all these combine to inspire a feeling of awe and fear in the observer.

Can Turtles Breathe under Water?

All turtles must eventually come to the surface for air, but certain species can obtain some oxygen from the water. This allows the reptiles to remain under water much longer than they could otherwise do.

In some species, such as the soft-shelled turtle, the throat just behind the mouth is richly supplied with blood vessels. The blood absorbs oxygen from the water that is then pumped in and out of the mouth, and this may allow the turtle to remain submerged for as much as several hours. Some turtles employ a similar method of obtaining oxygen except that the process occurs at the rear end of the body. Pouches branch from the intestine, and some oxygen passes through the walls of the pouch as water is drawn into the body and expelled.

The Most Valuable Turtle in the World

No member of the turtle clan has ever enjoyed the popularity that the diamondback terrapin of the eastern United States experienced during and before the roaring twenties. These terrapins are said to have been so named because the plates on their shells are diamond-shaped; but in the light of what one pays for the flesh of the reptiles, the name is quite appropriate without reference to the shell at all. During the height of their popularity, these terrapins brought as much as $90 per dozen "on the hoof." This ridiculous price may have had something to do with the demand for these creatures, but it has been maintained that few people can distinguish between diamondback and snapping turtle when the reptiles are cooked. Obviously, snapping turtle stew, so advertised, would not attract as many customers as would the diamondback.

Before the diamondbacks were in such demand as food, they were quite common from Massachusetts along the coasts to Mexico, where they inhabit the salt marshes and pools formed by the tides. This is the only species of turtle, incidentally, in North America that is apparently limited to this type of living environment.

The diamondback terrapins were almost eaten out of existence before they went out of style. This situation was probably due to the general public's changing food fads, and to the fact that edible terrapins became very difficult to obtain. Private terrapin "farms" were established, laws were passed protecting the reptiles, and various government agencies raised and propagated terrapins. The species now shows signs of increasing in numbers, and perhaps in the future gourmets may again have the opportunity routinely of spending a fortune for a microscopic quantity of the succulent reptile.

Other turtles that are eaten for food, either locally or commercially, include the alligator snapper, the common snapper, and several soft-shell turtles in various parts of the world.

Do Turtles Hibernate?

As in all reptiles the body temperature of turtles varies with the temperature of the air or water; if they did not hibernate during cold weather they would die. Many of the aquatic and semi-aquatic turtles burrow into the mud at the bottom of the body of water in which they live; land forms usually burrow into soft ground for a foot or so. During this winter sleep, they are in a stupor; they do not breathe at all unless they venture to the surface during warm spells. A hibernating turtle recovered from the bottom of a lake or stream appears to be dead, since all its body processes are slowed down. That all turtles do not successfully complete their hibernation is indicated by the number of dead turtles and shells found along the banks of lakes and streams in the spring. Many deaths are probably due to the impatience of the hibernating turtles—fooled by the early spring thaws into thinking that permanent warm weather has arrived—they emerge prematurely. Caught by a dropping temperature, they become stupefied with the cold, and, unable to return to their hibernating quarters, they die.

The Voice of the Turtle

Very few turtles have a voice in the real sense of the word. Many reptiles hiss their displeasure by sharply expelling air from the lungs, but only a few species have definite voices. Most of the giant tortoises that live on the Galápagos and a few other islands are capable of making sounds variously described as roaring, trumpeting, or bellowing. The males are prone to be especially noisy during the breeding season. Possibly these sounds, resembling those made by a bull, are supposed to be romantic.

According to one report, there are two species of turtles that possess such well-developed voices that all other turtles suffer by comparison: the tabulated tortoise of the West Indies and the leopard turtle of Africa. The noise-making ability of these turtles is said to be so well developed that a group of either species can produce a hubbub which almost anyone would mistake for several yapping dogs fighting with a squealing, grunting hog. But despite the novel possibilities of turtles that yap, grunt, and squeal, I have not been able to confirm the presence of such a well-developed voice in any of these creatures.

Turtles That Fish with Lures

The matamata turtle of the Amazon River and its tributaries is one of the queerest of the turtle clan. Attached to its long neck are a number of worm-like appendages that attract the fish, frogs, and other animals on which it feeds; and growing on its rough, irregular-shaped shell are various small water plants. When the turtle is resting on the bottom or moving slowly from one place to another, it is very difficult to distinguish from a rock or log overgrown with plant life.

The alligator snapper has a reddish filament attached to its tongue, which probably is used to attract fish. Observers state that the use of this lure by the turtles can be seen in captive specimens in aquaria.

How Large Do Turtles Grow?

Some of the present-day turtles are quite large, but they are all dwarfed by the size attained by several extinct species. One was a marine turtle called *Archelon,* which became extinct many years ago. An almost complete skeleton of one of these gigantic creatures may be seen at the Peabody Museum of Natural History at Yale University. The shell is over 12 feet long and the skull is 3 feet long. It has been estimated that the living turtle weighed about 6,000 pounds. Another species was a huge land tortoise that lived in India. One of the most complete skeletons of this tortoise, in the American Museum of Natural History, has a shell length of 7 feet 4 inches over the curve, and a straight line length of 5 feet 5 inches. It is thought that this creature weighed about 2,100 pounds when alive.

The largest of the turtles still in existence is the leatherback or leathery turtle, a large marine form. It is known that the maximum weight for this species is close to 2,000 pounds. One specimen caught off the coast of

Vancouver weighed 1,450 pounds, and another taken in the Pacific Ocean weighed 1,902½ pounds. The total length of one of these large turtles may be as much as 8 feet, and the front flippers may have a spread of 8 to 10 feet.

The probable maximum weight of other large species is indicated in the following table.

SIZE OF THE LARGEST TURTLES

Species	Probable Maximum Size	Remarks
Green turtle	800 to 900 pounds	A specimen weighing approximately 850 pounds has been caught in the West Indies. This species is the most popular of the marine turtles for use as a food.
Loggerhead	800 to 900 pounds	A turtle weighing approximately 850 pounds was caught in 1871. It had a flipper spread of 9 feet.
Giant tortoises	500 to 600 pounds	One specimen in Lord Rothschild's collection in England weighed 593 pounds when alive. These tortoises occur in small numbers on Galápagos, Seychelles, and Aldabra Islands.
Hawksbill	100 to 150 pounds	The smallest of the sea turtles. The species from which tortoise shell is obtained.
Alligator snapper	150 to 200 pounds	One in the New York Zoological Park weighing 113½ pounds, and one caught near Little Rock, Arkansas, weighed 117. An unconfirmed report lists one of 403 pounds.
Common snapper	50 to 100 pounds	A weight of 87 pounds is known for one that was fattened in captivity, but in nature, the maximum weight is probably less than this.

How Long Do Reptiles Live?

The most famous of the reptilian Methuselahs are the giant tortoises, although a few of the small tortoises and even crocodilians sometimes reach a ripe old age. It seems well established, however, that giant tortoises live longer then any other vertebrate animal.

The best known of the ancient tortoises include the Mauritius tortoise, brought from Seychelles to Port Louis, Mauritius, which was reported to be 130 to 200 years of age; Napoleon's tortoise, brought from Aldabra to St. Helena Island and said to be alive more than 100 years after Napoleon's death; and Captain Cook's tortoise from the Galápagos Islands, supposedly branded by the great English explorer in 1777 and left in the Tonga Islands. At late as 1959 Captain Cook's tortoise was reported to be still alive.

Most biologists who have studied this matter believe that some tortoises live more than 100 years and admit the possibility that the Mauritius tortoise may have survived from 152 to 200 years. Napoleon's friend is believed to have lived for more than a century. Captain Cook's tortoise had previously been given credit for at least 100 years, but a biologist is said to have discovered that it is a species from Madagascar that does not occur in the Galápagos Islands. No one knows just how old it is, nor how and when it arrived in the Tonga Islands. It appears now, however, that Captain Cook had nothing to do with its transportation.

Most evidence of old age in small tortoises comes from dates carved in their shells, the worn appearance of the carving, and the aged appearance of the reptiles; these often lend some weight to the contention that the tortoises are in truth as old as the age indicated. Much of this evidence is probably reliable, but a carved date can easily be forged. This possibility was pointed out some time ago by a man claiming to own a tortoise that had doubtless lived before the time of Christ, since it had the inscription "Adam I" carved in its shell. Biologists believe that there is evidence that the Carolina tortoise of the United States may live for 123 years.

Crocodilians, according to tradition, are also notably long lived, and we find writers crediting the sacred crocodiles of India with from 100 to 200 years of life. Established ages do not match this, although it is agreed that some crocodilians may well have lived longer than present records indicate. As far as authentic data are concerned, an American alligator holds the record, with a known life span of approximately 56 years. This reptile was in the Dresden Zoological Park, and was still alive at the time the record was made.

Four AMPHIBIANS

All amphibians are not amphibious, and all amphibious animals are not amphibians—an apparent ambiguity with meaning. Amphibians are animals that are classified into a group known as Amphibia. They include frogs, toads, salamanders, and a few relatively rare species known as coecelians. An amphibious animal, on the other hand, is any creature, irrespective of classification, that spends part of its time on land and part in the water. Beavers, hippopotamuses, crocodiles, and many other species are thus amphibious animals, but they are not classified into the group, Amphibia. It is true that most amphibians are amphibious in habit; in a majority of species the immature stages are passed in water, and the adults live on land for at least part of the time. But there are exceptions. Some salamanders, for instance, which are classified as Amphibia, live in water all their lives; strictly speaking, these salamanders are aquatic rather than amphibious in habit.

SOME FACTS AND FANCIES

The eggs of all Amphibia must be laid in water, or at least in moist areas, if they are to develop. Even toads, which seldom get in water except during the breeding season, descend on ponds and streams in the spring, literally in hordes, to lay their eggs. Amphibian eggs in the water occur as masses or strings of transparent jelly-like material containing a large number of small black objects.

The egg of an amphibian usually hatches into a tiny larval amphibian that is often quite unlike its parents in appearance. The youngsters of frogs and toads are the well-known tadpoles or pollywogs. As the tadpole grows, tiny legs develop, gills are gradually replaced by lungs, and the tail, contrary to popular opinion, does not drop off but is gradually absorbed into the tadpole's body and used for nourishment. When the day of the big transformation arrives the tadpole struggles into shallow water, passes through certain changes, and hops out on land as a miniature frog or toad. Unless a tadpole can get into shallow water, it will usually not change into a frog or toad. Thus tadpoles kept in deep aquaria do not go through this transformation.

Unlike birds and mammals, amphibians are cold-blooded, and their body temperatures thus vary with their environment. During cold weather, amphibians must protect themselves or they will freeze to death. They burrow into the soil or into the mud at the bottom of a lake or stream, and pass into the inactive state of hibernation. As a consequence, amphibians are conspicuously absent in temperate regions during this period.

There are fewer kinds of amphibians than any of the major vertebrate groups—only about 3,000 species—and, from man's standpoint, they are usually considered the least significant. However, even these creatures have a place—in man's economy and in the balance of nature.

Amphibians, unlike reptiles and fish, do not have scales. In fact, the skin of many species, such as most frogs and salamanders, is relatively smooth and moist. Many toads, on the other hand, have warty, relatively dry skin. Amphibians with smooth moist skins are usually confined to water or marshy areas, but the thicker-skinned toads may be found some distance from water.

Amphibia come in a greater range of sizes than is generally realized. The smallest amphibian, a minute frog, hails from Cuba. It has a body ⅜ of an inch long, and one could squat comfortably on a person's fingernail. The largest amphibian can be classified as a giant by most standards; it is a completely aquatic species that attains a length of 5 feet and a weight of almost 100 pounds. This giant among amphibians, as well as other large species, is discussed elsewhere.

What Amphibians Are Good to Eat?

On a world-wide basis among amphibians, the large frogs are certainly the most popular food source, although other species are eaten routinely in some countries. These include the American bullfrog, the goliath frog of the Cameroons in Africa, and the so-called edible frog of Europe.

In spite of the many people who will not eat frog legs, the amphibians are so popular in the United States that the wild frog population of the country cannot supply the demand. During some years more than half a million pounds of frog legs are imported and frog farms have been established with varying degrees of success.

The giant Japanese or Oriental salamander has long been eaten in Japan and China, and enterprising zoologists state that mudpuppies and hellbenders make good food.

What Is the Largest Amphibian?

The largest amphibian is the giant salamander, an entirely aquatic species found in Japan and parts of China. It may attain a length of between 5 and 6 feet, and there is a record of 5 feet 7 inches for a specimen caught in China. One captive giant salamander weighed 88 pounds when alive and 99 pounds after death, which indicates that the body probably absorbed water from the aquarium after the creature died. These salamanders inhabit swift mountain streams, subsisting on fish, insects, and worms. Formerly, the Japanese caught them in large numbers for food, and sometimes even used them for medicine. Recently, however, the government has given them protection to prevent their extinction.

The largest of the frog and toad group is the goliath frog, an enormous amphibian found in West Africa in the area known as the Cameroons. The body of this creature may reach a length of 12 or 13 inches, and the legs may be longer than the body, so that its over-all length may be more than 2 feet. The natives use these giant frogs for food, and the large thighbones are much prized for use in ceremonial rites. Consequently, very few specimens have found their way into museum collections.

The United States cannot do nearly as well in large amphibians, although a few get to be of respectable size. The longest amphibian in the United States is the congo eel, a slender salamander with minute legs; it may attain a length of 40 inches. The hellbender, which may attain a length of 27 inches, is probably the heaviest salamander in the United States. The bullfrog, with a body length of as much as 8 inches, is the largest tailless amphibian in the country.

How Long Do Amphibians Live?

In my reading I constantly come upon a reference to a toad that was supposed to have lived for 36 years. Usually its species is not indicated, but some authors manage to give the impression that it was an American toad. Actually, this famous toad was a common toad of Europe that was supposed to have been in the possession of a single family for 36 years. The late Major Stanley Flower, an authority on animal ages, carefully investigated this case and considered the report accurate. There is also a claim of 31 years for an American toad, but I have not been able to confirm this.

The greatest established age record among amphibians is held by the largest species, the giant Japanese salamander. One of these salamanders lived for approximately 52 years in a zoological park in Leyden, Netherlands, and its age at death was believed to be about 55 years. Another record which might be authentic claims 65 years for one of these salamanders. Passing to other groups, we find a hellbender that lived for 29 years, a congo eel for 26, and a siren for 25. An axolotl lived for 25 years in its larval form in Covent Garden, London, while in the adult stage one at Ann Arbor, Michigan, survived for 11 years. Even small tree frogs have been known to live for 7 to 16 years, and the North American bullfrog, sometimes credited with living for 30 years, has an established record of 16 years.

FROGS AND TOADS

What Is the Difference Between Frogs and Toads?

Both frogs and toads have long hind legs and, as adults, are completely tailless. Frogs, however, have a moist, relatively smooth skin and are agile jumpers; toads give clumsy short hops and their skin is rough, warty, and dry. In places where there are only a few species of each, as in parts of the United States and northern Europe, it is not difficult to distinguish between the two forms, but in some regions the line of demarcation between these two types of jumping amphibians is not so distinct. The term frog is acceptable when speaking of the frog and toad group in general.

Why Do Frogs Die in Dry Air?

Frogs spend part of their time on land, but they never venture far from water; if they do not have a moist environment, they will die. The reason is that the evaporation of the body fluids through the skin is so rapid that the frog must replace these fluids by periodically soaking itself in water.

I have seen a leopard frog, a species frequently used in biology classes, die within twelve hours because it was kept out of water. All amphibians lose a certain amount of water through the skin, but the rough-skinned toads lose it less quickly than the smooth-skinned frogs. Consequently, toads, with their thicker skins, are often found some distance from water.

Frogs That Fly

In Borneo, Java, and adjacent areas there are some tree frogs that have unusually large feet with webbed toes. For many years these frogs have been said to be capable of making prodigious leaps from trees, the spread of their webbed feet supposedly enabling them to glide much farther than they otherwise could. In a description of their flight or glide published in 1915, it was said that one frog was seen to jump from a tree and land some 30 to 40 yards away. Their ability to make tremendous leaps is now fully accepted, but some biologists contend that the large membranes of their feet are of no material help; the frog could jump just as far without them.

Frog

Toad

South America has a flying tree frog which apparently does as well without webs as the more famous flying frog of the big feet. One observer performed a large number of experiments with this species. When he tossed the frog into the air, it quickly righted itself, flattened its body and landed on the ground unhurt, belly side down. When he made the frog leap from a tower 140 feet high, it jumped, flattened its body and glided some 90 feet before it came to the ground. This same observer found that European frogs of comparable size fell vertically, and made no attempt to orient themselves so that they would land on their bellies and feet. More observations are needed, but at the present time there seems to be little doubt that certain species of frogs have some ability to glide.

A Male Frog That Makes a Nest of Its Vocal Pouches

The males of many species of frogs and toads have a pair of small vocal sacs or pouches which open into the mouth. Their principal use is to increase the volume of the voice. When the frogs croak, the sacs become greatly distended with air; at other times they are not noticeable. One group of cricket frogs in South America, whose pouches open from the floor of the mouth, has found a unique use for them—they carry the eggs in these sacs. During the incubation period, the pouches become so enlarged that they extend well over the undersurface of the body. The embryos remain in the pouches until they have completed their development and emerge as small frogs.

How Far Can Frogs Jump?

Frogs, with their well-developed hind legs, are able to make tremendous leaps. Even such small species as the cricket frog, whose body is only an inch long, can jump 3 feet, while the American bullfrog has the reputation of making leaps of 8 to 10 feet.

The famous Jumping Frog Jubilee of Angel's Camp, California, held in commemoration of Mark Twain's well-known story, is probably more fun than a three-ring circus. According to eyewitnesses of these contests, each frog is allowed three jumps, and the contestant that covers the greatest distance in the three jumps wins. The frogs' owners are allowed to punch each frog before the first jump, but not after this. Frequently the frogs are very uncooperative. Some will sit contentedly for a time and then take waddly jumps of a few inches; others will not budge until the owners in disgust try to pick them up, at which point they will make a tremendous leap of 6 feet or so, with no regard for the sweating, swearing, pursuing human being.

The winning jump is sometimes disgracefully short. In 1929 the total of the three jumps for the winning frog was actually less than a foot. Sometimes the frogs exert more effort. According to one writer, the winner in the 1938 contest broke previous records with a total of 15 feet 10 inches for the three jumps. In 1944 the record rose to 16 feet 2 inches; in 1954 to 16 feet 10 inches. Perhaps the waddly amphibians are gradually becoming more cooperative with their human masters.

Can Frogs Sing under Water?

Since frogs normally sing with their mouths and nostrils closed, they are able to sing even under water, although the water somewhat deadens the sound. Some time ago, while walking along the edge of a pond, I was attracted by the croaking of a frog. The sound continued for about five minutes, and although I closely examined all possible hiding places along the edge of the pond. I could not find it. Suddenly, about ten feet from shore there was a furious splashing of water, and a large water snake rose to the surface holding a croaking frog in its mouth. They had both been under water all the time I was trying to locate the source of the noise.

The so-called singing or croaking of frogs and toads is almost entirely limited to the males, although some females may make sounds when they are injured or disturbed. The male seems to use its voice principally to attract the female, but some of them certainly sing when their minds are not on mating, for a clamor of amphibian voices can be heard at night in almost any swamp long after the mating season is past. To sing, the frog or toad inhales, closes its mouth and nostrils, and forces the air back and forth between the mouth and lungs. Sound is produced by the action of the air passing over the vocal cords and causing them to vibrate. Many species of frogs have vocal sacs opening into the mouth, which during singing become greatly distended with air. These distended sacs, acting as resonators, are sometimes so large compared to the size of the frog's body that the creature seems to be a large, rounded sac to which a small frog is attached. The American bullfrog has the loudest frog voice known in the United States; the bellowing of ardent males may sometimes be heard for a mile or even more.

Why Is a Frog's Tongue Attached in Front?

Many frogs and toads depend almost entirely upon their tongues for catching food. In these amphibians, the tongue is attached at the front end and is free at its forked posterior end. When the frog spots a moving fly or similar creature, it flicks out its tongue, which is covered by a sticky substance, and the insect becomes hopelessly entangled.

This method of catching prey is doubtless quite efficient, otherwise there would be fewer frogs and toads; but sometimes the amphibian, which is attracted by movement, makes a mistake. One afternoon near dusk I flicked a burning cigarette from the porch to the ground. A toad hopped lazily into view; as I watched it came gradually closer to the cigarette. Smoke still curled upward. Suddenly the toad changed direction and hopped over to the cigarette. It eyed the curling smoke a moment, and then quick as a flash flipped out its tongue; the still-burning cigarette disappeared down its gullet, and the toad hopped unconcernedly away. The amazing part of the whole affair is that it never showed the slightest sign of discomfort, although I watched until it was out of sight.

What Amphibians Go to College?

Several kinds of amphibians are regularly used for study in biology and zoology courses at universities. Most often used are frogs of various kinds, and mudpuppies. Occasionally toads rather than frogs are used. The leopard or grass frog, a medium-sized species, is probably used more in elementary courses than any other single kind of amphibian. This frog is of a greenish color with black spots, with a body length of 3 to 4 inches.

The American bullfrog is another laboratory assistant, and the demand for these amphibians adds up to big business. One biological supply house boasts that it can fill an order of any size for these frogs, which seems logical in view of the tremendous number of these amphibians purchased by the company; during one week in June 1955 this company bought more than 10,000 pounds of bullfrogs. Later catalogs of this same company do not give specific figures, but the significant statement is made that bullfrogs alone have justified the investment in a large laboratory for the preparation of many kinds of animals for laboratory use.

The retail price of a bullfrog prepared for dissection suggests that the supply houses have to compete with dealers buying bullfrog legs for food. The amphibians are listed from $1.50 to $3.75 each, depending upon the size and the type of loving care to which they have been subjected.

An important objective in elementary biology courses is that of teaching the student something of the structure and function of the parts of his own body. Many structures and functions of man and other animals are similar, and many valuable biological and medical facts applicable to man are first discovered by a study of lower species. We can learn much about our own bodies even from the lowly amphibians.

A Toad That Uses Its Back as an Incubator

In parts of South America there is a peculiar tongueless amphibian called the Surinam toad—one of the few tailless amphibians to spend all its life in the water. It is a curious, flattened creature about 5 inches in length, with several projections arranged in the shape of a star on each toe of the front feet. Although the appearance of this amphibian is extraordinary, its reproductive habits are even more remarkable. At the time of mating, the male scrambles onto the back of the female, and clasps her tightly. The eggs are then expelled from a tube which protrudes from the end of the female's body and arches over her back under the belly of the male. The male presses the eggs into little pouches in the female's back, where they are held by a sticky secretion. There they remain, covered by a gelatinous lid, until development is completed. When the young finally push the tops from their prisons and emerge into the outside world, they are tiny toads, not tadpoles.

How Did the Midwife Toad Get Its Name?

There is a small toad in southwestern Europe that has been given the name of midwife or obstetrical toad, because of the way the eggs are cared for. The name midhusband seems much more appropriate, however, since it is the male of the species whose services are used. He gets his legs entangled in the strings of eggs and then goes into hiding. Occasionally he ventures forth at night, and moistens the eggs in water. Eventually, he goes into the water and stays there until the eggs have hatched. After this, he is again able to take his place in amphibian circles, unencumbered by entangling strands of developing youngsters.

Can Toads Live for Years Sealed in Solid Rock?

Every now and then newspaper headlines inform a receptive public that a toad has been found in a small chamber sealed in solid rock. The article is frequently supported by a statement from some "expert" in biology, such as the local mayor, that the animal must have been entombed for at least a hundred years.

Where biologists are concerned, this question was settled as early as 1777; nevertheless, in 1825, William Buckland of Oxford University, England, performed additional experiments. He took twenty-four toads, placed twelve of them in small cells in nonporous sandstone, and the other twelve in cells in porous limestone, sealed them all in their cells and buried them at a depth of 3 feet. At the end of a year, all the cells were opened. The toads that had been entombed in the nonporous sandstone were all dead, but most of those in the porous limestone were alive. It is thought probable that the living toads were able to survive because the porous walls of their chamber had allowed a certain amount of air to reach them, and may have also permitted an occasional insect to get in. The toads were again buried and left for another year, but when examined the second time they were all dead. Buckland also put toads in holes in trees and sealed them up, but all died within less than a year. His experiments prove that it is impossible for toads to live for any great length of time completely sealed or buried, although their survival for more than a year is itself quite remarkable.

It is certainly true that toads are sometimes found in the ground, or apparently sealed within rocks. However, people do not go out looking for entombed toads specifically, and to come upon one accidentally they must have at least partly destroyed the toad's chamber, making it impossible to determine how hermetically it was enclosed. The chances are that there were passages large enough to allow the toad to come and go as he chose, or at least large enough for insects to get in and keep him supplied with food.

Do Any Toads or Frogs Have a Venomous Bite?

In the 1890s a famous naturalist published an interesting book in which he described a South American barking or horned toad, or frog that was supposed to have a venomous bite. He gave two instances in which a dead horse had been found with the jaws of the toad still fastened to it, the conclusion being, of course, that death was due to the bite of the toad.

The barking frogs of South America, named because their cries resemble a dog's bark, are probably the most pugnacious amphibians in existence, but neither they nor any other known amphibian has a venomous bite. Barking frogs have well-developed teeth and their squat, dumpy bodies may be more than 6 inches long. If annoyed, they are likely to clamp their teeth upon any available portion of human anatomy. Once one of these frogs has clamped its jaws on an enemy, it holds on with bulldog tenacity, and it is very difficult to break the grip without killing the amphibian.

In addition to the barking frog, several of the other larger amphibians will bite under some conditions, as we have mentioned elsewhere. These include the hellbender, mudpuppy, and congo eel of North America, the giant Japanese salamander, and other large tropical frogs and toads. Some of these creatures have rather long teeth and are capable of inflicting a nasty wound.

A Common Toad Can Kill a Dog

This is a true statement, but I believe it is obvious that a toad is not likely to attack a dog and overcome it physically. If the dog dies because of the common toad, the amphibian will not be around to enjoy the end results. Many frogs and toads have glands in their skins that secrete a powerful poison; within a single toad there is enough poison to kill a small dog if it is stupid enough to eat a toad. Fortunately for the well-being of dogs, and the owners' peace of mind, dogs seldom eat toads. I have seen dogs capture toads many times and then drop them almost immediately, frequently frothing at the mouth. The reason for this is that the poison is quite irritating to the dog's mouth, and this irritation usually causes the dog to look for a more palatable meal elsewhere.

In some species this poison is considerable more virulent than in the common toads. At one time a small South American tree frog, *Dendrobates*, had the reputation of having such virulent poison glands that it was used by the natives to poison their arrows. This statement still occurs in relatively recent books, but certain experiments with the material strongly suggest that the idea is pure fiction. The experimenters state that the so-called poison is not even capable of killing small animals. It has been established, however, that two South American toads do secrete such strong poison that they should not be handled with unprotected hands. One of these is the giant South American toad mentioned on page 230. The other is a somewhat smaller but related species which, so far as I can find, does not have any recognized common name. The latter species is probably the most dangerous to dogs and other enemies, since dogs have been killed by simply carrying the amphibians in their mouths.

According to a reasonably reliable source, South American natives have used *Dendrobates* to stimulate the sale of parrots. This story must now be looked upon with suspicion in view of the experiments noted above. It may be that the secretions do cause the reported effects, and at the same time not be especially poisonous. At any rate, the supposed occurrences are sufficiently interesting to relate with a "tongue-in-cheek" attitude.

My informant stated that the natives would pluck out some of the normal green feathers of parrots, and rub the tree frog over the exposed skin. The new feathers that grew back in these areas were supposed to be of a striking yellow color. Whatever the truth of the matter, it is suggested that one should not succumb to the lure of a partially yellow South American parrot unless one of the tree frogs is furnished with each purchase. The yellow color is temporary, and when these feathers are shed, they will grow back the normal green color.

At least one frog in the United States may taste unpalatable even to snakes, several of which seem immune to the secretions of other species of amphibians. This is the pickerel frog, one of the commonest frogs in the eastern United States. It has spots, as does the well-known leopard frog, but in addition has a bright orange color on the inner surfaces of the hind legs.

A frog-eating snake has been seen to seize a pickerel frog, then quickly release the victim and rub its head vigorously in the sand. Persons collecting amphibians for study have had unpleasant experiences with this species. Other frogs placed in the same containers have been killed by their secretions within an hour or so. Even the hands of one particularly sensitive to this secretion will become inflamed after he handles one of these amphibians.

Some Frogs and Toads Eat Alligators

Several species of large frogs and toads will eat practically any living thing they can catch and overpower, including other frogs, small mammals, and birds. The American bullfrog has been known to swallow young water birds, and the barking frog of South America catches mice, birds, and similar creatures. The giant South American toad, with a body length of 7 to 8 inches, is one of the largest of the toads, and one of them holds what must be the championship for gastronomic ability in the toad clan. According to a story, several South American toads were received at a university for experimental purposes. Because of lack of space, the toads were placed in a cage with two young alligators, each about 11 inches long, where they all lived in harmony for several days. A week or so later, when it was decided to separate the toads and alligators, one of the alligators was unaccountably missing. Intensive search failing to turn it up, the toads came under suspicion, and all of them were subjected to X-rays. Sure enough, the missing alligator was discovered coiled within the stomach of one of the toads.

Dr. Frank Blair of the University of Texas supports this story with one of his own that is even better. In this case, a bullfrog with a body length of only about 5 inches and an alligator 10 or 11 inches long were involved. The two were in the same cage. One morning the alligator had disappeared, while the frog looked suspiciously distended and was quite inactive. The body of the alligator could be felt within the frog's body. The frog eventually recovered, but was not very active for several days.

Do Toads Cause Warts?

The cause-and-effect relationship between toads and warts is traditional. Some people believe that simply the touch of the toad's skin is sufficient to cause warts to develop, while others think that it is the toad's urine which produces them. Toads never cause warts, although it is easy to see how this idea originated. As previously noted, most toads secrete an irritating and poisonous substance, which in some species may actually burn or irritate the skin of anyone who handles them incautiously. Also many frogs and toads have a tendency to urinate when they are seized, and if the urine gets into a broken place in the skin it produces a burning sensation. But neither the poison nor the urine causes warts.

A Toad Horde

Most amphibians hibernate during the winter. The quarters selected vary with the different kinds of amphibians, but toads usually burrow into soft earth and remain there until spring. Emerging from hibernation, many species immediately mate and deposit the eggs in water, frequently descending upon the rivers and lakes in hordes. Several years ago I was fortunate in seeing such a mass emergence on a river in central Texas.

The late Dr. D. B. Casteel of the University of Texas, a biologist wise in the ways of toads, had agreed to take me to the river at the proper time. Near the end of February the weather became warm for several days, and the toad expert decided that the toad season was at hand. Several of us drove to the river one night, stopped the car motors, and turned out the lights. We were greeted by a chorus of male love songs which indicated that our guide had selected the proper time. As we approached the river, there in the glare of the flashlights were seemingly millions of toads. There were toads in the shallow water, there were toads along the bank, and for some distance back from the water the ground appeared to be hopping with toads—all headed for the river. There seemed to be all sizes: medium-sized toads, small, runty, male toads, and great waddly female toads, their bodies almost bursting with eggs. We collected over 1,100 of them within two hours, which gives some indication of how many there were. Toad lovers will be happy to learn that collections of this kind for classwork have now been discontinued.

A sight such as this can be seen in many areas if the proper time is selected. The first warm spell in the spring, particularly if accompanied by rain, will usually bring the toads from their hibernating quarters. They continue to emerge for a week or so, primarily at night, and after the eggs are laid, they scatter over the countryside in search of food.

Which Amphibians Are Man's Best Friends?

Some years ago, a government biologist estimated that toads, those warty amphibians that hop about our yards at dusk, were worth $19.44 each as insect destroyers. Within relatively recent years, the value to the farmers in Oklahoma of each individual of a species known as the Great Plains toad has been estimated at approximately $25.00.

In view of the fluctuating value of the dollar and many other factors, it is perhaps unwise to try to place a precise value on each of our chubby friends. There are many different kinds of toads, and their value varies somewhat under different circumstances. There have been sufficient studies of the food habits of the common toads, however, to indicate that in general they are the most valuable of the amphibians. Most of their food is composed of insects, of which many, such as cutworms, are definitely harmful.

A toad's appetite is amazing. One toad's stomach was found to contain sixty-five caterpillars of the gypsy moth, an important pest of shade and fruit trees. An authority has estimated that in three months a toad, under normal circumstances, would consume approximately ten thousand insects. If one of the amphibians is continuously supplied with food by an enterprising biologist, it seems to consider it a duty to swallow the material as long as the supply lasts. Under such circumstances, one toad swallowed so many earthworms in succession that digestion could not keep up the pace; eventually the worms were passing alive from the body.

Giant South American toads, also called marine toads, so large that one in a squatting position covers the major part of a dinner plate, have furnished proof of amphibians' ability to control insects. More than 100 years ago, these giant toads were introduced into Jamaica in the West Indies, reportedly to help reduce the number of rats that were chewing up the valuable sugar cane. These toads had no apparent effect upon the rat population, but they did help control the white grubs (immature stages of May or June beetles) and other insect pests of sugar cane. Some years later—possibly because introduced mongooses had gobbled up lizards and other insect destroyers—neighboring Puerto Rico developed grubworm troubles. Some of these toads were taken to Puerto Rico, and for a period of about ten years the grubworm troubles of the island were over. Then, for some unknown reason, toads decreased and the grubs increased. At the last report, cane-growers were using insecticides to supplement the work of their warty friends.

The same species of South American toads has recently been introduced into the Hawaiian Islands and other areas for the same purpose, and the reports to date have been encouraging. These amphibians will eat many kinds of insects, and they are not averse to devouring any other kind of animal they can overcome.

Tadpoles, as well as salamanders, eat many kinds of organic material, including substances that might otherwise pollute ponds and streams; they are thus considered valuable scavengers. It has also been found that the tadpoles of some species will feed greedily upon mosquito wigglers, sometimes entirely eliminating these pests from temporary pools. Their use for mosquito control on a large scale has been recommended. Certain aquatic salamanders are also known to feed upon mosquito wigglers.

In the balance of nature, it is of equal importance that amphibians furnish food for many kinds of animals. Food and game fish, such as bass, catfish, and pike, eat tadpoles and small frogs; relatively large amphibians may be eaten by snakes, water birds, and mammals. Perhaps the greatest value of amphibians as a source of food is indirect; they unwittingly serve as buffers between other animals and fish, and every amphibian that is eaten increases the chances of survival of other valuable food and game species.

SALAMANDERS

An Amphibian with Two Forms

The name axolotl was first given to a dark, yellow-spotted, gilled salamander found in some lakes around Mexico City. At the time it was
named, it was thought that the creature spent all its life in the water and
it was considered to be a normal species of salamander until around 1865.
About this time, several specimens were received in a zoological garden
in Paris. Shortly after their arrival, an interesting series of events occurred.
The axolotls mated; laid eggs which duly hatched into small gilled sala-

manders—thus far all normal enough. Then a peculiar thing happened. Some of the young axolotls lost their gills, underwent a few other changes and came out on land. Study revealed that these transformed axolotls were simply tiger salamanders, identical with or similar to a species common in many parts of the United States. But the disappointment the zoo director and his staff may have experienced in seeing a valuable exhibit transform into a very common species was more than compensated for by the intensely interesting discovery that the axolotl was actually the larval form of a well-known salamander. The most amazing part of the whole discovery, of course, was the fact that under other environmental conditions these immature forms actually reproduced. In some regions, that is, the sexual organs of the axolotl become mature and capable of reproduction, though it retains all the other features of the larval forms. In other regions —and this is what happened in the Paris zoo—the larvae develop into tiger salamanders and come out on land before they reproduce. The process of reproduction in the larval form is so seldom encountered that it makes the axolotl one of the most amazing vertebrates in the whole animal kingdom.

A Field Full of Sirens

In amphibian circles the name siren is not applied to a fascinating and dangerous female of the human species, but to a very peculiar group of salamanders. These snake-like creatures, which may grow to a length of 3 feet, have gills just behind the head, and only one pair of legs. Normally, they spend all their lives in the water, but if the swamp or stream in which they live dries up, they burrow into the mud and are able to survive even though the ground becomes quite dry. When the ground becomes wet again, they emerge from their burrows none the worse for their experience.

During a drought, a farmer had his son plow a dried-up swamp. After the boy had been working for a short time, he came running to the house in great excitement and gasped that the field was full of snakes. The farmer went to the field, fearfully accompanied by his son, and saw to his consternation that the plow had indeed unearthed a number of creatures greatly resembling snakes. They were not very active, so the man gingerly collected one in a bucket and departed for town to have it identified. The biology teacher at the school told him that the snakelike animal was a siren, and quite harmless. When placed in water the farmer's specimen shortly became very active and was soon swimming about, its small front legs clearly visible. Convinced at last that his son had not discovered a field of poisonous snakes, the farmer returned home, and with some difficulty persuaded the boy to continue his interrupted task. Several hundred sirens were uncovered before the swampy area was completely plowed.

Are Mudpuppies Poisonous?

These salamanders, also called water dogs and various other less-complimentary names, are often said to be capable of giving a person a painful nip. Although I have caught numbers of them barehanded, I have never been bitten by one, nor do I know of anyone who has. Whether they bite or not, they are definitely not venomous, although many fishermen are intensely afraid of them.

Once these salamanders have been identified, they are easily recognized in the future, for they have three pairs of gills just behind the head. In a live salamander, the gills are bright red and move back and forth in the water as the salamander rests on the bottom of the pond or stream, or walks slowly among the rocks. The legs are well developed, and the body is usually reddish-brown with darker splotches scattered over the surface. Its food consists chiefly of worms and similar organisms, and it will frequently seize a hook baited with them. In some regions they may be caught in large numbers.

Another salamander, also frequently caught by fishermen, is the hellbender; and in view of its ugly appearance it is appropriately named. It is somewhat similar to the mudpuppy, but it is larger, does not have the fluffy gills behind the head, and its skin is extremely wrinkled. Despite its formidable and hideous appearance, it is not venomous; indeed, no salamander known has a poisonous bite. As I have not had the privilege of catching hellbenders barehanded, I cannot speak from personal knowledge of their biting ability, but some biologists say that they can administer a rather vicious bite.

Are Any Amphibians Harmful?

Among the toad clan, anything that moves and can be captured is considered fair prey, and is greedily gobbled up. Obviously, some useful insects are eaten by many toads, and an occasional individual has been caught snapping up late arrivals at the entrance to honey bee hives. In spite of the bee's natural defense—its sting—one toad was found with thirty-two honey bees in its stomach; perhaps an immunity kept him comfortable.

The indiscriminate appetite of the American bullfrog, the largest frog in the United States, has earned it some criticism. These voracious creatures will eat anything alive that they can overcome, including insects, crayfish, tadpoles, other frogs, and even young wild ducklings, and other water birds. Nevertheless, bullfrogs are relatively innocuous compared with other enemies of wild ducks.

The hellbender and the mudpuppy are two of the largest salamanders in the United States. The hellbender, which may reach a length of more than 2 feet, is an ugly creature. Gill-less, with comparatively small eyes and skin so wrinkled that it appears too large for its owner, this amphibian has been described as an aged, shriveled, defunct cucumber. The mudpuppy, not quite as large as the hellbender, is not much prettier. It has gills that are a bright red color when the amphibian is alive.

Both the hellbender and the mudpuppy are entirely aquatic, and they are found in rivers and streams in the eastern and the midwestern parts of the United States. These two amphibians have been accused of enjoying meals of young fish, but just how much over-all damage they do is not known. The stomach of one hellbender was found to contain twenty-five small trout, and bluegills have been discovered in the stomachs of mudpuppies, along with a miscellaneous assortment of insects, worms, and other aquatic viands.

Five FISHES

Everyone knows that fishes have scales. But among fishes, as in most animal groups, we find exceptions to the rule; several kinds of fishes, such as some catfishes and the ocean sunfish, do not have scales. Eels, which seem to be scaleless, actually do have small scales embedded in the skin.

SOME FACTS AND FANCIES

Other characteristics of fishes include limbs in the form of fins, and in most species a method of breathing by gills. The fins of some species are so well formed that they afford their owners the ability to crawl along the bottom, and even in a few cases allow fishes to scramble about on land. Anyone who has cleaned a fish knows that many fishes have an air or swim bladder just below the backbone. In some fishes the swim bladder is connected to a region just behind the mouth. For these forms, it functions as a lung, and the fish can come to the surface of the water for air.

There are more than 25,000 species of fishes in the world—more different kinds than all other vertebrates combined. And the number of individuals within each species is also unrivalled among other kinds of vertebrates.

For instance, it has been estimated that more than 3 billion herring are caught each year. Even these tremendous numbers are believed to represent only a fraction of the total population of this one species in the oceans.

Persons familiar with the usual fresh-water fishes, and even with the common marine forms, do not usually realize what a variety of sizes are included within this class of animals. The largest fish, the whale shark, has been measured at 45 feet, and some authorities believe it reaches a length of 60 or 70 feet. A weight of more than 13 tons has also been reported for a 38-foot individual. At the other extreme some fishes as adults will stretch the tape at less than an inch.

The variety of breeding habits exhibited by fishes is almost endless. Some, such as sticklebacks, build elaborate nests and even guard the nest until the eggs are safely hatched. Others carry the eggs in their mouths until they are developed. After the eggs are hatched, the young stay with their parent for a time, and in time of danger may dash into the parent's wide-open mouth. It is well known to breeders of tropical fish that some species give birth to living young, although a majority of fishes lay eggs. The eggs of some are laid in hollows scooped out of the bottom of a stream or lake, and in some species the eggs are guarded by one of the parents until they hatch.

One of the most amazing breeding habits among fishes is to be found in the grunions, small fish that belong to the family known as the silversides. The fish, which occur along the coast of southern California, actually lay their eggs on land. During the spring and summer, these fish dash up on the beach at a high spring tide. The female digs a small hole in the sand and lays the eggs that are fertilized by the male. Papa and mamma fish then flap back into the water and forget about the whole affair. Two weeks

later, at another high spring tide, the eggs are washed out of the sand, the young grunions hatch, and swim happily away.

Scientists have recently been studying the number of eggs an individual fish may lay. These estimates are based upon the examination of the eggs found in female fishes and should thus be reasonably accurate. A marine fish called the ling was found to contain more than 28 million eggs; a turbot, 9 million; and a codfish more than 6.5 million. If all these eggs developed, the oceans would be literally crawling with fishes within a short time. Some authorities estimate that for many species only about one egg in a million laid ever becomes an adult.

What Is the Largest Fresh-water Fish?

It is generally thought that the largest fresh-water fish is the arapaima or piraruca of the rivers of South America. This fish is said to reach a length of 15 feet and a weight of 500 pounds. However, there are several kinds of sturgeons that are much larger than the arapaima. Some of them spend most of their time in fresh water, while others come into fresh water only to spawn. The largest of the sturgeons is the huso or giant Russian sturgeon. There is an established weight of 3,221 pounds for one of these fish, and a length of up to 26 feet has been reported. Other large fish, such as sharks and sawfishes occasionally get into fresh water, but they do not spend as much of their time there as do the sturgeons. There are several species of catfishes, wholly fresh-water species, that also rival or exceed the size of the arapaima. One of the largest of these is the wels of European rivers. This fish is said to attain a length of 15 feet and a weight of over 700 pounds, but I have not been able to confirm these figures.

Several very valuable fish products are obtained from sturgeon, and for this reason they have been caught so extensively that large specimens are now exceedingly rare. The product most in demand is obtained from the eggs or roe. These are treated and sold as caviar.

Which Fishes Contribute Most to Man's Economy?

Reliable statistics of the value of different kinds of fishes on a world wide basis are hard to obtain. However, from the standpoint of food and various other fish products used directly by man, several kinds of fishes are of prime importance. Certain kinds of closely related fishes are difficult to distinguish from each other, hence the following discussion applies to groups of species rather than to single species.

On the basis of volume, probably more herring and related species are caught than any other kind of fishes. Herrings are used in the manufacture of certain kinds of anchovies and, in the United States at least, the so-called alewife is a kind of herring. Herring are most in demand as cured or processed fish—salted, smoked, or kippered—rather than as fresh fish, and because of the tremendous numbers used, the herring is considered to be the most important cured fish in the world.

Also of great commercial importance from the food angle are various kinds of flatfishes such as flounder, halibut, and turbot. Although salmon rank far down the line in quantity of fishes caught, it is believed by some authorities that, from the monetary standpoint, the salmon is the most valuable fish in existence.

Fishes furnish us with a large number of valuable products in addition to food. According to a recent estimate, approximately one-third of the world's catch of commercial fishes is used for the manufacture of products other than food. Fish meal and fish oil are the most important of these products. Fish meal was formerly used primarily for fertilizer, but it is now used as an important ingredient of various types of foods for animals such as hogs, cows, and chickens.

Fish oil, obtained by treating waste products and even whole fish, is used in the manufacture of various types of soap, paints, and varnishes. Other by-products include fish glue, used in the manufacture of stamps, books, and in photoengraving work, and fish liver oils.

Both vitamins A and D were formerly obtained from fish liver and at first the principal source was the codfish. Today many other fishes are used, including sharks and dogfishes; the livers are processed primarily for vitamin A. Vitamin D is now produced by methods easier and cheaper than obtaining it from fish livers.

Millions of people are employed in one phase or another of the fish industry. A United Nations Food and Agricultural Organization estimate places the annual value to fishermen at more than $3 billion. Aside from farm products, fish is the most important food source in the world for human beings.

The Role of Fishes in Controlling Disease

Despite the discovery of DDT and even more powerful insecticides, man still depends upon fishes to help him in his fight against disease-carrying mosquitoes. There have been, and still are, scientific debates over the exact value of fishes in this fight, but a complete study of the evidence shows that fishes are often extremely efficient. Biologists who need mosquito larvae or wigglers for their work have long been aware of the competition from fishes, and thus of the need to find fishless ponds for their specimens.

Among the species that are particularly effective in destroying mosquitoes are sunfish, goldfish, and killifish. A little top minnow, named *Gambusia*, that is found in the United States and other temperate areas, is probably the most famous of these mosquito-killers. A single specimen may devour more than a hundred wigglers within eight hours. Recognizing the prowess of *Gambusia* and other species, many mosquito-abatement districts have specialists who rear fishes and distribute them to mosquito-infested area. This method of control has been most successful in Italy, and there is now no major region of the world which has not received some of these fish.

Do Fishes Prey on Their Own Kind?

One biologist has remarked that fishes would be their own worst enemy except that so many other kinds of animals also include fish in their diets. Almost all species will eat other fishes under some circumstances.

Swordfish and sawfish swim rapidly into shoals of smaller fishes and strike back and forth with the sword or saw. The dead and dying victims are then eaten at leisure. Few fishes are likely to escape a hungry sailfish by speed alone. Sailfish are thought to be the swiftest known species. The swimming speed of hooked sailfish reportedly has been timed with stop watches and some specimens have taken out one hundred yards of line in three seconds. If correct, this means that, for one hundred yards at least, sailfish can swim at the incredible speed of approximately 68 miles per hour.

Some carnivorous fishes swim in groups or shoals. These include the dogfish, the barracuda, and the bluefish, a species that somewhat resembles a bass in general appearance. A group of dogfish has been known to herd a school of its quarry into a relatively compact mass before swimming in from all sides and chopping the victims to bits.

Barracuda have been credited with a habit, that, if true, certainly shows a degree of intelligence uncommon in the fish clan. A large barracuda, upon discovering a shoal of fish, gorges itself to capacity. Then, if near shallow water, instead of allowing the remainder of fish to escape, the barracuda is said to drive them into the shallow water and stand guard until its meal has been digested and it is ready for another.

Most biologists are in agreement that, from the standpoint of destructiveness and ferocity, the bluefish is near the top of the list. These fish hunt in huge shoals, and will dash into a group of weaker fish with their jaws working like chopping machines. Their trail is marked by dead and dying victims which stain the ocean waters with their blood. The bluefish seem to feel that their mission is to maim or destroy as many fish as possible,

because they kill and injure far more than they can eat. Bluefish often
occur in tremendous numbers. On the Atlantic coast of the United States it
has been estimated, they are responsible for the destruction of more than
a quadrillion fish per year.

Not only are bluefish outstandingly ferocious and bloodthirsty, but there
is considerable evidence that as gluttons they have no peer. It has been
maintained that a bluefish is not satisfied if more fish are still available
after it has eaten its fill. The creature simply regurgitates and starts over
again!

How Long Do Fish Live?

It seems as though few people can talk or write about fish without exag-
gerating a little; and the champion fish story of all time, believed even by
biologists for many years, concerned an ancient and hoary pike fish. This
fish, according to the story, was caught in a lake in 1497. Attached to its
body was a ring bearing an inscription to the effect that the fish had been
put in the lake by Emperor Frederick II. The aged fish, supposedly 267
years old, was thereafter called the Emperor's pike, and its skeleton was
preserved in a German museum for many years. Its fame spread far and
wide, and its great age was apparently accepted by many biologists, including Metchnikoff of the Pasteur Institute, who used it as an example
of the longevity of fish. The bubble of its fame exploded with considerable
repercussion, however, when a German anatomist, reverently studying the
famous skeleton, found to his disgust that it was not a single skeleton at
all, but was composed of the bones of several different fish.

Carp also have traditionally long lives. Buffon, a famous biologist,
vouched for ages of as much as 150 years, but modern study shows that
he was probably mistaken. The oldest verified age for a carp of which I
could find a record was 24 years, but it is thought that some may live
longer, as noted below.

The species of fish with the greatest verified age record is the European
catfish or wels. There is very good evidence that two of these fish have lived
for over 60 years in a lake in England, and at the last report they were
still alive. Eels, both European and American species, come in for their
share of attention. The late Major Stanley Flower, an expert on animal
ages, accepted ages of 40, 42, and 55 for the European eel, and a probable
50 is listed for the American form. One of the European eels is of particular
interest, because it was owned by a single family for more than 40 years.
A European sturgeon was kept for 38 years in the Brighton aquarium, and
even the lowly perch has been known to live for 12 years in the New York
aquarium.

The most accurate method for determining the age of a fish, as well as the ages of other animals, is by the observation and study of specimens in a zoological park, or in some other situation where mistakes in identities are not likely. Within recent years, however, somewhat indirect methods have been used to determine the ages of fishes caught in nature.

It has been found that the scales and certain bones of some fishes show annual growth rings, somewhat similar to the growth rings of a tree. Age determination using these methods must be done by experts, and even so, there is still possibility of error. However, Dr. Alex Comfort, well-known authority on animal ages, lists the following probable ages, based upon scale and bone studies: carp, 30 to 50 years; a halibut, 10 feet long and weighing 500 pounds, 60 years; beluga sturgeon, 75 years (ages 80 to 100 probable for large specimens).

The fishes with the shortest lives are doubtless some of the gobies. Most of these fish are small, and some species are used as aquarium fish. Some of these might be called "annuals," since they hatch, grow up, reproduce, and die all within a single year. These fish, and possibly the ice fish, of China, are the only vertebrate animals known with such a life history; they thus have the dubious honor of being shorter-lived than any other known vertebrate animal.

HERRINGS

What Are Sardines?

Sardines are sardines only when they are safely in the can. According to the United States Bureau of Fisheries, sardines are any of the small fish that belong to the herring family. Different species are emphasized by the sardine industry in different parts of the world. Off the coast of California, most of the fish caught are the so-called California sardine, while in Maine fishermen collect the sea herring. The canneries of France and Portugal can young pilchards, and in Norway the sprat receives the lion's share of attention. Some of the fish that are used as sardines have the scientific name *Sardina*, and it is probable that the common name of sardine derives from this.

SALMON

A Marine Fish That Breeds in Fresh Water

It has been known for many years that some marine fishes, such as salmon and alewives enter fresh water to breed. In the case of the salmon,

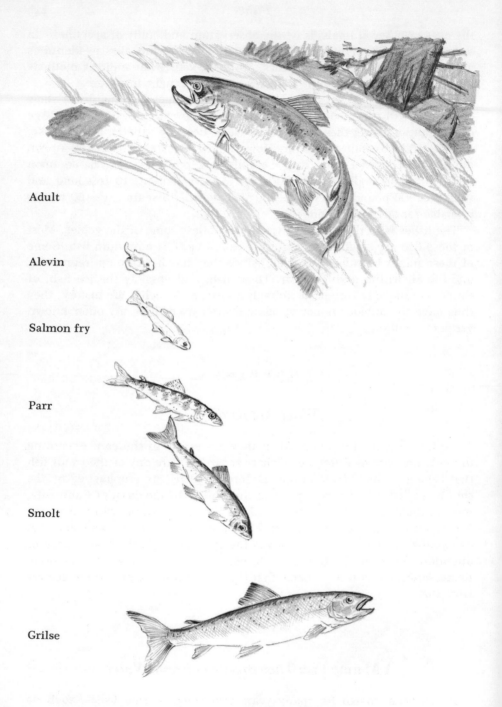

Adult

Alevin

Salmon fry

Parr

Smolt

Grilse

Atlantic Salmon's Cycle of Life

after the eggs hatch the young salmon swim to the ocean, became mature, and return to rivers and streams to lay their eggs. By marking young salmon, it has been found that they always return to the same stream in which they were hatched.

Until recently, one of the greatest of animal mysteries was how the fish could find their way back to the stream of their birth several years later. Careful studies now indicate that the fish do this by their well-developed sense of smell. Fish with their nostrils plugged returned to streams, but they often blundered into the wrong ones. Those without plugged nostrils always returned to their home streams. It is believed, therefore, that the "homing instinct" of salmon depends upon the association of particular water odors that is impressed upon the young fish during their brief residence in the stream after hatching.

FOUR-EYED FISHES

What Fish Has Four Eyes?

In parts of Central and South America are fish that have eyes unlike those of any other vertebrate animal. They are called four-eyed fish but, although the structure of their eyes is remarkable, the term "four-eyed" is somewhat misleading. There are only two eye sockets and in each eye socket there is only a single eye, but the eyes are constructed for two types of vision. The fish are sometimes called double-eyed fish, a name more descriptive of the actual construction of the eyes. Each eye is divided into an upper and lower part by a dark stripe, and the fish usually swims with its head partly out of the water so that the water surface lies along the

Upper pupil

Pupil screen

Lower pupil

Four-eyed Fish

dividing line of the eye. Detailed studies of the structure of the eyes indicate that these fish have double vision. The upper half of the eye is thus probably used for seeing objects out of the water, while the lower half peers around for food beneath the surface.

SHARKS AND RAYS

How Dangerous Are Sharks?

There are probably more stories told about sharks than about any other group of fishes, and most discussions have dealt with whether or not they will attack human beings. Even before World War II there were a number of authentic instances of sharks attacking human beings, but some biologists were nevertheless unconvinced that such attacks ever occurred. Now, I suspect that even the most stubborn skeptics are believers because of extended studies and full verification of many attacks. Dr. Leonard P. Schultz, of the United States National Museum, has reported on over 700 authenticated cases of shark attack. Of this number, 408 people died and 319 recovered. During World War II the armed forces of the United States considered the hazard of shark attack so important that they developed a chemical shark repellent. This material proved satisfactory in experiments with some species, but had no effect on others. Several agencies, including the Office of Naval Research and the American Institute of Biological Sciences, are supporting research toward developing a good shark repellent. Results to date are encouraging, but as yet there is no sure way to prevent sharks from attacking a person in open water.

It should perhaps be mentioned that, at this writing, the largest fish recognized by the International Game Fish Association as having been caught on rod and reel is a white shark. This fish, caught off the coast of Australia in 1955, weighed 2,536 pounds.

Although it is definitely known that some sharks are dangerous, many shark stories have been considerably exaggerated. There are about 150 different kinds of shark, and of this number very few account for most human casualties. These are the white shark or man-eater, the tiger shark, the blue shark, and the hammerhead; but even they attack man only rarely and are less dangerous in some areas than in others, which perhaps is one reason for all the controversy regarding their appetites. The difference may be due to temperament, and also to the presence or absence of food in a given area. Where sharks are well fed from garbage or slaughterhouses, natives will frequently dive among them to recover coins, but where food is scarce no amount of money will tempt the divers into the water. Con-

sidering the number of exposures, we can be sure that no shark prefers a human being to all other articles of diet. Nevertheless, it is a wise person who heeds the warning, "Never trust any species of shark."

Of What Use Are Fish Scales?

Everyone is aware that fishes display an enormous variety of colors. Some of these colors are caused from actual color cells, containing pigment, whereas others are a result of light reflection and interference by small crystals on the scales. These crystals are responsible for the silvery appearance and for the iridescence which occurs in many species.

Many years ago it was found that if the shiny material from fish scales was applied to beads it would give them a luster quite similar to pearls. This was a big factor in establishing the costume jewelry industry. This shiny material used to make imitation pearls is called pearl essence. It is derived by subjecting the scales to special treatment, which results in a separation of the crystals from the scales. After purification and other treatments, the resulting pearl essence is mixed with various kinds of liquids, into which beads are dipped and allowed to dry. The quality of the imitation pearls depends upon the kind of beads used, and the number of times the beads are dipped in the essence concoction. Pearl essence is also used to decorate many other articles, such as jewelry boxes, toilet sets, and even automobile fixtures.

Pearl essence is by far the most important commercial product derived from fish scales, although the scales of some species, such as the tarpon, are used for making trinkets and souvenirs. Scales are of tremendous importance, however, to those biologists who are interested in fishes. By studying the scales an expert can estimate its age rather accurately. As a fish grows, rings similar to the growth rings of a tree are added to the scales. During the summer, when food is plentiful and the temperatures are warm, a wide light area of growth rings is added to the scales; in winter, growth of the fish is slower, and the growth-ring region is narrower and darker. Knowledge of how long fishes live, how large they are at a certain age, and the rate of growth under various conditions is of importance to those interested in the problems of propagating and conserving food and game fishes.

Shark scales are small tooth-like structures that impart a rough surface to the skin. At one time pieces of sharkskin, called shagreen, were in demand as abrasives. Carpenters, cabinet makers, and even metal workers used the material for smoothing and polishing surfaces. Today cheaper abrasives, such as sand paper, have largely replaced sharkskin, and about the only use for the skin with the scales still attached is for decorative purposes. Within recent years, however, a method of successfully removing the scales has been discovered, and the tanned skin of certain species produces highly satisfactory leather. The demand for such shark leather products as wallets, tobacco pouches, shoes, and handbags now far exceeds the supply.

Are Dogfish Edible?

I have not had the privilege of eating dogfish, but those who have tried it tell me that the flesh has a strong taste of ammonia. Apparently the flesh needs special treatment to be palatable.

The flesh of the dogfish has appeared on the menus of many restaurants and on the tables of people throughout the world, but not under the name of dogfish. In Canada and the United States we have "grayfish," in England it is "flake," while the name "sea eel" is used in Germany. In all cases, it is our old friend the dogfish parading under an assumed name.

What Are the Medicinal Values of Fishes?

One fish may take part of the credit for training our doctors. The dogfish, a small shark, is one of the principal animals studied in college and university courses of comparative vertebrate anatomy, and the successful completion of this course is required for entrance to many medical schools. In this course many premedical students get their first training in dissection; though the bodies of people and fish differ, the gross organ systems of each are surprisingly similar.

Dogfish are used in medical training for several reasons. They are numerous and relatively easy to obtain in large quantity. The organ systems are more similar to those of man than are those of many other fishes. Also, the skeleton of the dogfish is composed of cartilage rather than bone. Cartilage, which is much softer than bone, allows a student to make successful dissections of such complex structures as the brain, the nerves connected to it, and the delicate tubes of the inner ear. In many other animals these structures are enclosed in a hard bony covering, which makes dissection much more difficult for an inexperienced student.

Until put to this use, the dogfish was regarded as an unwelcome species. It has sharp teeth, a voracious appetite, and often swims in large schools. Unfortunately for fishermen, dogfish have a taste for herring and other fishes of commercial importance. When accidentally caught in a net they express their displeasure by testing the strands with their teeth. The overall damage to the fishing industry by dogfish has been estimated at several hundred thousand dollars annually, but within recent years fishermen have finally been able to make a profit from them. Thousands of the "dogs" are used each year in zoology courses and many of the fish are captured for the vitamin content of their livers.

Death-dealing Rays

Sting rays, or stingarees, are very flat fish with a long whiplike tail near the base of which is a sharp jagged stinger. These fish have earned an evil reputation which is at least partially deserved, but the chances are that they are not deliberately vicious. They habitually lie partially buried in the sand and will naturally defend themselves if someone steps upon their backs. Their only weapon of defense is the long spine or stinger which they know too well how to use.

The jagged wound inflicted by the barb of a sting ray may be quite serious. Aside from the usual danger of infection, there is the fact that the barb releases into the wound a poison secreted by a gland connected to the spine. The effects of the sting frequently persist for weeks or months, and in some instances permanent injury to a limb has resulted. Tropical species are probably more dangerous than those found in temperate areas. One death in the United States from a sting ray's sting was reported between 1950 and 1954. Most sting rays are marine, but a fresh-water species in the Amazon River seems to be about as dangerous as any. Richard Schomburgk, an early South American explorer, had several experiences with these fish. Two of his native helpers were stung by sting rays, and in both instances the men suffered excruciating pain and had violent convulsions. Although the wounds were treated at once, the lives of the men were saved only with difficulty. Several days later Schomburgk was visiting at an estate when one of the laborers was stung, and although the man was young and vigorous he died in convulsions some time later. Other explorers have reported similar experiences.

Dr. Bruce W. Halstead, of Loma Linda University, states that the L-C treatment, mentioned elsewhere, has been used for sting ray stings with reportedly good results.

Other fish that have dangerous venomous spines include the scorpion fish and the weaver fish. These have poison glands connected to spines along their backs, and a few persons have died as a result of stepping on them or handling them incautiously. Both these fishes live in the ocean. There are many other fishes that have venomous spines, but most of them are not dangerous to man. Common examples include the spiny dogfish, a marine form, and various catfishes that are found in both fresh and salt water. Some tropical catfishes apparently have more potent spines, since fatalities following their stings have been reported.

Several kinds of fishes are capable of delivering electric shocks, such as the marine group called torpedos, electric rays, or crampfish. All are somewhat flattened, and are related to the sting rays; these fishes occur in both the Atlantic and Pacific oceans. Torpedos spend much of their time resting on the ocean bottom, and they can be potentially dangerous for the unwary persons who step unceremoniously on the middle of their backs. A large specimen can knock a man flat on his face with the attendant possibility that the victim will drown.

ANGLERS

Fish That Trick Their Prey

Angler fish have very peculiar and suggestive devices for attracting their prey — usually lures of some kind which float above their mouths. In certain cases the lures are simply movable barbules, while in others the resemblance of the lure to a fishing rod and line is remarkable. In some species there is even a three-pronged hook on the end of the line. Many names have been given to the more common species, including fishing frog, goose fish, toadfish, and allmouth. This last name is especially appropriate since, when its mouth is open, the fish looks like a large mouth with a small body attached to it. The angler's habit is to lie buried in the mud or otherwise concealed, with its lure dangling over its wide open mouth. Any fish curious enough to investigate the dangling lure disappears with a dull snap down the cavernous maw.

Angler fish will eat practically any living thing that comes within reach, even an occasional sea bird. A rather remarkable story has been told about two boys, an angler fish, and a duck on the eastern coast of the United States. The two boys were fishing close to shore when they were attracted by the peculiar actions of a flock of ducks some distance away. Some of the ducks appeared to be diving tail first, and all the birds seemed to be somewhat alarmed. The boys rowed toward the ducks and, as they approached, saw in the clear water a huge angler fish come close to the surface, seize a duck, and swallow it. The boys went back to shore for a harpoon and returned to the place where they had seen the fish. When they spotted the angler on the shallow bottom, they harpooned it, towed it to shore, and then were surprised to see that its sides were moving rather vigorously. Concluding that it must be the duck, they cut open the fish and found the duck, still alive, covered with the angler's stomach secretions. When cleaned, the duck was none the worse for its experience, and the boys kept it as a pet for some time, naming it, quite appropriately, Davey Jones.

Fishes That Swallow Larger Fishes

Imagine if you can a man weighing 150 pounds sitting down to a table and eating a 300-pound hog at one meal, and, what is more, swallowing it whole. Angler fish regularly and successfully (thanks to the stretching powers of their stomachs) swallow objects larger than their own bodies. Their voracious appetites, however, sometimes make them overly ambitious. Specimens have been found floating helplessly at the water's surface with fish in their stomachs that were more than twice their own size. Appetite alone is not to blame, however. Their teeth are so arranged that once they have seized a victim they cannot turn it loose. The angler must finish any meal it begins or endure being dragged through the water by its prey.

Some species of deep-sea fishes, smaller than the anglers, equal or even exceed the angler in swallowing ability. These fishes, which include the black or great swallower, and the so-called widemouths, customarily swallow fish larger than themselves and are reported to have successfully downed fish three times their own size.

A Male Fish That Grows on the Body of the Female

While the female angler fish may measure three feet or more and weigh twenty or thirty pounds, the tiny males of some species have a maximum length of about four inches, and in some cases are so small that they can be seen only with difficulty.

A short time after hatching, the male attaches himself to the body of the female, and although the female continues to grow, the male does not to any extent. The tissues of the two fuse together, and the two blood systems become connected. After this happens, the male is absolutely dependent upon the female, and draws nourishment from her blood stream. In 1936 one of these female anglers was caught in a net off the coast of Massachusetts at a depth of 600 feet. This fish was 33½ inches long and it weighed 20 pounds. Study revealed that a tiny male, only 1½ inches in length, was attached to the skin of the female's body just behind the gill covers.

It is not known why this peculiar association should have developed, but its advantages are apparent. Most anglers of this type are deep-sea fish and live in relative darkness most of their lives. Since the two sexes are attached almost from birth, when the breeding season arrives the males and females do not have to go blundering around in the darkness seeking a mate. Comparable associations between male and female animals without backbones are known, but the angler fish are the only known vertebrates in which such a situation occurs.

EELS

Does the Moray Have a Poisonous Bite?

Morays, of which there are many kinds, are eels that live in the ocean. Many of them have long sharp teeth and the snake-like body of large individuals may be more than 10 feet long.

Also known as the murry and muraena, these fish occur in the Mediterranean Sea, adjacent parts of the Atlantic Ocean and in the Pacific. In the days of the Roman Empire, large numbers of murrys were reared in specially built enclosures. The fish were so popular as food that Julius Caesar is said to have served more than 6,000 of them at a single banquet.

The notoriety of these morays, however, did not arise from their popularity as food. Rather, it was because the Romans used the fish for sport. The bodies of dead slaves were fed to the fish and, if reports are correct, this practice was not confined to the dead. Pliny is quoted as authority for the statement that the threat of the *piscina* or rearing pools was an important factor in maintaining discipline among the slaves.

The Romans believed the bite of the moray to be venomous, and this belief persists among many people even today. But many people hunting for abalones off the California coast have been bitten by morays and, so far as I know, no poisonous effects were reported.

Morays are greatly feared by fishermen, although they seldom attack without provocation or unless the fish mistake a probing hand for a marine animal that they can eat. But if captured and pulled into a small boat, a large moray is likely to make things lively for all hands.

Dr. Vernon Brock, director of the Hawaiian Fish and Game Division, once speared a 10-foot moray near Johnston Island, south of the Hawaiian Islands. The fish did not struggle so he assumed it to be dead. He therefore dived into the water and grasped the spear in order to tow the specimen

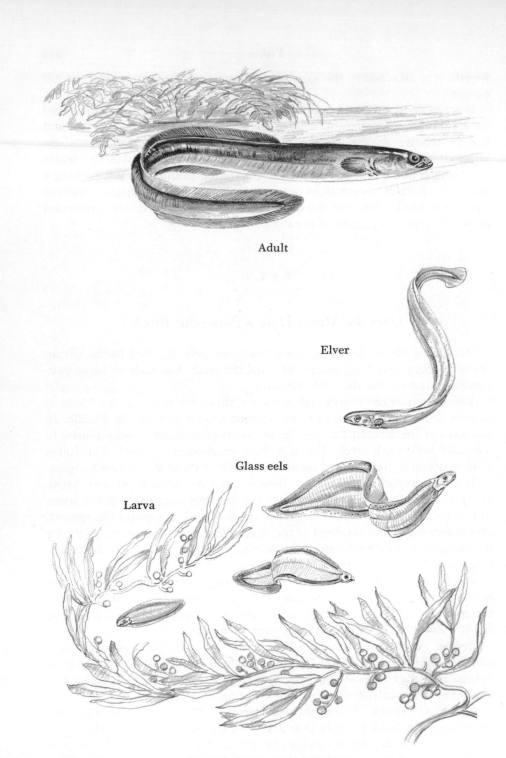

Adult

Elver

Glass eels

Larva

American Eel—larva to adult

to the boat. Suddenly the moray came very much alive and lunged straight at its attacker. Dr. Brock instinctively threw up an arm to protect his face. The moray seized the arm; then, after chewing it savagely, released its grip. Dr. Brock swam to the boat with considerable difficulty; a torniquet had to be used to stop the flow of blood. Fully three months elapsed before he regained the use of his arm.

Do Eels Jump About in the Pan While Cooking?

It is probably the snake-like form of the eel that causes many people to regard this interesting species with distaste. There are a number of different kinds of eels, many of which live in salt water, but much to the disgust of feminine "Isaak Waltons" there are also fresh-water eels, some of which may be caught occasionally on hooks. It is said that when eels are being cooked they will jump about in the frying pan, and I had one enthusiastic person tell me that he once had to tie on the lid of a frying pan to prevent the eel from jumping out onto the floor. This story was certainly an exaggeration, unless the man was talking about a live eel. I have seen pieces of a freshly killed eel move slightly in a pan, and the muscles quiver in the hot grease, but in most instances these movements are not noticeable unless one is watching for them. The movements are caused by muscular contractions, and they may also occur when one is cooking other kinds of meat, such as frogs' legs.

The flesh of eels is, of course, not poisonous, and the creatures do not have a poisonous bite. I have handled a fair number of fresh-water eels and have yet to be bitten by one.

Fresh-water Eels That Breed in the Ocean

A few fresh-water fishes, such as eels, reverse the procedure of the salmon and breed in the ocean. Perhaps it is appropriate that fresh-water eels, about which so many fish stories have been told, should have unusual breeding habits. Fresh-water eels become mature when several years old, and shortly thereafter start downstream toward the ocean. Huge numbers congregate in a common breeding ground in the Atlantic Ocean, south and southwest of Bermuda. Here the adults spawn and, having performed their parental duties, die within a short time. The egg hatches, not into a respectable-looking eel, but into a curious flattened leaf-like creature called a larval eel. Biologists were familiar with this larva long before its connection with the adult eel was established, but it differs so radically from the adult that it was regarded as a different kind of fish. Some biologist gave these larvae the scientific name of *Leptocephalus,* and now that they are known to be immature eels they are frequently called leptocephalus larvae. The larvae eventually find their way back to shore, but before they can enter fresh water they must change into another larval form called an elver. The elvers swim up the streams and remain in fresh water until they become mature.

Curiously enough, the American and European eels, although different species, use the same general breeding grounds; sometimes even intermingling. Yet the two species remain distinct, and an American eel has never been found in European waters or vice versa. It is quite possible that the larvae may occasionally make a mistake and swim off in the wrong direction, but if they do it is unlikely that they live to boast of their travels. The reason lies in their different rates of development. The larva of the American eel takes only a year to develop into an elver, but the European form takes about three years to attain this same stage. It takes approximately the same time for each species to reach its respective homeland. If the larva of an American eel were to swim toward Europe, it would find itself in the embarrassing position of changing into an elver in the middle of the ocean, 2,000 miles or so from shore. European larvae wandering toward the American continent would arrive a couple of years before they had reached the stage where they were ready to live in fresh water. During the waiting period, the chances would be very much against the survival of the infant Europeans.

CARP, ELECTRIC EELS, AND CATFISHES

Rough Fish

Rough fish are usually considered to include any fresh-water fishes that are normally not valuable for food or sport. Species usually classified as rough fish include the gars, buffalos, suckers, carp, and fresh-water dogfish or bowfins.

Rough fish in large number are considered objectionable for several reasons. Some, such as the gars, feed almost entirely on other fish and thereby destroy large numbers that might otherwise end up in the frying pan. Some rough fish do not normally eat other fish exclusively, but they may consume or destroy so much of the food of more valuable fish that the latter are reduced in numbers. Carp especially have objectionable food habits that may cause trouble for other fish. They feed primarily upon aquatic organisms that are found on water plants and in the mud on the bottoms of lakes and streams. In searching for their food, carp grub about in the mud, and in so doing they often uproot and kill much aquatic vegetation. If they occur in large numbers, they may keep the water so muddy that it becomes unsuitable for other species.

Although rough fish in large numbers are usually objectionable, a certain number have their place in the balance of nature; even when they make up a large percentage of the fish population, people can find a use for them. It has been found, for instance, that the removal of predatory rough fish from many lakes will not necessarily result in a larger yield of food and game fish. In fact the contrary is often true. The removal of the predatory fish allows so many of the young game fish to survive that not enough food is available to enable them to grow as fast as usual.

When rough fish occur in large numbers they are sometimes caught by commercial fishermen for the manufacture of fish meal, fertilizer, and other products. The Falcon Dam on the Rio Grande River, the boundary between the United States and Mexico, has created Falcon Lake. Commercial fishermen have taken as many as forty-three tons of rough fish per month from this lake.

Where Did Carp Originate?

Carp are so common in the ponds and streams of Europe and America that it is hard to believe that they are not natives of either continent. Asia is the original home of these fish, and in China they have been cultivated for food for more than 1,500 years. Carp were introduced into Europe several hundred years ago and into the United States before 1900.

There is probably no fish in the world that has been cussed and discussed more than the carp, but the fish are sometimes useful both directly and indirectly. Carp are probably cultured more for food than any other single kind of fish. This is especially true in Asia and parts of Europe where the cultivation of fish in ponds has been flourishing for many years. Carp are so hardy that they are capable of living under conditions that would kill most other species. This, plus the fact that they gain weight rapidly with a minimum of attention, probably accounts for their popularity as a cultured fish.

Even in the United States, where sportsmen in general regard carp as fit only for pigs, millions of pounds of these fish are marketed as food. Restaurants may call the dish by a different name but what frequently lies beneath their fish sauce is a carp.

The well-known goldfish is actually a kind of carp. It was developed by selective breeding many years ago, and now there is disagreement as to

whether Chinese or Japanese fish fanciers were responsible. As long as
goldfish are kept in a small amount of water, such as an aquarium, they
do not grow excessively. If they are placed in a larger body of water, however, they often grow to tremendous size, lose their gold color and look
very much like carp. I have seen fish 2 feet in length that developed from
tiny goldfish.

At this writing there is increasing evidence that other fishes may soon
be competing with carp in popularity as a cultivated fish. These are native
African species called tilapias and largemouth kurpers. They are easily
raised in many types of water and reproduce at astounding rates. Some of
the fish have been raised successfully in Thailand, Egypt, and the Hawaiian
Islands.

What Is the Most Dangerous Fish in the World?

Several kinds of fishes, such as sharks and barracudas, have earned
the reputation of being dangerous, but none can compare in ferocity with
some small fresh-water fishes of South America. These fishes—distant relatives of the carp—have various names, including piranha, carabe, and
pirai. No land animal, however large, may be considered safe from these
little balls of fury.

Observing a piranha in an aquarium, one gets no impression of the
latent ferocity contained within that relatively small body. One sees a fish
somewhat resembling a perch in general shape. But look closely at the
large mouth with its pugnaciously protruding jaws. Observe that along
the margin of each jaw are razor-sharp triangular-shaped teeth which seem
too large for such a small fish.

Piranhas have the nasty habit of hunting in schools, and any animal
that is attacked becomes the center of a seething maelstrom of activity until
every shred of flesh has been ripped from its bones. It is reported that they
sometimes turn savagely upon their fellows and devour them with equal
relish. Several naturalists have written interesting accounts of experiences
with the piranha, and many South American explorers, as well as natives,
bear scars as a result of unpleasant encounters with them. One explorer,
while fishing for piranhas, lost his balance and fell headfirst into a school
of them. Before he gained the shore, only a short distance away, he was
severely bitten in several places. Another naturalist reported that a native
on muleback passed through the camp on his way home. A short time later
the mule returned to camp, riderless. Following the mule tracks to a
stream, the naturalist found the native's skeleton a short distance from the
stream crossing, completely stripped of flesh. Piranha will fasten their
razor-sharp teeth upon the first part of the anatomy that comes within

reach, and will continue their attack even out of water. Wooden planks and sticks will be chewed up with insatiable fury, and several men have had their fingers terribly mutilated when they attempted to remove a hook from a piranha's mouth.

Are Electric Eels Dangerous?

The electric eel, which inhabits the rivers and lakes of South America, actually is not an eel at all but belongs to the same group as the carp. It may attain a length of 6 to 7 feet and is capable of delivering a very powerful electric shock. Doubtless many exaggerated stories have been related regarding the strength of the current generated by these fish, but some of the stories contain an element of truth. I do not know of anyone who has ever been killed directly by the shock of an electric eel, but some reported cases of death by drowning following an electric shock are very probably authentic.

Alexander von Humboldt, a South American explorer, wished to obtain some electric eels for experimental work, but he found that the natives feared them so intensely that he had to devise a special plan for catching them. A herd of horses was driven into a stream inhabited by electric eels in order to stir them up, and thus facilitate their capture. The eels attacked the horses with discharges of electricity, and the horses plunged and reared wildly and made for the bank, only to be driven back into the water by the natives. During the confusion, a few eels came close enough to shore to be captured. When the horses were finally allowed to come ashore, they were hardly able to walk, and two of them had drowned.

Another man saw a native boy, who was swimming in a river, suddenly shocked into insensibility by an electric eel. Only a prompt rescue by the boy's friends saved him from drowning, and the effects of the shock lasted for several hours. Many other naturalists and explorers have witnessed similar occurrences, and all agree that the electric eel is a potentially dangerous fish.

FLATFISHES

Can Fishes Change Color?

Some years ago I was idly watching some fishes swimming about in a clear park stream, the bottom of which was peculiarly marked with large areas of contrasting light and dark spots. As the fishes swam about searching for food, they would occasionally stop for a short time over one of these areas and within a few minutes, much to my amazement, they would become almost invisible. I watched for an hour or more, and they always changed color to harmonize with the background. Many species of fishes have this power of color change developed to a certain extent, but some are much more adept than others. Some of the flatfishes, including the flounders and the turbots, are probably the champion blenders of the fish world. Experiments have shown that if they are placed even on a checkerboard background, within a short time it is almost impossible to tell where background ends and fish begins.

Fishes Whose Eyes Migrate

A flounder, when laid on its side, will stare up with both eyes at the same time. In most fish the eyes are on opposite sides of the head, and only one is visible when the fish is laid on its side. All fishes belonging to the flounder or flatfish group pass through the same peculiar changes during their development, so that their eyes eventually lie very close together. When the young flatfish hatches, it is a normally formed fish with eyes on opposite sides of its head. After a short period of growth, however, the body becomes flatter, and one eye starts to move toward the top of the head, and continues to move until it reaches a position on the opposite side very close to the other eye. In most cases, a definite twisting or turning of the head occurs at the same time. These fishes lie on the floor of the ocean on their side; when they swim, they do so on one side watching for food above them.

A Mouth Full of Eggs

The males of some marine catfishes and others found in the rivers of South America carry the eggs in their mouths until they hatch. So far as is known, they do not eat at all during this period. The father's interest in his duties does not wane even after the young fish hatch. He swims with them for a time and, when danger threatens, holds his mouth open until the frightened youngsters can dash in to safety. The tilapias or largemouth kurpers, mentioned previously, are also mouth breeders.

In all fairness to the female, it should be mentioned that in the case of some African fishes related to the perch, the female rather than the male carries the eggs in her mouth and, in time of danger, allows the young fish to seek safety therein.

A Fish That Shocks its Meal from Other Fish

In the Nile River of Africa lives a fish called the electric catfish. Like the electric eel, it generates a current and, if we are to believe supposedly authentic reports, uses its electricity not simply for defense but to secure its food. It swims along until it discovers another fish in the process of digesting a meal, swims near, and flicks on its current. The astonished victim vomits its meal in surprise and pain, and the catfish rapidly gobbles up the stuff.

STICKLEBACKS

The Stickleback, Champion Nest Builder

Many fishes build nests of one type or another, but the small stickle-backs—most species are only a few inches in length—are probably the champions of them all. The nests are built by the male from twigs, stems, leaves, and similar rubbish, which, using his mouth, he fashions into a hollow structure with a single entrance, cementing the material with a sticky substance secreted by glands connected to the kidneys.

The nest when completed is a comparatively elaborate structure usually attached to reeds or some other suitable foundation. The stickleback then

sallies forth in search of a wife whom, by persuasion, or even by such strong-arm methods as sticking her with his spines, he induces to enter the nest. Once inside, the female deposits the eggs and then breaks through the back wall of the nest and swims away. The males of some species are not satisfied with a single conquest but, after fertilizing the eggs, go out and repeat the whole process. When sufficient eggs have been procured from females willing to be pilfered, the male guards the nest until the eggs are hatched and the young are old enough to shift for themselves.

SHARK SUCKERS

Hobo Fish

Shark suckers (other names include sucking fish, pilot fish, and remora) are slender grayish fish 2 to 3 feet long. On top of their heads is an oblong sucker-like disc, with which they attach themselves to almost any kind of moving object, such as whales, turtles, or even ships, although they are most often found associated with sharks. The reason for their peculiar habit is not entirely clear. They do gain a certain amount of protection from their hosts and sometimes eat scraps of food left by them. They also gain free transportation, but the shark sucker is a good swimmer and indeed can frequently swim faster than the shark to which it is attached. Possibly they are just naturally lazy and prefer to spend their energies in ways other than swimming.

Contrary to popular opinion, the shark sucker does not directly harm the shark by attaching to it. However, if a shark is host to several suckers, it must expend considerably more muscular effort in swimming. Very thin sharks have been found to which several of the sucking fish were attached, and it is thought probable that these hobos contributed to the shark's poor physical condition.

In some parts of the world, especially in the South Seas, natives use the shark suckers as fish hooks. They tie a line to the tail of a sucking fish and, when the game, fish, or turtle, is spotted, toss the remora overboard. It is allowed to swim about until it fastens onto its prey, which is then slowly hauled within capturing or harpooning distance. A remora attaches to its host so firmly·that it is almost impossible to pull it off without tearing its sucker.

At one time it was believed that shark suckers could stop ships. According to one story, it was a large shark sucker that attached itself to Marc Antony's ship, thus delaying his arrival for the battle of Actium and thereby causing his defeat.

PARADISE FISH, FIGHTING FISH, CLIMBING PERCH, AND GOBIES

Fishes That Blow Bubbles

Several kinds of fishes, including the Siamese fighting fish, the paradise fish, and the gouramis, make nests by blowing bubbles from their mouths. Several of these bubble nesters have recently become popular as aquarium fish, and their nesting habits are well known to many fish fanciers. The nest is built by the male bubble fish, who goes to the surface of the water, takes some air into his mouth, and blows a number of bubbles which stick together and float on top of the water. He then goes on the prowl for a wife, whom he herds under the bubble nest. After the eggs have been deposited and fertilized, the male takes the eggs in his mouth, encases them in a bubble and releases them so that they will float upward and stick to the nest.

The male then chases the female away and himself guards the nest and repairs it until the eggs are hatched. In many cases the male will swim with his brood for a time, fighting any enemy that appears, but he frequently loses all his parental feeling after a few days of careful watchfulness and may suddenly dash forward and devour all that he can catch. The young scatter in all directions, and fortunately a few avoid their greedy parent and escape to carry on the race.

Fighting Fish

According to an article written some time ago by a "widely traveled" person, sporting people in the Far East match Siamese fighting fish in separate glass containers. They place two jars side by side, and the two fish dash themselves against the glass trying to get together. This exciting combat continues until one of the fighters become so enraged that it literally explodes. But eyewitnesses of these encounters tell a somewhat different story.

The males are used for fighting, and when two fish are matched they are put in the same container. As the fighters approach each other, they display brilliant colors of red, blue, and green, each one apparently trying to outshine the other. These preliminaries last for several seconds, after which one or both fish will suddenly launch an attack almost too quick for the eye to follow. They nip vigorously and may lock jaws and remain in this position for some time. The fighting continues until one of the fish is no longer able to fight, whereupon his opponent is declared the winner. The loser is usually removed before it is killed.

Siamese fighting fish are found in the natural state in Thailand (Siam), parts of China, and the Malay Peninsula, and for many years they have been bred in Thailand for their fighting qualities.

Despite the small size of these fish, which have a maximum length of about 2½ inches, their courage, fighting qualities, and endurance are remarkable. Wild males are quite pugnacious and are more than willing to fight, but they usually quit within a few minutes. However, the best pedigreed stock that has been bred for fighting qualities has been known to continue the combat for as long as six hours.

Fish That Climb Trees

Travelers in India, the Far East, and parts of Africa are likely to be astonished at the sight of small fish skipping nimbly about on land. Perhaps the most efficient of these land scramblers are the climbing perch and the mud skippers. The common eel also has been known to make excursions overland, but it is not so efficient as the fish mentioned above.

The climbing perch of India and adjacent areas are small fish that vary in length from about 3 to 8 inches. They get about by spreading the rows of movable spines on their gill covers so as to brace themselves on the ground, and pushing vigorously with tail and front fins. The gills of these land-inhabiting forms have become modified so that they can breathe in the air for a time.

The first definite report of the climbing prowess of these fish was made in 1797 by someone who caught a climbing perch on the trunk of a tree 5 feet above ground and apparently trying to climb higher. Since that time, specimens have been found in rather high branches of trees, and although some biologists believe that these fish were dropped by birds others think that they definitely can climb, especially if the tree trunk is growing at an angle. At any rate, the fish are called climbing perch, and the name is likely to stick.

The mud skippers of Africa, Asia, and Australia are even more efficient than the climbing perch. They can climb up leaning trees and up on logs in search of insects; in some places they are called tree-climbing gobies. In appearance, the mud skippers have features of both tadpoles and frogs. The front part of the body is enlarged and tapers toward the tail like the body of a tadpole, while the head is surmounted by a pair of toad-like bulging eyes. With their modified front fins, the creatures are able to skip about on land rather rapidly. When not actively searching for food, the mud skipper frequently rests on the edge of the bank with its tail in the water. The tail region is so richly supplied with blood vessels that the fish gets some oxygen from the water through this part of the body to supplement the air breathing it can do through its modified gills.

What Is the Smallest Vertebrate Animal?

Very few anglers vie with each other in attempts to catch the smallest fish, but these smaller creatures are just as interesting as the giants. As opposed to the possible 60- or 70-foot length of the whale shark which is the largest fish, the smallest fish must be measured in fractions of an inch. The smallest fish in the world are found in lakes in the Philippine Islands. There are several species that belong to the goby group, the largest of which measures only about ½ inch, and the smallest, called *Pandaka pygmaea*, only slightly more than ¼ inch.

These fish are the smallest living animals with a backbone, but despite their small size they are an important article of food in some parts of the Philippine Islands. They occur in such enormous numbers in some lakes that they are collected by the thousands and cooked into a concoction that is flavored with peppers and spices.

A Fish That Shoots Its Food

Of all methods of obtaining food, that used by the archer fish of India, Burma, and adjacent areas is easily the strangest. This fish feeds on insects that live along the banks of streams and ponds. When it sees an insect hovering near the water surface or perched on an overhanging branch, it swims slowly until near its prey and carefully raises its mouth close to the surface. It then shoots a drop of water from its mouth with unerring accuracy, striking the insect and knocking it into the water where the fish can get it. Another indication of the archer's accuracy is that on more than one occasion, one of these finny marksmen has been known to extinguish a lighted cigarette, much to the astonishment of the smoker. Within recent years some of these fish have become available as aquarium exhibits, and many will display their marksmanship in captivity.

How Does a Swordfish Differ from a Sawfish?

Some people have the idea that swordfish and sawfish are very much alike, but the two are actually quite different. The sword of the swordfish is sharp on the end and smooth along the sides, while the saw of the sawfish is blunt on the end, and it has large teeth along each edge. In addition, the sawfish is flattened; the swordfish is compressed from side to side. Young sawfish are born alive, with the saw well developed but enclosed in a sheath which prevents injury to the mother. Young swordfish hatch from eggs without a sword; the sword develops rapidly as the youngster grows. The sawfish is classified in the same group with the shark, dogfish, and sting ray; the swordfish belongs with fish such as bass, catfish, perch, and salmon.

Some of the habits of the two fishes are similar. Both feed on fishes and collect their food by swimming into shoals of fishes and lashing back and forth with their swords or saws. Both fishes have been reported to attack larger fishes or whales, and as often as not will emerge victorious in the encounter. It is only fair to say that some biologists do not believe these stories.

The sawfish especially has a reputation for unprovoked attacks on human beings. These fish are not confined to salt water, but have been reported as going some distance up rivers and attacking human swimmers. It has even been stated that in parts of India sawfish have attacked people and cut them completely in two with their jagged saws. I have not confirmed these stories completely, but it is certain that a large sawfish would be capable of inflicting terrible wounds. The swordfish itself is not entirely harmless to human beings. Many years ago a man was supposed to have been killed off the coast of England by a swordfish, and other people have been wounded at one time or another.

Both the swordfish and sawfish grow to a considerable size. The largest sawfish caught by rod and reel that I know of was taken off the coast of Galveston, Texas, and weighed 736 pounds. However, lengths of 27 to 29 feet with weights up to 4,500 pounds have been reported. I have not been able to find the probable maximum size of swordfish, but they certainly attain a weight of well over 1,000 pounds. One of 1,182 pounds, caught off the coast of Chile, is recognized by the International Game Fish Association.

Can a Swordfish Sink a Boat?

There have been numerous reports of swordfish that attack ships, even causing small craft to sink. The reasons for their attacks are not clear, but it is probable that they mistake the ships for whales or some other living animal that is invading their domain. The velocity attained by an attacking swordfish must be tremendous, for the sword is sometimes so deeply embedded in the wood that the fish is unable to withdraw it, and breaks it off in its attempts to escape. In a museum in England there is part of the bow of a ship into which a swordfish stuck its sword 13½ inches deep through solid wood; and in the British Museum there is an exhibit of a timber from the side of a ship through which a swordfish's sword has penetrated for no less than 22 inches.

PUFFERS AND OCEAN SUNFISH

Fish That Swell Like Balloons

One of the oddest types of defense is that used by the puffer, globe, and porcupine fish. They are able to inflate their bodies to several times normal size by taking air or water into a special bladder-like sac connected with the gullet or esophagus. When one of their enemies, such as an enterprising shark, swims into view, these fish immediately start swelling, presumably discouraging the astonished pursuer. Some species have inedible spines scattered over their bodies, so that when they are inflated they look more like pincushions than tasty morsels. Many of the fishes that employ this type of defense are forced to float on top of the water like ballons until the air is expelled.

Their ability to inflate themselves is curious enough, but an even more remarkable habit was reported many years ago by Charles Darwin. According to his story, it would be disastrous for any shark to eat one of these fish, because the fish would gnaw through the stomach and body wall of the shark to get out. Darwin reported this story in good faith, and until recently it was believed by many biologists. Now, however, it is regarded simply as a fish story, too good to be true.

Are Any Fish Poisonous to Eat?

A number of fishes including the toadfish, the parrot fish, the porcupine fish, the puffers, and the file- or triggerfish have poisonous flesh. Of this group, the most dangerous to eat are probably some of the toad and puffer fish which inhabit the waters near several South Pacific islands, and which have been responsible for many deaths, especially in Japan and adjacent areas. It has been claimed that the poisonous material is contained in the reproductive and digestive organs and that if they are quickly removed after the fish is killed it is not likely to be poisonous. Yet, Japanese, trusting in this belief, have marketed the fish alive and still many people have died from eating them. Even cooking these fish does not make them safe to eat, since heat does not destroy the poison.

Fortunately, some of the most dangerous species may be avoided by the application of a very simple rule: Never eat a fish that does not look like a fish. This statement, stupid as it may sound, is essentially good advice. Many poisonous fish do not have the usual fish form, but are frequently odd or even ugly in appearance. Puffers blow up their bodies with air or water; some species have spines rather than scales; while another has a hard bony beak resembling that of a parrot. All poisonous fish are marine —so far as known, there is no fresh-water fish with poisonous flesh.

Certain tropical morays, discussed elsewhere, also have poisonous flesh. These fish are actually marine eels, most of which inhabit tropical reefs. According to one authority, human mortality from eating poisonous morays is about 10 per cent.

Monster Parents with Midget Children

Ocean sunfish are very large, but their eggs and newborn young are astonishingly small. The eggs, which are only about $\frac{1}{20}$ inch in diameter, hatch into small fish $\frac{1}{10}$ of an inch in length. These tiny atoms grow into adults which may be over 8 feet long and weigh more than 1,200 pounds. It has been estimated that the young sunfish must increase its weight approximately 60 million times before it can attain the maximum size for the species. There is probably a greater size difference between the young and adult of ocean sunfish than between the young and adult of any other animal. Even the difference in size between the young and adults of the kangaroos and opossums, great as it is, shrinks into insignificance by comparison.

FLYING FISH

One of the most interesting experiences of an ocean voyage is to see a school of flying fish suddenly break the surface and go sailing over the waves like so many streaks of light. The "wings" of flying fish are variants of the normal front fins, in that they are greatly enlarged. In flight, these fins are spread and held at an angle to the body; some species also spread the rear pair of fins. It was at one time thought that the fish flapped its fins like the wings of a bird, but this is not true. The fish swims rapidly through the water, with part of its body breaking the surface. It may swim in this fashion for some distance, gaining speed by vigorous movements of the tail. When the fins are spread and held rigid, its speed lifts it bodily into the air, and it may sail or glide for several hundred yards before dropping back into the ocean. It can lengthen the initial flight by striking the crests of the waves and picking up additional power with a few vigorous strokes of its tail. It may fly quite high—not infrequently flying fish land by accident upon the decks of large steamers. Flying fish have been reported as flying at speeds of from 35 to 45 miles per hour.

What Fish Can Live out of Water?

Droughts hold no terrors for the lungfish of Africa. When the swamps and streams start drying up, these fish simply burrow into the mud for a foot or so, fashion themselves comfortable rooms and coil up for a nice summer's sleep. They secrete a mucus that, mixed with the mud, hardens and forms a kind of cocoon about their bodies. Air is obtained through a small opening that is left at the top of the burrow, and most breathing is carried on during this period by the swim bladder, which is really a well-developed lung.

Under ordinary conditions, the fish remain in their sleeping quarters until the rains come again and flood their sun-baked homes. Thanks to their habit of forming cocoons, lungfish are to be seen in many aquariums throughout the world. Collectors locate the buried fish by pounding on the earth until they find a spot that sounds hollow. The fish are then dug up, packed and shipped, cocoon and all. At their new quarters, the cocoons are placed in water and when the mud has dissolved the lungfish swim happily about.

A Fish Said to Raid Hen Houses

A. Hyatt Verrill, well-known writer and South American explorer, relates one of the most amazing fish stories that this writer has ever heard. His story concerns the South American lungfish, which is a peculiar and somewhat large fish found in the rivers and swamps of northeastern and central South America. It is related to the African lungfish previously mentioned. In certain areas when the rivers and swamps dry up, as they do occasionally, the fish reportedly get out on land in search of food which, during this period, consists of lizards, mice, rats, and similar creatures. According to Verrill, the lungfish is not satisfied with catching wild animals, but frequently turns marauder and raids the hen houses of natives living near the stream. It is well known that some fish, such as the angler, will eat ducks or other birds if they happen to get within reach, but that a fish should go hunting for chickens across dry land is really incredible. However, in parts of South America, according to the story, these raids are accepted without furor by the owners of the chickens, who simply capture the thief and have fish for their next meal instead of chicken.

LAMPREYS AND HAGFISH

What Are Lampreys and Hagfish?

Lampreys and hagfish are elongated fish-like creatures which grow to a length of 2 or 3 feet and resemble eels. They are similar to fish and are called fish by most people, but they differ in so many important respects that biologists have classified them as a separate group called cyclostomes. One of the most noticeable differences is that cyclostomes do not have any limbs at all. The only fins they have are along the center of the back and tail, and on the undersurface of the body near the rear end. Their skin is entirely scaleless, and skin glands secrete so much slime that it is almost impossible for a person to hold a cyclostome in his hands. Lampreys are found in both fresh and salt water, but hagfish are wholly marine.

Fish That Cannot Close Their Mouths

The mouth of the lamprey and the hagfish puts them high on the list of nature's oddities. Instead of having jaws, the mouth is surrounded by a band of cartilage. The creatures are thus doomed to swim through life with their mouths always open. However, the circular mouth is a very efficient sucker, with which they can attach themselves to rocks and stones and even to other fish.

Most of the cyclostomes that live in fresh water do not eat at all during their adult stages, and consequently are never taken on hooks. An occasional specimen is caught in a net or trap, much to the horror of fishermen, many of whom believe that the fish are venomous. The creatures are not venomous, and since they do not have jaws it is improbable that they are capable of injuring human beings. During the Middle Ages lampreys were in demand as food, especially among the nobility, and it has been said that Henry I of England died as a result of eating too many. Today, however, they are seldom eaten.

What Fish Can Climb Cliffs?

Many marine lampreys come into fresh water to breed. As they go upstream they sometimes encounter waterfalls too swift for easy swimming. Faced with such an obstacle, the lampreys use their sucker-like mouths to advantage. Attaching themselves to rocks to hold themselves against the current, they gradually work their way toward the falls by swimming forward short distances and again attaching to rocks nearer the falls. To climb a perpendicular cliff and enter the stream above the falls, as they sometimes do, the lamprey attaches its sucker to the cliff, wiggling its body vigorously and inching the sucker upward at the same time. At times they may be entirely out of the water. Huge numbers of them have been seen, either anchored near the foot of falls or laboriously climbing over them.

When lampreys swim up a river to lay their eggs, they search for a place where the current is relatively slow. There they construct a crude nest of stones which they collect and move into place with their efficient mouths. The person who first called these creatures lampreys must have observed this habit, for the name means "to lick rocks."

The Ravages of Lampreys and Hagfish

The toothed sucker of the lampreys, and the tongue which also has teeth, are well adapted to the way in which many of them get their food. Certain kinds of lampreys feed by attaching themselves with their suckers to the bodies of fish; these suckers work like suction discs. The toothed tongue is then used to rasp a hole in the body of the fish, and the lamprey sucks its blood and body juices. The wounds may ruin the commercial value of a fish and large numbers die later as a result of the lamprey's action.

The accidental introduction of the sea lamprey into the Great Lakes is an excellent example of serious consequences that may result from introducing an alien animal into a new environment. At one time Niagara Falls prevented ships from passing between Lake Ontario and the remainder of the Great Lakes. These falls were also an effective barrier to any marine animals that might want to take a fling in any of the lakes other than Ontario. Then came the Welland Canal, which by-passed Niagara Falls thus opening a free channel from the lakes to the sea. The reverse was also true, and full advantage of the situation was taken by the sea lampreys. The fresh water was no barrier, since sea lampreys routinely enter fresh water in order to spawn.

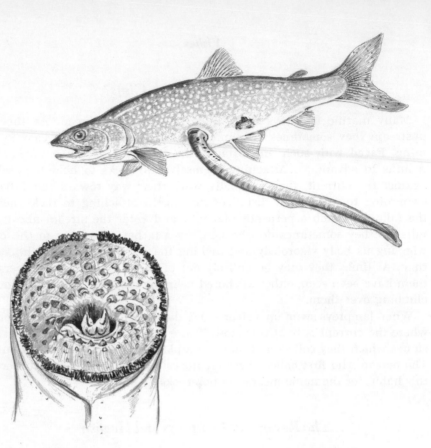

Lamprey Eel and Lake Trout (*showing eel's suction disk*)

The commercial fishermen soon felt the results of the sea lamprey's presence. At one time lake trout was one of the most important of the food fishes in Lakes Huron, Michigan, and Superior. In 1939 more than a million pounds were taken from Lake Huron; in 1951 the catch had dwindled to 25 pounds. More than 5 million pounds of trout were caught in Lake Michigan in 1945; only 400 pounds were take in 1954.

Millions of dollars have been spent in an effort to control the sea lamprey, and the Great Lakes Fisheries Research Committee has made lamprey control one of its prime objectives. Control measures have included efforts to market the lamprey as human food, thereby having the general public help eat the creatures out of existence; the erection of electric barriers to electrocute migrating lampreys; and attempts to find selective chemicals that would kill lamprey larvae and not harm other fish and water life.

Until recently all these efforts have been in vain; the lampreys flourished despite all persecution. Then experiments began on a chemical with the formidable name of 3, 4, 6-trichlor-2-nitrophenol. Fortunately this chemical proved selective in experiments; also, fortunately, the manufacturers gave the chemical the trade name, DOWLAP. It will be some years before the ultimate results of the use of DOWLAP and similar chemicals are known, but as of now, the application of this larvicide to Great Lakes tributaries seems to have arrested the growth of lampreys in the several hundred spawning streams, and as a result is reducing their number in the Great Lakes.

The feeding habits of the lamprey would present a problem if it had to get its oxygen from the water as most fish do by allowing the water to flow into its mouth, over the gills and out through the gill slits. If it had to release its grip on a fish to take water into its mouth, it would find that its meal had run away while it was breathing. The gills of the lamprey, however, lie in pouches in its body, and during respiration they expand and contract, drawing water into the gill slits and expelling it at the same place.

The hagfish as a rule is not satisfied merely to attach itself to the outside of another fish. It usually bores its way right into the body of its victim and, working from the inside, eventually consumes almost the entire fish. Fishermen sometimes net large fish that are nothing but a skinful of bones, with a well-fed hag complacently reposing within.

Six ARTHROPODS

There are more different kinds of animals among the arthropods than within any other group of the animal kingdom. And the arthropods represent a tremendous variety of "shapes, forms, and fashions." Insects, crabs, spiders, centipedes, and crawfish all belong in this classification, as do barnacles, pill bugs, and a host of similar species.

SOME FACTS AND FANCIES

The word arthropod means jointed feet or legs. This characteristic of the legs is easily seen in most species such as crabs, lobsters, and insects. Another distinguishing feature is the exterior skeleton. The shell of a crab or lobster is really its skeleton, which surrounds the muscles and other tissues of the body. The hard skeleton of arthropods helps to protect them from injury, but it has certain disadvantages. It is composed of dead material which, when it gets hard, will neither grow nor stretch. Since this is true even for young arthropods, the skeleton must be shed from time to time so that growth can take place. A new skeleton forms under the old one, the old skeleton splits, and the creature slowly creeps out. For a time, the new skeleton is soft and can be stretched, and at this time growth takes place. After a new skeleton becomes hard, the arthropod grows no more until it sheds its skeleton again.

Soft-shell crabs are not special kinds of crabs, as often believed; they are crabs that are captured and killed just after they have shed their skeletons and before the new skeleton has hardened.

Arthropods of one kind or another are found all over the world, from high mountains to the depths of the ocean, from the arctic to the antarctic, and from the tree tops to deep in the soil. Some can live under such adverse conditions that it has been predicted that they will be the eventual inheritors of the earth.

INSECTS

Insects have been described as man's chief competitors on earth and it is certain that from the human standpoint they form one of the most important of animal groups. Many insects destroy crops and other products, and many carry important diseases, both animal and human. The cost of harmful insects in human misery and suffering is incalculable, but in cold dollars and cents it has been estimated that, within the United States alone, they cause a direct loss of more than $3½ billion per year.

Because the harmful insects are most often brought to our attention, we often forget that other insects are beneficial. Many of them are of inestimable value both directly and indirectly.

How Many Kinds of Insects Are There?

There are many different kinds of insects, and they have such a variety of habits and preferences that there is no place on the face of the earth that is entirely free of them. There are actually so many different kinds that even entomologists cannot agree as to the exact number. I have seen estimates ranging from a conservative 500,000 to an enthusiastic 1.5 million, so far as known species of insects are concerned. One of the most recent attempts to be reasonably accurate that I have noticed was an estimate in 1954 of approximately 753,920 known species of insects. Because of the tremendous numbers involved, and the fact that many new species are being described each year, any such figures can be only an estimate. However, all biologists do agree that the number of species of insects far exceeds the combined total of all other members of the animal kingdom. The source noted above estimated that in 1954 approximately 164,340 living species of animals other than insects were known.

Actually, of the known insects, only a relatively few can be considered major pests. Some years ago the United States Bureau of Entomology and

Plant Quarantine * estimated that there are approximately 84,000 kinds of insects in the United States, and of that number only 600 caused enough damage to be considered important. On a world-wide basis it is believed that there are approximately 10,000 kinds of important harmful insects. The harmful species, however, make up in numbers what they lack in kinds.

A biologist once estimated that if all the offspring of a single pair of houseflies lived and reproduced throughout the summer, within six months more than 191 quintillion flies would be produced, enough to cover the earth to a depth of forty-seven feet. Thanks to lack of food, natural enemies and other limiting factors, such a situation never arises. But these figures help to explain why flies and certain other insects can appear suddenly in large numbers in the summer.

How Large Are Insects?

Most of us probably think of the sizes of insects in terms of such familiar species as houseflies and honey bees. A majority of the familiar species should probably be considered as medium in size, but there are also giants and midgets in the insect world. An entomologist has aptly described the situation with respect to the size of insects. He states accurately that the largest insect is larger than the smallest vertebrate animal, and that the smallest insect is smaller than the largest of the one-celled animals, the protozoans. The longest insects are some of the walking sticks, and Dr. A. B. Gurney, of the United States National Museum, states that a species from Borneo has the longest body. There is a specimen 11 inches long in the National Museum, and others up to 13 inches have been reported. One would be tempted to hunt some of the larger moths with a shotgun. The atlas moth of Asia, the hercules moth of Australia, and a noctuid moth of South America have wingspreads of 10 to 11 inches.

The largest insects in the United States are also walking sticks and moths. A walking stick in the southwestern states has a body length of 6 inches, and the cecropia moth of the eastern United States has a wingspread of over 6 inches.

The smallest insects are little wasps that are parasites within the eggs of certain insects. These minute parasites, appropriately called fairy-flies, are only 1/100 of an inch in length.

---

* The Bureau of Entomology and Plant Quarantine has recently been discontinued as such, and the various branches incorporated into other government bureaus.

What Is An Insect?

Even some well-trained people have a tendency to call any creature an insect that to them is bug-like in appearance. One of the easiest ways to distinguish an insect from similar classes is to look at its legs. Most adult insects have only three pairs of legs, but similar arthropods have more than this. Insects have a single pair of "feelers" or antennae attached to the head near the eyes and these are easy to distinguish on butterflies, beetles, and other large species. Any arthropod that flies is an insect, although all insects cannot fly. All the gnats, beetles, moths, and other arthropods that buzz about lights at night are true insects.

Flies, beetles, bees, butterflies, moths, and certain other insects have several stages of metamorphosis before the adult emerges. The egg hatches into a worm-like little creature called a larva. The larvae of moths and butterflies are usually known as caterpillars, those of many flies are maggots, and beetle and bee larvae are often called grubs. These larvae feed for a time, shed their outer skeletons or "skins" like other arthropods, and grow. After passing through several larval stages the next stage, called the pupa, is formed. Moth pupae are often enclosed within a silken cocoon that is attached to tree branches or some other object; other insects form their pupae, often naked, in the soil or some other concealed spot. Some pupae, such as those of the housefly, are surrounded by a tough membrane, so that they resemble small brownish seeds. The adult ultimately comes from the pupa, and if it is a flying insect it allows its wings to dry and expand before flying. Once the adult stage is reached the insect no longer grows. Thus, despite belief to the contrary, small flies, beetles, gnats, bees, and butterflies do not grow into larger insects. Larger similar insects are adults of different species.

The eggs of many insects such as crickets, grasshoppers, squash bugs, and cockroaches hatch into young insects which, except for size, resemble their parents. A person would not have much difficulty in recognizing a young grasshopper as such.

The question is often asked as to the difference between a bug and an insect. Popularly, the terms "bug" and "insect" are used indiscriminately for many arthropods such as true insects, scorpions, spiders, ticks, and centipedes. To the entomologist, however, a bug in its limited sense is a true insect that belongs to a particular group. This group is known as the Hemiptera, and included within it are such insects as squash bugs, bedbugs, stink bugs, chinch bugs, and assassin bugs.

How Fast Do Insects Fly?

Some insects have the reputation of being able to fly with tremendous speed. The species with the greatest reputations are some of the deer bot flies, the immature stages of which are parasites on deer. Estimates of as much as 800 miles per hour have been given for the possible flight speed of these flies. The flight speed of these insects has never been accurately measured; consequently, no one knows for sure just how fast they can fly. They are probably among the fastest of insects, but few entomologists who have investigated flight speed believe they can fly as fast as formerly maintained. For example, Dr. E. O. Essig, of the University of California, believes that 50 miles per hour is about the maximum speed these flies can attain.

The flight speeds of many species of insects have been measured, and reported figures of some of the fastest, which seem reasonably reliable, include: sphinx moth, 33 and 34 miles per hour; horseflies, 30 and 31.5 miles per hour; dragonflies, 22 and 30 miles per hour. Other dragonflies have been recorded at 45 and 55 miles per hour, but I would like to see these reports confirmed.

How Dangerous Are Dragonflies?

A pond in bright sunlight in the summer would seem strange without winged insects darting about over the surface or perched on a water plant. Some of these are quite large, with a wingspread of 3 or 4 inches; the wings are membranous and they may be clear or splotched with color. These swift-flying insects, so much a part of the landscape of every pond, are called dragonflies by biologists. Damselflies, related to dragonflies, are also found about ponds, but their flight is not so swift and they spend considerable time perched quietly on a water plant or on the bank. The wings of damselflies are often beautifully colored with red, green, or purple.

Various common names have been given to these insects and most of them imply that they are terrible creatures indeed. Common names include snake doctors, snake feeders, devil's darning needles, and mule or horse stingers. It is firmly believed in some areas that dragonflies administer to sick snakes and that they are capable of bringing dead snakes back to life. They are also reported to sting horses and mules to death. According to local tradition, boys who wade in water had best beware because the devil's darning needles are likely to sew up their ears!

Actually these insects are not only harmless to man and larger animals,

but they do a considerable amount of good. Their food consists principally of insects which they catch on the wing, many of them mosquitoes and harmful flies.

The immature stages of both dragonflies and damselflies live in water, where they feed upon other aquatic insects and similar creatures. They have been accused of eating small fish and they may occasionally vary their diets by capturing one. However, the little harm they may do in this way is certainly outweighed by the beneficial habits of their parents. It is also true that the youngsters themselves make up for their petty crimes by serving as food for larger fish.

What Are Kissing Bugs?

Kissing bugs are kinds of assassin bugs, already mentioned, that feed on the blood of ground squirrels, opossums, armadillos, and certain other species of animals. They sometimes get into houses and feed on sleeping people. The insects are common in parts of the southern United States, Mexico, Central and South America.

Kissing bugs in houses have habits similar to bedbugs; they hide in cracks and dark areas during the day, and come out at night to make a meal off the first sleeping person they can find. It has been known for a long time that these insects transmit a disease, called Chagas disease, south of the United States border, and within the last few years, several cases have been discovered in Texas. It may be, therefore, that more cases of Chagas disease occur in the United States than formerly supposed, since the disease is often difficult to diagnose.

The assassin bugs that feed upon people and certain other animals are called kissing bugs because they often bite a person around the mouth. It has been suggested that the kiss of a kissing bug is considerably more potent than the kisses with which most people are familiar. The "kissed" person may become nauseated, have a fever, and break out in a rash, even though the insect is not infected with Chagas disease. These reactions are probably caused by saliva, which the bug injects at the time of feeding. Other common names for these insects include big bedbug and Mexican bedbug.

What Is the Blue Tail Fly?

The song, "The Blue Tail Fly," sometimes called "Johnny Crack Corn," was written many years ago. It was reputedly a favorite of Abraham Lincoln. Until a few years ago most people supposed that the blue tail fly existed only in the mind of the writer of the song; then the song became popular again and listeners began asking biologists if any such insect existed.

Dr. C. H. Curran, of the American Museum of Natural History, decided that he would investigate the matter. The song obviously deals with a biting fly, apparently with a blue tail, that packs a terrific bite. After studying many possibilities, Dr. Curran decided that the blue tail fly is a real insect, probably the so-called black horsefly. This is a large fly about an inch in length, common in parts of the United States east of the Mississippi River. It is black or dark brown in color, and the tail has a definite bluish sheen. Called the blue fly in parts of the southern United States, it is a serious pest in some areas. Groups of horses and cattle, when attacked by these insects have seriously injured each other by kicking or hooking, and horses pulling buggies and wagons have been known to run away as a result of the bites of the flies.

Horseflies and some of their relatives called deer flies often try their sharp beaks on people. The bite is painful and the insects are known to carry certain human diseases: tularemia or rabbit fever, and African eye worm disease. African eye worm disease occurs only in parts of Africa, and the disease is transmitted by the bite of a deer fly.

Are Fruit Flies of Any Value?

The name fruit fly has been applied to many kinds of insects. Some of them are harmful because they destroy edible fruits. One group of fruit flies, however, is among the most valuable insects in the world. They have been of tremendous importance in the science of genetics, dealing with the inheritance of organisms.

Many years ago, when the study of genetics was in its infancy, biologists searched for an animal that would be satisfactory for experiments in this field. Fruit flies with the scientific name, *Drosophila*, were selected for several reasons. They are easy to rear in the laboratory, and their small size makes it possible for many colonies to be kept in a minimum of space. Also, equally important, the life cycle of the insects is so short that many generations can be reared per year, and thus many experiments can be completed within a relatively short time. Many principles relative to the inheritance of organisms, and applicable to other animals, have been discovered for the first time by a study of *Drosophila*.

Fruit flies are quite small, and the average person would doubtless call them gnats. They are called fruit flies because some species are attracted to ripe and decaying fruit. Another name for these insects is pomace fly.

Will Singing Mosquitoes Bite?

There is a common belief that mosquitoes that sing or buzz will not bite, but anyone who has had much experience with these pests knows that this idea is not entirely true. Some small gnats similar to mosquitoes do not bite, but will buzz around a person's ears; this is probably one reason for the mistaken belief. Another reason is the difference in the habits of male

and female mosquitoes. Only female mosquitoes are the bloodthirsty sex; male mosquitoes do not bite, but many of them at times seem to enjoy singing in human ears. Male mosquitoes feed upon innocuous substances such as plant juices, and nectar—never upon blood as do the females.

The mosquito's "song" is made primarily by the rapid movements of the wings, as is the buzzing sound of flies, bees, and other flying insects. The reason a noise results from wing movements may be better appreciated if we note how fast some insects can move their wings. These figures, in times of wing-beat per *second*, may seem incredible to most people, but the measurements were made with accurate instruments: housefly, 180 to 330; cabbage butterfly, 9 to 12; honey bee, 190 to 250; dragonflies, 20 to 28; mosquitoes, 278 to 587; a midge, 988 to 1,047. As compared to these figures, hummingbird wing-beats have been measured at from 40 to 50 per second.

Contrary to the prevailing belief that mosquitoes are entirely harmful, there are a few that are potentially beneficial. The wigglers of some mosquitoes feed upon the wigglers of other species. Some such feeders do not bite at all as adults, but certain kinds are enormous mosquitoes called gallinippers, the bite of which packs a terrific punch. As yet we do not know exactly how much good these cannibalistic wigglers do, but they certainly destroy many other species that would otherwise develop into blood-hungry females. Within recent years some of the "wiggler-eating wigglers" have been introduced into new areas to see if they will reduce the numbers of harmful species. The experiments are still being studied.

Many insects "sing" or make noises in ways other than the buzzing of wings. These sounds are not songs in the same sense as are those of birds and people; insects do not have vocal cords or other throat modifications for their noisemaking. Grasshoppers, katydids, and crickets "sing" by rubbing two parts of the body together such as two wings, two legs, or a leg on a rough part of the wing. Cicadas, discussed on p. 310, have two special sound-producing structures, one on each side, near the center of the body. Fortunately, perhaps, and unlike the human species, only the males of most insects are equipped with special sound-producing structures.

What Is the Most Dangerous Animal in the World?

The housefly is certainly a competitor for this designation. In view of the number of diseases it carries, few people would argue with this description. Yet the housefly does not bite. The mouthparts are formed in such a way that the creature could not bite even if it wanted to. There is another kind of fly that does bite and is so similar to the housefly that the average person has difficulty in distinguishing between the two. This species is called the stable fly and the dog fly; it breeds in wet hay, grass, and even in seaweed. During rainy weather it is often driven indoors; hence the commonly held belief that houseflies bite during rainy weather.

Scientific studies of the insects show that the housefly and its relatives may serve in the transmission of approximately thirty diseases and parasites. Some of these are among the most serious maladies in the world, and include typhoid fever, cholera, anthrax, tuberculosis, leprosy, plague, and polio. In all fairness to flies, it must be said that people can get these diseases in ways other than from the insects.

When DDT and similar insecticides were first put into general use, it was believed that houseflies and other harmful insects were doomed to extinction. However, strains have developed that are resistant to DDT and related materials.

What Are Screw-worms?

Screw-worms are maggots that have the revolting habit of developing in open wounds of domestic and wild animals, and sometimes even in man. The maggots are the immature stages or larvae of a greenish fly, about twice the size of a housefly, with three black stripes on its back. This insect occurs over practically the entire southern half of the United States and on into Mexico, Central and South America.

The eggs of these flies are deposited near a wire cut, dehorned stub, or other wound, and the resulting maggots burrow into and around the wound preventing it from healing. Hundreds of thousands of these maggots may infest a single animal, and unless the victim is treated, death usually results.

In the past, screw-worms have been considered one of the greatest pests of wild and domestic animals and losses of as much as $10 million per year have been estimated for the United States alone. Human cases with an occasional death have occurred in the United States, and in 1945–1946, 81 cases occurred in Chile within a relatively small area. An unknown number of game animals, such as deer, also are doubtless killed each year by this fly.

Many methods for controlling screw-worms have been tried, but until recently results have been discouraging. Then some clever entomologist discovered, while investigating the love life of the screw-worm, that the female mated only once during her life. It was also found that exposure to X- and gamma-rays would sterilize insects, but that certain doses of the radiation did not have any other apparent adverse effects upon them.

Dr. E. P. Knipling, director of the Entomology Research Division, Dr. Arthur W. Lindquist, and some of their colleagues, got the bright idea of sterilizing male screw-worms and releasing them to compete with normal males for the attention of ardent female flies. The idea was that if enough sterile males were released, many would mate with the females; the females would not mate again and would deposit sterile eggs. Continuous release of sterile male flies in large numbers, it was hoped, would drastically reduce the screw-worm and possibly even eliminate it in the treated regions.

Within the past few years literally billions of screw-worm flies have been reared, sterilized, and released in the southeastern United States, and as of this writing, the insect is virtually eliminated in the tier of states east of the Mississippi River and bordering the Gulf of Mexico.

Stockmen in Texas and other areas in the southwest became interested in these accomplishments, and in 1962 a large screw-worm laboratory was opened at Mission, Texas. Some flies have already been released in the state, and preliminary results are most encouraging. Unless control measures are extended into Mexico and adjacent regions, complete eradication in Texas is doubtful, but it is probable that the expected reduction of screw-worms will be well worth the time and money involved.

In some areas screw-worms help to take a tremendous toll of the deer population. Thus one possible result of screw-worm control is a great increase in the numbers of these animals. Whether or not this would be an unmixed blessing remains to be seen.

Which Insects Are Most Important in Pollination?

Plants are unable to produce fruit or seeds unless they are pollinated. That is, pollen grains must be carried from one part of a flower to another, or from one flower to another.

The agents most important in pollination vary with the different kinds of plants, but they include wind, insects, and gravity. Insects are by far the most potent pollinating agents for a majority of our flowers, vegetables, and fruits. Leading insect pollinators include bees, wasps, beetles, and moths, and in the United States alone it has been estimated that the annual yield of insect-pollinated plants is approximately $4½ billion.

Certain insects are more efficient than honey bees in pollinating specific plants, but on an over-all basis the bee is by far the most important pollinating insect in the United States. One authority estimates that honey bees are responsible for more than 80 per cent of the insect pollination of our commercial crops. Approximately $50 million worth of honey and beeswax is produced in the United States each year, but the pollinating activities of honey bees are obviously their most valuable contribution.

Each year thousands of colonies of bees are rented by fruit growers and producers of other crops, and kept near the orchards or fields during the flowering of the plants. This practice has materially increased the yields of many crops.

The honey bee is not native to the United States, but the insects were imported into this country several hundred years ago. Before that, plants were pollinated by native bees and other insects. Clearing and plowing large tracts of land have destroyed the natural habitats of the wild benefactors; consequently, these insects are now relatively rare in many areas.

For certain crops other insects are more efficient in pollination than are honey bees. Red clover, for example, often does not attract honey bees, and the flowers are so constructed that pollination by honey bees is difficult. Bumble bees, on the other hand, like red clover, which they pollinate easily.

Although we could probably survive without the pollinating activities of insects, our ways of life would certainly be greatly modified. Many kinds of plants now used for food would die out, and the yield of others would be greatly reduced. The spring hillsides and woodlands would be drab without many of our flowers, and the development of "bad lands" would be encouraged by the dying of plants that help to bind the soil.

Do Bees Die After Stinging?

If you have been stung by a honey bee, it may be some small consolation to know that many of these insects pay with their lives for stinging a person. The stingers of honey bees have several small hooks or barbs near the end. When this stinger penetrates relatively thick skin, the barbs catch on the skin and prevent the bee from pulling the stinger free. Even an angry honey bee does not want to sit on a person's skin all day, tied down by the stinger, and it struggles to pull loose. The stinger often breaks from the bee's body and stays in the wound. The breaking of the stinger so injures the insect that it dies within a short time.

If a bee leaves its stinger in a person's anatomy, the victim should remove it by scraping the stinger out with a fingernail or knife. Do not try to grasp the end of the stinger because poison glands are often still attached to the protruding end. Grasping this end is likely to squeeze the glands and force more poison into the wound. The stingers of many wasps, hornets, and yellow jackets are not barbed and they may sting a person without paying the extreme penalty. Some of these insects are also capable of stinging several times in succession.

It has been known for many years that an occasional person has been killed as a result of wasp or bee sting, but until recently, it was thought that these occurrences were quite rare. In fact, one biologist has estimated that approximately 500 honey-bee stings would be required to kill a person. This may be true for many people, but it is now known that deaths from the sting of a single wasp or bee are much more common than formerly believed. Dr. H. M. Parrish, a physician, collected information on the number of people killed in the United States by various kinds of venomous animals. He found that from 1950 through 1954, 215 people had died in the United States as a result of bites and stings. One of the most important —and perhaps surprising—things about these figures is that 86 of these people were killed by the stings of wasps and bees. During this same period only 71 people died as a result of the bites of venomous snakes.

These figures certainly emphasize that wasp and bee stings may be seriously injurious to many people. Anyone showing severe reactions to the sting of a wasp or bee, such as nausea, difficulties in breathing, faintness, fever, or convulsions, obviously should be rushed to a physician at once. People sensitive to stings should consult with their doctors about the possibilities of taking treatments to overcome the sensitivity.

Ants Milk Cows

Ants, of course, do not milk real cows, but they have developed an association with aphids or plant lice that is similar to the one between man and cow. The plant lice are small fragile insects that feed on plants, and during spring and summer some of them can be seen in groups on the stems and leaves of many species.

If you look closely among a group of plant lice, you are likely to see several ants hurrying about. The association between these two kinds of insects is one of the most interesting in the whole insect world. The plant lice are actually milked by the ants. Plant juices taken into the aphids' bodies are changed into a substance called honey dew. The ants like this

honey dew, and they have found a way to cause the aphids to give them some. A hungry ant will approach a plant louse and stroke it with its feelers or antennae. The aphid apparently enjoys this tickling, for it will secrete a small drop of honey dew which is gobbled up by the hungry ant. In return for this food, ants carefully watch over their "cows," and move them from one place to another when food becomes scarce. In some cases the ants carry the insects into their nests at night and during the winter.

The association between ants and aphids, while intensely interesting, has also resulted in considerable harm to people. Perhaps the best known case in the United States involves the corn root aphid and the cornfield ants. The ants gather the eggs in the fall and keep them in their nests until they hatch. The young aphids are then carried to the roots of various plants, from which they suck juices. Unfortunately for gardeners and farmers, corn is the favorite food of these plant lice. The ants seem to realize this, and have been known to carry their charges more than 150 feet so that the creatures can feed upon their favorite food. Large amounts of corn may be killed if the insects are numerous.

In view of the protection given many aphids by ants, and the enormous reproductive capacity enjoyed by these insects, man is fortunate in having several insect friends on the opposite side of the fence. These include ladybird beetles, green lacewings, and the larvae of certain flies known as hover flies. A single hover fly larva has been seen to eat more than 800 aphids, a fact that indicates how important these insects are in the battle to control other insect pests.

Why Do Ants Carry Umbrellas?

A long line of ants, each one carrying a piece of leaf in its mouth, is a common sight in the southwestern United States, Mexico, South America, and other parts of the world. The piece of leaf often almost conceals the ant carrying it, and because of this the insects have been called umbrella or parasol ants. They are also called leaf-cutting ants.

The leaves do shield the ants from the sun to some extent, but they are much more important than mere umbrellas. Without the leaves, the ants would actually starve to death. The leaves are not eaten, but they are used to grow a fungus on which the ants feed. Once within the nest the pieces of leaves are chewed into a paste by smaller ants. This material is then used as a base upon which the fungus is grown.

In some areas leaf-cutting ants occur in such large numbers that crops and fruit trees cannot be grown successfully unless the ants are controlled. Such large numbers of these ants may occur that a large tree will be completely stripped in a single night. The ants are unwelcome neighbors in most cases, but in Brazil the natives take advantage of the situation when the insects occur in large numbers. Here the *sauba* ants, as they are called, are collected, fried, and eaten.

Ants have a tenacity that makes a bulldog seem mild by comparison. Once the jaws of an ant have closed on an object, it holds on no matter what happens. This grip often does not weaken even though the ant's head is cut off, and after a battle between different kinds of ants, the victors often stalk about with the severed heads of their victims clinging to their legs.

In India, Africa, South America, and perhaps other parts of the world, practical advantage is taken of this characteristic. The ants are used for

suturing wounds. The edges of a wound are held together, and the wide open jaws of large ants are applied to the two edges. When the irate ants clamp their jaws together, one jaw catches on each side of the wound. The bodies of the ants are then cut off, and the wound is sealed almost as neatly as though clamps had been used. Different kinds of ants are used for this purpose in different countries, but the natives of South America frequently use the largest individuals or soldiers of a species of leaf-cutter.

What Is the Most Feared Animal of the Jungle?

Many animals—lions, tigers, elephants, crocodiles, and even venomous snakes—are feared by a majority of jungle creatures. At one time or another, however, each of these admittedly dangerous animals contacts an especially brave, stubborn, or foolish individual of another species that contests its right of way. But there is one group of animals that is feared by all species; when they appear, every living thing—including human beings—beats a hasty retreat. These most feared of jungle animals are ants.

The ants in question are the driver ants of Africa. The insects are so called because they move in great armies containing millions or even billions of individuals, and they literally drive everything before them. Ants in South America, known as legionary ants, have habits similar to those of the drivers.

Driver ants are primarily meat-eaters, and if we can believe reports, everything living in their paths from insect to elephant is likely to be overwhelmed and dismembered. Each ant is only a quarter- to about a half-inch in length, but their incredible numbers and the efficiency of the individuals more than make up for their small size. The little demons swarm over their intended victims, bury their jaws in the flesh, and tug. People who have had the misfortune to be bitten by driver ants state that the insects almost invariably succeed in yanking out a bit of flesh each time they bite. Multiply these small bits by millions or billions and one can see how even a large animal could be literally torn to pieces by them.

These ants do not have a permanent home, but often take up temporary quarters in a hollow tree, a hole in the ground, or some secluded spot before marching into new territory in search of more profitable hunting grounds. Direct sunlight will kill them within a short time; as a consequence, the insects travel mostly at night or in shadow.

If a house or even a village is in the path of a marching column of drivers, the buildings are likely to be invaded by the hungry hordes. Under such circumstances the inhabitants, prudently vacate the premises until the ants decide to move on. This interruption of routine is often actually appreciated by the natives, for as the ants swarm through the houses, all unwelcome vermin from scorpions to rats are either killed or chased out of the building. All domestic animals must, of course, be removed during such an invasion, or they too will fall prey to the voracious drivers.

The Values of Parasites

Some years ago, I found a large green caterpillar about 3½ inches long, and decided that I would attempt to rear it. I placed it in a jar with some leaves and did not examine it for several days. When I looked at the caterpillar again, I was disgusted to see that its back was almost covered with small oblong white objects. The caterpillar died, and my efforts to rear it were at an end.

It is not at all uncommon to find dead or very feeble caterpillars on leaves or limbs, their backs studded with such white objects. These objects are not eggs as sometimes supposed, but are the cocoons of many small insects which have been living inside the caterpillars. Small wasps lay their eggs in the bodies of the caterpillars and the eggs hatch into tiny grubs or larvae. These feed on the internal organs of the caterpillar, but before they change into wasps, they come to the outside and spin small cocoons on the caterpillar's back. When the adult wasp has formed inside each cocoon, it cuts a small hole through which it escapes.

Insects that kill other insects, as the wasps killed the caterpillar, are said to be parasites. Lice, fleas, and similar creatures that feed on people and animals are also called parasites, and probably for this reason most people think of a parasite as something harmful or dangerous to them. However, some insect parasites are among man's most valuable animal friends. As a matter of fact, parasites are considered to be one of the most important factors in keeping harmful insects in check.

Almost all insects that attack man's crops have parasites and other enemies that destroy great numbers of them. These destructive insects are often not an important problem in their native lands because their enemies, by their activities, help maintain the balance of nature. But a different situation may develop if the pest is accidentally introduced into a different country. Here, unhampered by its natural enemies, the pest may soon become a major problem. This has been demonstrated repeatedly in the United States and other parts of the world. The pink boll worm, the Japanese beetle, the boll weevil, the European corn borer—all these culprits and many more are foreign introductions. In a final analysis there are few extremely important crop pests that are native to the area where they are causing the damage.

Fortunately, the importance of insect enemies of other insects has been recognized by entomologists for more than fifty years. Thus when a new insect pest appears, one of the first problems has been to discover the enemies that hold it in check in its native land. Hundreds of insect parasites have been shipped from one country to another in an effort to control introduced pests. Often the results have been spectacular. Today parasites and other types of insect enemies are reared by the millions and sent to other regions for the control of many of our most important insect enemies.

Are Ladybirds the Parents of Plant Lice?

Dr. Frank E. Lutz, a late curator of the American Museum of Natural History, used to relate a story that illustrates a common misbelief regarding these insects—also called lady beetles and ladybugs.

Some of Dr. Lutz's friends were collecting insects on a piece of land when the owner approached and asked what they were doing. One of the men replied that they were making an insect collection, and showed him a ladybird he had just caught. The owner was quite pleased and urged them to collect all the beetles they could find, since he knew that the insects were the parents of plant lice which infested his crops. He said that the beetles were always present with large numbers of plant lice or aphids, and he could not be convinced that the beetles were not responsible for the pests.

It is true that ladybirds are often seen associating with plant lice, but the beetles are not the fond parents of the lice. Instead, the beetles are there to feed on the plant lice. Actually, the lady beetles are considered to be among the most beneficial insects in the world, because both adults and larvae feed upon plant lice and many other harmful insects. Their value is indicated by the estimate that each larva and adult can eat from fifty to one hundred aphids per day. Apparently the beneficial activities of these beetles were recognized even in the Middle Ages. They were then known as Beetles of the Blessed Lady, which today has been shortened to lady beetles, or ladybird. In Sweden the beetles are called "Virgin Mary's Golden Hens," and in parts of France are known as the "Cows of the Lord."

The lady beetle was one of the first insects used by man on a large scale to control an important insect pest. About 1872 the cottony cushion scale was discovered on citrus trees in California. This insect feeds on the sap of the leaves and twigs, and within a few years it had spread so rapidly that the entire citrus industry was threatened. The cottony cushion scale was known to occur in Australia, where insect predators and parasites held it in check, and it is thought that the pest may have been introduced into the United States accidentally on nursery stock. The most important enemy of the scale insect was found to be a lady beetle, and a total of 514 beetles were introduced into the United States. Within two years the beetles had multiplied so rapidly and had eaten scales with such gusto that the pest was under control. The expense involved in introducing the ladybirds was less than $5,000.00. The tiny benefactors have, to say the least, saved citrus growers millions of dollars; they may have actually saved the industry itself.

Within recent years the use of insect parasites and predators has expanded tremendously. Today millions of them are reared in insectaries in various parts of the world. From the insectaries the insects are sent to orchards or fields to be released at the appropriate time.

What Beetle Shoots at Its Enemies?

There are some beetles in the United States, Europe, and other parts of the world that have a reddish head and legs and a bluish body. Certain species are about half an inch long and may be found under rocks, logs, or stones. If you try to catch one of these beetles you are likely to get the surprise of your life. The little rascal will actually shoot at the collector! This habit has earned it the name of bombardier beetle. When disturbed it discharges a liquid that suddenly changes to gas as it comes in contact with the air. The resulting pop can be heard for several feet and the gas forms a smoke screen. This combination of noise and the cloud of gas may so astonish an attacker that the beetle makes its escape in the confusion. The discharge of some of the large tropical species is reported to be irritating to the skin.

Bombardier beetles belong to a very large group of insects called ground beetles because they are often seen scurrying rapidly along the ground. They are frequently attracted to lights, and will attack and eat other insects in the vicinity. Large ground beetles most often seen around lights are of a black or greenish color. They are flattened and some are more than an inch long. If one of these insects is disturbed it will give off a liquid that is irritating and unpleasant. The material has an acrid biting odor and it pollutes the air for several feet around the irate beetle.

Despite the unpleasant odor associated with many ground beetles, these insects are among our most valuable allies. Both adults and larvae feed upon other insects, many of which are harmful. Some species are so fond of caterpillars that the beetles are known as caterpillar hunters in certain regions. Some years ago a large green and blue fellow was introduced into the United States to help combat the gypsy moth, a pest of shade trees in the northeastern part of the country. The beetle is now well established, and the insects take a tremendous toll of the gypsy moths. The larvae or immature stages of the beetles like gypsy moth caterpillars so well that they climb trees in search of the pests.

What Are Grubworms?

Grubworms, or grubs, are familiar to all who have dug for fishing worms or who have spaded up their gardens. They are whitish creatures with a brown head and three pairs of short legs near the front end of the body. Grubworms, of which there are many kinds, are really youngsters of beetles and not true worms at all.

One kind of grubworm develops into the well-known brownish may beetle or junebug. Large numbers of these insects are sometimes seen on warm summer evenings buzzing about lights or alighting on screen doors or windows. The grubs of these beetles live in the ground and feed on the roots of grass and other plants. In the soil of lawns, in large numbers, they may do considerable damage to the grass by cutting the roots.

Another kind of beetle in the southern United States is also called a junebug. This is a bright green insect with brownish markings that is related to the may beetles. Another name for this beetle is fig-eater, because the adults eat figs and they are often attracted to fig trees in large numbers.

The young of the Japanese beetle, an insect first recorded from the United States in 1916, is also a grubworm. Since its introduction the Japanese beetle has spread along the Atlantic seaboard and into several midwestern states. Adult beetles, which are of a greenish-bronze color and about half an inch long, feed upon many different kinds of plants. The grubs cause extensive damage by eating the roots of grass and other plants. It has been estimated that this pest causes damage worth approximately $10 million per year to fruit trees and many other crops, lawns, and golf courses.

Almost fifty different kinds of parasitic and predatory insects have been imported into this country in an effort to stem the spread of the beetle hordes. Within recent years the number of beetles has declined in some areas, as certain of the beetle's enemies have become well established. There is now a hope that some day the Japanese beetle will be as relatively unimportant here as it is in Japan.

Grubs as pests of sugar cane are discussed elsewhere.

The largest beetles in the world belong to the same group as the Japanese beetles, the junebugs, and the may beetles. The large species include the goliath beetles of Africa, the rhinoceros beetles of Central America, and the hercules beetles of South America and the West Indies. The males of some of these giant forms have long horns on the front of the head and body, and they may be over 6 inches in length. Many of these large beetles can fly, and although they fly slowly they do so with tremendous power. Some have been reported as flying into an electric light and actually breaking the bulb.

What Insects Are the Most Important Scavengers?

Many different kinds of insects feed on animal excrement and the bodies of dead animals. Their activities are of tremendous importance in the economy of nature, since they speed up decomposition and thereby enrich the soil; in some cases small carcasses and other objectionable materials are buried by the industrious insects.

Among the most important insect scavengers are the blow flies, flesh flies, dung flies, burying beetles, and the tumblebugs. The latter two insects go about their business in a rather spectacular fashion. Burying beetles, as their name implies, bury the carcasses of small animals. This they do by digging around and under the animal until it sinks into the loosened soil and eventually becomes covered. Eggs are then deposited on the body, which serves as food for the beetle larvae that hatch.

Tumblebugs are often seen industriously rolling a ball of dung along a path or road. It is buried at a suitable spot and an egg deposited on it. The dung is used for food by the developing youngster.

The sacred scarab or scarabaeus of the ancient Egyptians is also a tumblebug or dung beetle. According to authorities this insect and its representations were regarded as symbols of immortality and resurrection; the rolling ball of dung was supposed to represent the earth and its movements through space. Chances are that those originally responsible for the adoption of the beetle as a symbol did not know the composition of the ball.

What Is the Spanishfly?

The true Spanishfly is a European insect sometimes found in England. Not a fly at all, it is a brilliantly colored green and blue beetle, ½ to ¾ inch long.

This beetle is best known because of a substance that is formed within its body. This material, called cantharidin or sometimes simply Spanish fly, has been extracted from the bodies of these beetles for many years. Cantharidin has been used as an aphrodisiac, as a vesicating agent, and as a counter-irritant. It is dangerous to take internally, and even when applied to the skin may have harmful effects on the kidneys.

Although the true Spanishfly is confined to Europe and adjacent areas, beetles of the same group occur in other countries, including the United States. They are called blister beetles because many of them also form cantharidin in their bodies, and if you crush one on your skin, a large blister will result. Some of them will even cause a blister merely if they are handled and not crushed. Rather common in some areas, they are easily found on wildflowers and weeds. They are sometimes attracted to lights. There are a number of different kinds and sizes, including solid black, solid gray, yellow with black stripes, orange wings with black head and body, and so on.

Adult blister beetles eat the leaves of many plants including potatoes, tomatoes, and other vegetables. They are called old-fashioned potatobugs in some sections, and they may at times cause considerable damage to various types of crops. The immature stages of some species of the insects, however, feed on grasshopper eggs and thus compensate somewhat for the sins of their parents.

The Chief Scourge of the Apple Orchard

The codling moth, which occurs in all apple-growing districts of the world, is the major insect pest of the orchard. It was accidentally introduced into the United States from southeastern Europe many years ago. If the insect is not controlled in an orchard, it is likely to destroy most of the crop. Even with control measures, the moth causes millions of dollars worth of damage per year.

The adult does no damage directly, but the females lay eggs near developing apples so that the young can find the fruit. The small caterpillars bore into young apples and eat the seeds. The insects are pinkish-white with brown heads and they may be as much as ¾ inch long. Before the caterpillars change into moths, they leave the apples and make small cocoons under bits of bark.

Another insect responsible for "wormy" apples is the apple maggot—the immature stage or larva of a fly, slightly smaller than a housefly. It is unappetizing to bite into a nice red apple and to find inside brown burrows containing an insect larva; it is even more unappetizing to discover only half a larva in a burrow.

Moths Do Not Eat Clothes

Clothes moths are sometimes called millers because their wings and bodies are covered with fine scales, resembling flour, which are easily rubbed off. The moths, of which there are several kinds, are a brownish color and have a wingspread of about ½ inch. They are sometimes seen crawling over clothes or flitting aimlessly about the house.

The moth itself does not eat clothes; it could not even if it wanted to. Like other butterflies and moths, its mouth is in the form of a soft tube which cannot injure clothing. The moth is the adult stage of the insect, and it is the caterpillar or larval stages that are so destructive.

Clothes moths have a life cycle similar to that of other moths and butterflies. The eggs are laid by the adult moth on clothes or similar material where they hatch into caterpillars or larvae. These are the villains that make meals of our woolen clothing, upholstered furniture, and even furs. The caterpillars of some kinds of clothes moths live in small silken cases which they drag about as they move from one place to another. When quite small these cases resemble small bits of dust and more than one person has been startled by seeing such a piece of "dirt" walking away.

Other kinds of insects also destroy clothing, rugs, furs, and similar material. The most notorious are beetles that belong to a group known as skin beetles or dermestids. These animals feed on a variety of materials including rugs, furs, leather, stored foods, and even museum animal specimens of various kinds.

Some biologists have taken advantage of the beetles' appetite for dried animal material. The skull and often other skeletal elements of various animals are among the most important parts for scientific study. Cleaning the bones properly without injuring them is a difficult task. In many biology laboratories colonies of dermestid beetles are maintained for this purpose. A partially cleaned skeleton dropped into such a colony of beetles will be as clean as the proverbial hound's tooth within a few days.

How Can You Recognize a Bedbug?

Any insect that flies or jumps cannot be a bedbug; neither can one that is brightly colored. An adult bedbug is a flattened, wingless insect, brown in color, and about ⅓ inch in length. Immature bedbugs are similar but smaller, and they also like to feed on people. If crushed, the insects emit a disagreeable odor.

Bedbugs may occasionally be found on clothes as well as on beds, or even crawling across the floor. They feed especially at night on people who are in bed, but have been known to bite in theaters and other public buildings during the day. After they have fed to their satisfaction, they go into hiding. This may be in cracks about the room. The insects are often difficult to find because of their retiring habits, and a room may be heavily infested without the occupants' knowing it.

Until the development of DDT, ridding a house of a bedbug infestation was a very difficult task. By using DDT the task is now relatively simple, unless the bedbugs happen to be resistant to the insecticide. As of this writing, DDT is still the insecticide of choice in the United States, but in some countries it is necessary to use other insecticides, such as malathion.

Spare Those Cockroaches

The cockroaches that live in houses are considered objectionable insects because they contaminate food and because of the possibility that they may carry the germs of certain human diseases. Of the hundreds of species of cockroaches, however, only a few prefer to live in houses. Most of them are respectable insects that live under bark, in leaves, and under rocks. All are scavengers that feed upon dead plant and animal material. These wild cockroaches seem to rate as important members of nature's "sanitation department."

What Are Rain-trees?

One occasionally sees rain-trees or weeping-trees discussed in sensational newspaper or magazine articles. These are trees in tropical areas from which liquid drops in noticeable amounts; this moisture in turn may even keep the ground under the trees relatively wet. It has even been suggested that trees of this type should be planted in deserts to supply the ground with moisture.

The trees do in fact furnish the liquid, but the showers are not produced directly by the trees. The showers are caused by large numbers of insects which are called by various names, including leafhoppers and froghoppers. These insects suck the sap from the trees, and act as "middlemen," so to speak. The sap passes into the body, the insects use part of it as food, and pass the remainder out as drops of liquid. It has been estimated that less than one hundred of these insects can eliminate a quart of water in an hour and a half. Since thousands of leafhoppers may occur on a single tree they can readily produce visible showers.

Even in the temperate zone, including the United States, the same thing may happen on a smaller scale. Under such a tree you are likely to get splattered with an occasional drop of liquid, and parked cars may accumulate a coat of sticky material within a single night.

Leafhoppers are ¼ inch in length and they are often colored green or brown. They hop and can fly for short distances. Small green and light brown species are attracted to lights, and they will frequently bite if they get on the skin. Many of them are of considerable economic importance. Large numbers sucking plant juices often cause the plants to wilt or die. In addition, certain species transmit plant diseases which cause losses estimated at several million dollars annually.

What Causes the Black Death?

Throughout the Middle Ages, and until relatively modern times, a disease known as the black death was the scourge of the human race. The malady struck with devastating suddenness; during the fourteenth century, it killed approximately one-fourth of the entire population of Europe. In 1665 the great London plague accounted for some 70,000 lives.

This disease, called the black death because it turns the skin a bluish or blackish color, is also called plague; one form of it is known as bubonic plague. Not until after 1900 was it discovered that the disease is transmitted to human beings by the bites of fleas that have the germs in their bodies. Plague is also a disease of such rodents as rats, ground squirrels, prairie dogs, and chipmunks. The fleas get the germs from infected rodents. Intensive control measures against rats and rat fleas, and the development of a vaccine, have effectively reduced the incidence of the black death. In the United States, 534 cases of human plague have occurred from 1900 to 1960 with 345 deaths. Three cases with two fatalities were reported in 1961.

A word should be said about the jumping ability of fleas. One of the insects can easily jump 12 inches horizontally and 7–8 inches high. An equivalent leap for a human athlete would involve a high jump of 450 feet and a broad jump of approximately 700 feet.

Fleas also transmit to man a disease known as endemic or murine typhus, which is not as serious as plague; the disease is widely distributed throughout the world including the United States. This malady is not the same as epidemic typhus, which is carried by body lice.

During World War I severe outbreaks of epidemic typhus occurred in Poland, Serbia (now part of Yugoslavia), and other European countries. The disease immobilized the Serbian army, and during the epidemic more than 150,000 people died. During World War II epidemic typhus occurred in civilian populations, but very few cases developed in the Allied armies, thanks to the use of an efficient vaccine and of DDT and other substances for louse control.

Epidemic typhus is not transmitted to man by the bite of the louse. The organisms causing the disease are found in the body juices and these get into breaks in the skin when lice are accidentally crushed by the person scratching. Typhus germs can also penetrate mucous membranes, such as those of the lining of eye sockets and the mouth. It is thus literally true that it is more dangerous for a man to bite a louse than for a louse to bite a man.

The Beetle of Bad Omen

People are frequently surprised to hear a ticking sound coming from their furniture or from the walls of their houses. This noise, resembling the ticking of a clock, can be heard for some distance; it is especially noticeable at night. For many years the cause of these ticking sounds was not known —it was a popular superstition that they predicted death.

The sounds are caused by small beetles that live in the wood and bore through it. During the mating season, which occurs principally in April, May, and June, the ticking is more common and it is believed to be a mating signal. The beetles tap on the walls of the tunnels with their heads. After the cause of the mysterious ticking was discovered, the insects were called deathwatch beetles, and even today their tapping is often considered an ill omen. The noises bode ill indeed for the wood through which the insects are industriously chewing. In time, extensive damage to buildings and furniture may result.

Many other small beetles, some related to the deathwatch beetle, also bore through wood and cause considerable damage. These include the furniture beetles and the powderpost beetles.

In California is found a small beetle that bores through the lead sheathing of telephone cables. These holes allow rain to come in contact with the wires and cause short circuits. The beetle responsible for the damage is often called the short circuit beetle as well as the lead cable borer. In parts of the state these pests have been reported as causing approximately one-fifth of all damage to aerial telephone cables.

The Virtuous Termite

It is well known that termites attack houses and other wooden structures, thereby causing damage totaling millions of dollars each year. Not so well known is the fact that the insects also make considerable positive contributions to man's well-being.

They are among the few animals that can digest wood, and the insects often use this ability in one of the most important cycles in nature. As plants grow, they take materials from the soil and use them in growth. When plants die, they eventually decay, and the important elements in their bodies get back into the soil and help to enrich it. The decay of dead plants that fall to the ground is hastened; the tree is exposed to the moisture of the soil and many kinds of organisms, such as bacteria, fungi, and insects are able to attack the softened wood. Dead trees that remain standing, however, often become so hard that most of the organisms that assist in decay cannot attack the wood very rapidly. But such trees are not immune to termites. The busy insects burrow into the trees, felling them to the ground. Except for termites, many of the trees might stand for years, cluttering up the forests, preventing new growth, and keeping valuable elements from the soil.

For a long time it was not known how termites managed to digest wood. It was discovered that the process was accomplished by many minute one-celled animals or protozoans that live symbiotically in the insects' intestines. The protozoans chemically change the wood so the termites can use it for food. This symbiotic relationship is so complete that neither the termites nor the protozoans can live without the other.

Termites also serve as food for useful animals such as birds, and even for human beings. When the winged males and females of a termite colony become mature, they emerge from their burrows, sometimes in enormous numbers, fly about and mate. The insects may emerge in houses, and this is often the first indication to the home owner that his house is infested with termites. One such large mating flight was seen to be followed by fifteen species of birds, all stuffing themselves to capacity.

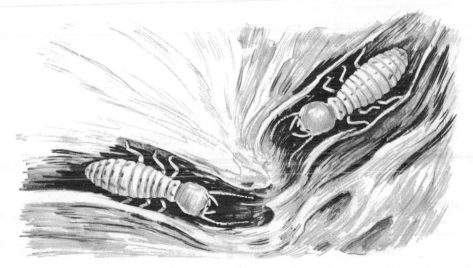

Termites are eaten regularly by the natives of Australia, India, and Africa. On the latter continent the insects are often parched over a slow fire like peanuts; the taste of these dainties has been described as similar to that of sweetened cream.

Do Insects Destroy Weeds?

Anyone who has farmed, or who has tried to grow vegetables or flowers, has received the impression that the appetites of insects are limited to a taste for useful plants. Actually, however, many insects are useful because they feed on weeds and other plants that compete with cultivated crops.

An outstanding example of how useful weed-eating insects can be occurred in Australia some years ago. Before the development of aniline dyes, carmine—a brilliant red dye—was obtained primarily from the bodies of certain insects. These were known as cochineal insects, and the raising of these insects on prickly pear, a type of cactus, was a thriving industry for many years. About 1800 prickly pear plants were introduced into Australia in an effort to establish the dye industry in that country.

For a time the introduced cacti kept within respectable limits but then they suddenly started overrunning the landscape. By 1925 the prickly pears had spread over some 60 million acres, and they showed every indication of occupying a large part of the continent to the exclusion of native plants and grasses. A Prickly Pear Commission was established and frantic efforts were made to find methods which would help hold the rebellious cacti in check. For approximately ten years chemical and mechanical means were tried and more than fifty kinds of insects were introduced in an effort to halt the marching prickly pears. At last success was attained in the form of a small moth caterpillar from South America which feeds voraciously upon the fleshy stems. This insect, appropriately named *Cactoblastis*, literally blasted the stubborn cacti into oblivion. Whole acres of the plants were killed, and within seven years after the insects were introduced the prickly pears were brought under control. These caterpillars are such specialized feeders that there does not appear to be any danger that they will attack cultivated plants. The total cost of this project has been estimated to have been less than a penny an acre. This compares to many dollars per acre for the unsatisfactory chemical and mechanical controls previously tried.

A similar project began in the United States a few years ago. In California, Oregon, Washington, and other western states hundreds of thousands of acres of land were overgrown by an undesirable plant known as Klamath or goat weed. This plant, which is poisonous to livestock, is a native of Europe, where it is known as St. Johnswort. It also occurs in the range lands of Canada, New Zealand, and Australia. In 1944 some leaf-eating beetles, which Australians had found to have a taste for Klamath weed, were introduced into the United States. American entomologists tested these insects on more than fifty different kinds of crops, and found that from the human standpoint the beetles were gratifyingly stupid; according to reports they will starve to death rather than eat anything except Klamath weed! Thousands of these beetles were released; they have chewed away voraciously, and to date the results have been most encouraging. As of this writing many thousands of acres have been cleared of the weed.

Recently the insect cudgel was used against a weed variously known as puncture weed or vine goathead, and Mexican sandburr, which is widely distributed over the western United States. These weeds grow nasty burrs capable of puncturing everything from bicycle tires to the skins of horses, cows, and human beings.

This weed apparently came originally from Spain, and in looking for natural enemies, biologists found the puncture-vine weevil. Experiments over several years have indicated that native plants are safe from the attack of the weevil, but that the immature insects develop within the seed pods of the puncture weed, thereby destroying them. Large numbers of these weevils are presently being released, and it is hoped that the puncture weevil proves as harmful to the puncture weed as *Cactoblastis* did to Australian cacti.

What Was the Manna of Biblical Times?

The story of the wanderings of the Israelites in the wilderness after they were banished from Egypt tells of their finding large quantities of a white flaky material that was good to eat. Many authorities believe that the manna of the biblical story was actually a substance secreted by insects. In various parts of the world are insects that secrete a material which becomes white and flaky upon contact with air. These insects, called scale insects, are related to the infamous San Jose scale, which is an important pest on fruit trees in the United States and other regions. The flakes formed by the insects that occur where the Israelites presumably wandered, are especially large and succulent. Even today the Arabs use these flakes for food and call it "man."

Some botanists suggest that manna may have been a lichen, a kind of plant that occurs in the area. So far, no one has been able to settle the controversy to everyone's satisfaction, but zoologists stoutly maintain that an insect was responsible.

There are few insects—of species that are large enough and which occur in sufficient numbers—that have not been eaten by man. These include succulent grubworms, grasshoppers, giant water bugs, termites, and many kinds of caterpillars. Some are often available in the United States through importers of rare foods. One of the latest fads, chocolate covered ants from South America, is surprisingly popular.

What Are Hellgrammites?

There are few fisherman who would not recognize a hellgrammite, and many are the anglers who have caught fish by using them for bait. Hellgrammites grow to 2½ to 3 inches in length; they are flat, with three pairs of legs near the head. They also have a pair of large jaws which they know how to use.

Hellgrammites are usually found in relatively swift water under rocks and stones. They live in water for about three years, and then transform into large insects known as dobsonflies. Dobsonflies are sometimes found around lights at night in the vicinity of lakes and streams, and their large size often attracts attention. The male is certainly one of the weirdest looking of insects. Two curved projections more than an inch in length extend from the head and cross each other. These projections, somewhat resembling the tusks of an elephant, are the jaws, but they are not likely to injure anyone since they are not very powerful. The female dobsonfly is about the same size as the male, but she does not have the greatly oversized jaws. The female can give a painful nip to anyone who handles her carelessly.

What Insects Are the Most Important Fish Food?

According to some authorities, insects make up the most important part of the food of small to medium-sized adult fresh-water fish. And even such large food and game fish as bass, catfish, and pike feed on insects when they are young. Among sunfish, crappies, and many others, insects may make up as much as 70 per cent of their diet.

Examinations of the stomachs of large numbers of fish have shown that many kinds of insects are eaten, but one of the most important is the immature mayfly. Mayflies, also called dayflies and fishflies, pass their immature stages in the water. Here they live for months or even years before they emerge as adults. Mayflies are among the shortest lived of insects as adults; they may become adults, mate, lay their eggs, and die all within twenty-four hours. The insects, which are often yellowish with two long filaments on the ends of their bodies, sometimes emerge from the water in tremendous numbers. They are attracted to lights, and I have seen so many flying about lights on bridges that they created a traffic hazard.

According to one report, fishing has deteriorated recently in parts of Lake Erie. This situation is blamed in part upon the dumping of mill products and sewage into the lake, which has in turn greatly reduced the mayfly population—a staple of the fishes' diet.

Other insects important as fish food include aquatic beetles, backswimmers, and water boatmen. Of special importance are the immature stages of certain small flies known variously as gnats and midges. The immature stages of some species are red in color and are called bloodworms. These midges sometimes also emerge from the water in tremendous numbers, and although they do not bite, they may cause considerable annoyance to anyone in the vicinity.

Will Devilhorses Spit in Your Eyes?

Devilhorses are among the most misunderstood of insects. The real name of these creatures is preying mantids, although they are also called mule killers, soothsayers, and various other uncomplimentary names. Some people think that they can kill mules and horses; others believe that the insects are poisonous.

The insects are sometimes called *praying* mantids because they continuously keep their front legs folded up near their bodies as though in an attitude of prayer. The position of the legs, however, serves a practical purpose. The front legs have long spines on their edges, and they are kept folded so that the mantid is always ready to seize any unwary insect that comes within reach.

Any animal, such as a mantid, that feeds exclusively on insects and similar species, is almost invariably hailed as a benefactor to mankind. However, while I have seen mantids in nature eating mosquitoes, grasshoppers, and moths, and there have been other reports of incidental observations, so far as I know there has never been a detailed analysis of the food habits of the many species of mantids under different conditions. In the absence of such information, we must assume that a beneficial insect tastes as good to a mantid as does a harmful one.

Mantids are among the few insects that have both the inclination and strength to overcome and eat an adult vertebrate animal. They have been known to capture and eat hummingbirds, and one was discovered eating a field mouse.

One of the most common beliefs connected with mantids is that they can spit for some distance, and in so doing, deliberately aim for the eyes. If this spit gets into the eyes, so the story goes, great pain and possible

blindness will result. Preying mantids are actually quite harmless. The belief that mantids will spit in one's eyes has probably arisen because they have been mistaken for another insect. Stick insects, or walking sticks as they are sometimes called, are somewhat similar to mantids, and I have even known biologists to confuse them. Certain kinds of walking sticks have been seen to eject an irritating fluid for several inches. People who have gotten the material in their eyes have suffered intense pain. Stick insects do not spit the fluid, but they secrete it from glands that open along the sides of the body.

Which Insect Is the World's Worst Crop-destroyer?

Since early biblical times, and probably for many ages before that, certain countries of Africa and Asia have been invaded by plagues of locusts. The insects often occur in countless millions, and when they have finished eating and moved on not a green sprig remains in the fields on which they had settled.

The name locust has been used for at least two distantly different kinds of insects. One is the cicada, an insect discussed in the next section, but biologists limit the term to certain kinds of grasshoppers. These are the short-horned grasshoppers, with relatively short "feelers" or antennae, the family name of which at one time was *Locustidae*. Those that are most destructive have tremendous appetites for crops of various kinds, and most of them are strong fliers. The insects often migrate long distances in hordes, and they may occur in such tremendous numbers that a flight literally darkens the sun. The term locust generally designates grass-hoppers that are migratory.

Residents in the eastern United States sometimes experience a local outbreak of grasshoppers or locusts, but the damage in this part of the country is minor compared with that in the states farther west. During a twenty-five year period, from 1925 to 1949, it was estimated that grass-hoppers or locusts had caused damage worth more than half a billion dollars in twenty-three states in western United States. Today grasshoppers are still considered to be among our most important insect pests, and millions of dollars are spent in their control.

On a world-wide basis it has been estimated that grasshoppers have caused more direct crop loss than any other insect. As a result, millions of people have starved to death. The locust problem in the United States, serious as it is, is small compared with the situation in other areas. South America has its difficulties, but the countries of the Middle East and adjacent areas are usually the hardest hit. Countries invaded within the past few years include Iraq, Iran, Turkey, Ethiopia, India, Afghanistan, Eritrea, and many others. Some of the swarms contain astronomical num-bers of locusts that chew up every cultivated plant in their paths. One is reported to have covered 2,000 square miles; another in Brazil is said to have migrated on a 60-mile front, and to have taken four hours to pass a given point. And, during a control campaign in Turkey, more than 400 tons of eggs and 1,200 tons of grasshoppers were collected within three months.

The Insect with a Childhood of Seventeen Years

The life cycle of most insects is relatively short, and many kinds pass from the egg to the adult stage within a few days or weeks. Others spend the winter months in the egg or other immature stage, and a few may require several years to become adults.

The prize for the longest life cycle known in the insect world, however, must be awarded to the seventeen-year cicada. Cicadas are called locusts in some sections, but as we have seen, this name should be limited to certain members of the grasshopper clan. The rather common cicada which often gives a concert from trees during the day and early evening is familiar to many people. These insects are similar to the seventeen-year cicada, but their life cycle is completed in from two to five years.

The immature stages of cicadas are passed in the ground, where they burrow about and feed on the roots of various plants. Those of the seventeen-year species stay in the ground for seventeen years. So far as is known, they do no serious damage to the plants on which they feed.

The rate of development of these numerous insects is about the same, and when they come from the ground they do so in tremendous numbers. At last the big moment arrives, and out from the soil pops droves of the queerest insects you ever saw. Superficially they do not resemble adult cicadas to any extent. They are about an inch long, and have large toothed front legs which cause them to resemble chubby crawfish. On the head is a pair of large eyes, and small wing pads can be seen on the back. These nymphs, as they are called, must now transform into adults. Each one grasps a rock or twig, or crawls up a tree trunk and catches the bark. The "skin" or outer shell then splits down the back. Gradually the adult insect works its way out of the skin, which remains attached to the spot as a light brown shell.

Seventeen-year cicadas emerge over a period of several days, and the adults may live for two or three weeks. Unlike the human species, only male cicadas can "sing," but while they are alive, a concentration of the insects can make life miserable for human beings.

While attending a midwestern university I experienced an emergence of these insects. The campus has a large number of trees, and the cicadas accumulated there in droves. These insects have a tendency to sing in unison, and very shortly the professors had competition from the outside. Louder and louder grew the chorus as the numbers of cicadas increased; louder and louder shouted the professors, until bets were placed on the lasting qualities of the teachers versus the insects. Fortunately, the worst of the competition was over in about three weeks, and sounds gradually returned to normal.

Cicadas of one type or another occur in many parts of the world, but the seventeen-year species is confined to the eastern United States; a variety in the southeast requires only thirteen years to complete its life cycle. Most of the states east of the Mississippi River, and a few to the west, have one or more broods of these insects. There are many different broods, and each one emerges at a different time. Government and state agencies have studied these various broods, and can predict the time when a particular group is to be expected.

The cicadas sometimes cause damage to trees, but the destruction is not as much as one might expect from such tremendous numbers. Essentially all harm is done by the egg-laying females. The cicada pushes the ovipositor or egg-laying tube into the bark of small twigs and limbs, and the eggs are deposited in the tissues of the plant. The twigs are punctured and splintered during the process, and valuable fruit trees may be heavily damaged or even killed if enough cicadas are present. When the eggs hatch, the nymphs drop to the ground, burrow into the soil, and remain there for their destined thirteen or seventeen years.

Few insects can compete with the seventeen-year cicada in length of life, if we include the immature stages. Queen termites and queen ants are probably the most serious competitors. There are reports of queen ants being kept in captivity of from fifteen to nineteen years, and an age of at least fifteen for some queens is accepted by Dr. Charles Michener of the University of Kansas, and others who have investigated insect ages. Some authorities on termites believe that queen termites may live forty to fifty years, but here the evidence is indirect. At present this possible incredible age for an insect cannot be considered as established fact.

SPIDERS

Most spiders feed on insects and other arthropods and they have a poisonous bite with which they kill their victims. Some spiders capture and overcome their prey by the use of a large web. The spider squats patiently on the web until something gets entangled in its strands, then rushes out and seizes it. But other spiders hunt actively for their prey. Some hide in flowers or under bits of trash and pounce when their victims get within reach.

The so-called bolas spiders capture their food by one of the most amazing devices known in the entire animal kingdom. These spiders actually use a casting line to snare flying insects. The spider spins a strong line, on the end of which is a ball of sticky silk. Near dusk, when insects become more active, the hunter takes up a station on the branch of a tree and waits. If an insect flies past—the bolas is heaved toward the flier. If the sticky ball strikes its target, the insect is stopped in mid-air, the spider hurries down the line, bites the insect, and enjoys the fruits of a successful cast. Bolas spiders and their relatives are widely distributed in the United States and certain other countries.

The common expression that the female is deadlier than the male is appropriate for spiders. Female spiders are often larger than males; after mating, they may make a meal of their erstwhile lovers. But this practice is not invariable.

After mating, the female spider usually encloses the eggs in a silken cocoon which may be attached to the web or hidden in some secluded spot. The female of some species, such as the so-called wolf spider, attaches the cocoon to the tip of her abdomen, and lugs it around as she looks for food. The wolf spiders are gray or brown, with a leg spread of 1½ to 2 inches. One would hardly associate motherly love with a spider, but many species will fight fiercely to defend their eggs. The mother wolf spider actually opens the cocoon when the youngsters are ready to face the outside world. The young spiders scramble out and swarm all over the mother's body. Here they cling for a week or so as the mother engages in her normal activities.

We have seen that spiders, scorpions, mites, and ticks are not true insects, although many people refer to them as such. All these species are classified into a group known as the arachnids.

Of What Value Are Spiders?

Spiders are sometimes found in enormous numbers in certain areas, and since they eat insects, the chances are that they do a considerable amount of good under certain circumstances. Many "spiderologists" have collected the arachnids intensively in some regions and have estimated the number that probably occur over a large area. These estimates have ranged from approximately 11,000 per acre in a woodland to more than 2 million in grassy areas.

Dr. Willis J. Gertsch, of the American Museum of Natural History, cites an instance of spiders eliminating an infestation of bedbugs in Athens, Greece. Camps occupied by Greek refugees had supported thriving colonies of bedbugs for more than a year, when there was a sudden and dramatic decrease of the blood-thirsty pests. Investigation showed that there were large numbers of little crab spiders in the barracks, and that a single spider might kill thirty to forty bedbugs in a single day. Thanks to these spiders, the bedbugs were completely wiped out.

In any large spider web you can usually find the remains of several insects. It is true that the spider is not selective; beneficial as well as harmful insects may be killed. However, even the ill-reputed black widow spider probably does some good. One female was given credit for killing 250 houseflies plus several other kinds of insects during its life.

The Uses of Spider Webs

The silk of spiders is secreted by several glands inside the spiders' abdomen. These glands open to the outside through finger-like processes called spinnerets. The spinnerets are movable, and there may be six or eight of them, depending upon the kind of spider. The different kinds of silk glands secrete different kinds of silk, each of which may be used for a specific purpose such as parts of the web, the egg cocoon, and so on. Sometimes the strands come from only one type of gland, but often they are a combination of two or more kinds of silk. The silk is liquid as it comes from the spinnerets, but once in the air it hardens quickly.

Spider silk, for its size, is among the strongest materials known. It will stretch one-fifth of its length before breaking, and its tensile strength exceeds that of steel. Small wonder that large flies and other insects are held firmly by webs that appear fragile.

All of us have seen spiders launch themselves into space and float easily downward, suspended by a strand of silk that is attached at the spot from which the jump is made. This silken strand is called the dragline. As spiders roam about from place to place they play out this dragline, which is attached at intervals. When the spider jumps into space, the anchored dragline checks its fall and is gradually played out from the spinnerets. If the spider scrambles back up the dragline, it catches the strand on one of its legs and rolls it into a ball as it climbs. Once arrived at a safe perch, the balled dragline may be discarded or, if the spider is hungry, it may be eaten.

The webs of some tropical spiders are as much as 6 feet in diameter and are so strong that they have been known to hold birds. Natives in several regions have found many uses for these webs. The complete web is often employed as a fish net and will hold a catch of three or four pounds. In Australia twisted strands of silk are used for fishing lures. When the fish bites the end of the lure its teeth become entangled in the silk, allowing the catch to be landed by the native angler. Small bags for carrying trinkets are often woven from the silk, and even relatively waterproof hats have been fabricated from it. It must not be supposed, however, that uses for spider silk are limited to primitive people. Even today spider silk is used for the cross hairs and lines of reference in various kinds of optical instruments such as levels, telescopes, and surveying transits. But during the past few years fine platinum wires and etchings on glass have replaced spider silk to some extent.

Many years ago a Frenchman believed that spider silk could be used for clothing. According to English biologist Dr. Theodore H. Savoy, this man made a pair of stockings from the material in 1710. Scientific circles were thrown into an enthusiastic furor. The Paris Academy of Science commissioned René Antoine Ferchault de Réaumur, a famous French biologist, to investigate the possibility of using spider silk on a large scale. Visions of quick riches, however, quickly faded as Réaumur's investigation proceeded. It was found that spiders' appetites included a taste for their fellows, and consequently each one had to be kept in a separate cage. Much of the silk produced was not usable, and many thousands of spiders were needed to produce a pound of silk. It was concluded that the amount of labor and expense involved was prohibitive, and since that time this type of silk has not been used for clothing except for an occasional novelty.

How Dangerous Are Spiders?

Most spiders have a bite that is poisonous to insects and other animals upon which they feed, but relatively few are normally dangerous to human beings.

The species in the United States with the worst reputation are the tarantulas and the black widow. The big hairy tarantulas are especially prevalent in tropical and subtropical areas; tropical species sometimes occur in bunches of bananas shipped to other areas. The tarantulas in the United States, and even those in tropical countries, are not likely to cause death in man. People who have been bitten by various kinds of tarantulas describe the effects as similar to those of bee stings.

Some of the tarantula group found in South America are the largest spiders in the world. Dr. Willis J. Gertsch, of the American Museum of Natural History, gives a body length of 3½ inches and a leg span of 9½ inches for a large female from Brazil. A somewhat more slender male from French Guiana spanned 10 inches. The venom of these monster spiders has been found to have little effect on man, but because of the large mouthparts, a bite from one of these would doubtless be quite painful. It is true that not all tropical tarantulas have been tested, and it is possible that some of them might be dangerous to man.

The black widow is quite different from tarantulas. One biologist, who suffered no ill effects from the bites of several kinds of tarantulas, had to be taken to a hospital when he allowed a black widow to bite him. Young children and aged individuals are most likely to die as a result of black widow bites, but studies now indicate that more deaths occur than commonly believed. It is known that 39 people died in the United States from the bite of this spider from 1950 through 1954, and the chances are good that other deaths from this cause were not officially recorded.

Anyone bitten by a black widow spider should go to a physician at once, since doctors now have treatments which relieve the symptoms of the bite within a relatively short time, usually by an injection of calcium gluconate or a similar substance.

The black widow is so called because the female is black in color, and she has the nasty habit of eating the male after they have mated. The female, which is the only one that bites, has a body about as large as the end of one's little finger, and a leg spread of an inch or so. It is easy to identify: on the undersurface of the body is a red or orange-colored spot that has the shape of an hourglass. The general shape of the body and the coal-black color also make the spider easy to recognize even without seeing the red spot.

Black widow spiders are found under rocks, in piles of wood, in garages, and outhouses. It is not likely to bite unless one brushes against its web or unless one of them happens to get in clothes or shoes. In the United States the black widow is most common in the south and southwest, but it has been reported from most of the states and parts of Canada. In areas where this spider is common, it is wise to teach children to avoid spider webs, and to shake out shoes and clothing that have not been worn for some time.

In 1958 attention was called to another kind of venomous spider in the United States. This species, called the brown spider, and *Loxosceles*, is brown in color with a wide black stripe from the front part of the head to the middle of the back. The bite of this spider causes the development of ulcers or sores which may require several weeks to heal, and which often result in unsightly scars. This species is rather widely distributed in the midwestern, southern, and southwestern United States. The brown spider occurs in barns, garages, and other outbuildings, and in some cases, even in houses. Death usually does not occur from the bite of this spider, but according to Dr. Maurice T. James, of Washington State University, the death of a four-year-old boy has been recorded by the attending physician.

Dangerously venomous spiders in other countries included relatives of the black widow which are widely distributed over the world, a species of funnel web spider in Australia, and a species in southern Brazil.

SCORPIONS

Scorpions do not look much like spiders, but the two are related. One easily seen similarity is their jointed legs, characteristic of all arthropods. Unlike spiders, scorpions do not have a poisonous bite; the business end is the tail, which is equipped with a poisonous stinger. Insects, spiders, and similar creatures that scorpions eat are overcome by the powerful pincers at the front end of the body, but if the victim offers too much resistance, the stinger helps to subdue the unwilling prey.

Scorpions are not sociable even with their own kind, and if two meet the chances are good that one will furnish a meal for the other. There is a common saying of considerable truth that two adult scorpions are found together only if they are mating, or if one is eating the other.

During the day scorpions hide under logs or stones or in similar spots, and at night ramble about searching for food. Where the creatures are common, they often manage to get into houses. Scorpions are seldom seen by the average person, but this fact has not prevented the development of misconceptions and superstitions. One is that young scorpions eat their mother shortly after they are born. This idea has developed because the youngsters, after being born alive, hang on to the back of the female as she wanders about. In order to grow, young scorpions, like other arthropods, shed their outer skins or skeletons from time to time. These shed skins sometimes stick to the back of the female giving her a ragged appearance. Not too much imagination is needed to interpret these ragged edges as made by the hungry jaws of the mother scorpion's developing brood. Young scorpions usually do not eat at all while they are being lugged about by the female. After they have developed for a time, the youngsters straggle off to fend for themselves.

Another prevalent myth is that scorpions routinely commit suicide by stinging themselves if in danger. The truth is that many scorpions are immune to their own poison.

The so-called whip- or whip-tailed scorpions have large front pincers and a slender tail that accounts for their common name. They are also arachnids, but are classified in a different group from scorpions. They are dangerous-looking creatures, and the chunky body plus the pincers may be 3 inches in length. Some of them emit a vinegar-like odor when irritated, and for this reason in parts of the United States they are called vinegarones or vinegaroons. Whip-scorpions are believed to have a poisonous bite or sting, but such is not the case. They do not have a stinger, and the bite has been described as about as severe as a pin-prick. The material causing the vinegar-like odor might irritate tender skin, and if it gets into an open wound will cause a burning sensation.

How Poisonous Are Scorpions?

As one might expect, the effects of scorpion stings vary tremendously according to their particular species. There is also some variation in people's sensitivity to the venom. Fortunately, there is only one region in the United States where scorpions are generally dangerous to human beings. This is Arizona, where more than two dozen deaths from scorpion sting have been recorded; all these victims were young children, but it seem possible that an especially sensitive adult might be killed. The Arizona scorpion is related to the infamous Durango scorpion, a still more dangerous species that occurs in the state of Durango, Mexico, and adjacent areas. The Durango species has been known to kill an adult in less than an hour, and over a period of 35 years, it has been responsible for the death of approximately 1,600 people. Dangerous scorpions also occur in Africa and several other tropical countries.

Within recent years a good antivenin has been developed for the sting of the Durango scorpion, and the use of this has greatly reduced the mortality rate. This antivenin has also been used successfully for the stings of the Arizona scorpions which are relatives of the Durango species.

Dr. H. L. Stahnke, of Arizona State University, has developed a treatment for scorpion sting which he states is quite successful. This treatment, called the L C treatment consists of:

1. Applying a tight ligature between the site of the sting and the heart if the sting has occurred on an arm or leg.

2. Immersing the stung area in a pan of water and cracked ice. The ligature should be removed after it has been on for five or ten minutes.

3. Keeping the wound area in the ice solution for at least two hours.

The idea behind this treatment is to slow up the circulation in the region of the sting so that the venom will be absorbed slowly, thereby giving the body time to build up a defense against it. According to Dr. Stahnke, this treatment is sufficient for the stings of the two Arizona scorpions, and the victim will not suffer any serious ill effects if it is properly administered.

CHIGGERS

In many parts of the world, including the United States, people who ramble about in the woods and fields have had painful experiences with chiggers. Chiggers, redbugs, harvestbugs, and bête-rouge, as they are variously called, are tiny red mites that are almost invisible to the unaided eye.

Chiggers are to be found in a variety of locales, including meadows, fields, and woods. They feed on many kinds of animals, such as rodents, rabbits, and even box turtles and snakes. If one of these is not available, a human being is an acceptable substitute. The little rascals swarm over the body, attach themselves to a convenient spot on the skin, and begin to feed. As a result, large numbers of sizeable red welts which often itch severely appear on the body and legs and may persist for days.

• After a chigger has fed for a time it drops off and completes its life cycle. The adults do not feed on other animals, but there are usually enough youngsters to make life miserable for a good percentage of the population. In parts of Europe and Australia some chiggers are important pests of domestic animals such as horses, cattle, and sheep.

So far as is known, no chiggers in the United States or Europe carry any human disease, although an occasional individual might become ill as a result of large numbers of bites. In parts of Asia, Australia, Japan, and adjacent areas chiggers carry a disease that has a mortality of from 5 to 30 per cent. This disease is called scrub typhus as well as the formidable name, *tsutsugamushi* fever. In Australia a similar or possibly identical malady is known as Mossman fever. During World War II there were more than 7,000 cases of this disease among American troops.

Good insect repellents have been developed that also work against chiggers. Materials used include dimethyl phthalate, dibutyl phthalate, and diethyl toluamide. Some of these substances are now generally available, and the user should follow the manufacturer's directions.

I have found good emergency measures to include taking a hot soapy bath and allowing the suds to dry on the body before rinsing. After rinsing and drying off, apply rubbing alcohol all over the body, being careful to avoid tender spots.

At the present state of our knowledge most activities of chiggers seem

to fall on the negative side of the ledger. As information accumulates, however, we might find that these creatures do a certain amount of good. A
biologist who was experimenting with chiggers found that the eggs of insects were among their favorite foods, and we may eventually determine
that the little mites serve as an important insect control.

TICKS

Ticks are all parasites of animals of one kind or another, and a number
of them will feed on people. The home life and habits of different kinds
of ticks vary, but are all of the same general pattern in the most common
species.

The eggs are usually laid on the ground in sheltered spots, and they
hatch into very small ticks which most people call seed ticks. By various
means these seed ticks find an animal such as a mouse, rabbit, or even
a human being, attach themselves to its body, and feed for a time. The
seed tick may then drop off its host, shed its skin, and transform into the
next stage. This procedure is repeated until the ticks become adults.

When filled or engorged with blood a female tick may be several times
as large as a male tick of the same kind. Average-sized ticks, both male and
female, are approximately ¼ inch long when not filled with blood. As the
female feeds her body expands until it may get to be as large as a fingernail. Male ticks do not take in as much blood as females do and their
bodies do not enlarge to any extent.

Do Ticks Carry Human Diseases?

Ticks carry both animal and human diseases. One of the most widespread human diseases is spotted fever, formerly called Rocky Mountain Spotted Fever because it was thought to be confined to the Rocky Mountain area of the United States. It is now known that the disease occurs in at least forty-five of the United States, the District of Columbia, and in parts of Mexico, Central and South America. In 1961 there were 219 cases in the United States. Other tick-transmitted human diseases include tularemia or rabbit fever, Q fever, boutonneuse fever of the Mediterranean area, Colorado tick fever, tick typhus, and a type of relapsing fever.

Among the most important tick-transmitted diseases of animals, in addition to rabbit fever, which people get from infected rodents and rabbits is one that strikes cattle all over the world. Known variously as red water fever, splenic fever, and Texas cattle fever, it causes a death rate among infected cattle often as high as 75 per cent. This disease in the United States was called Texas cattle fever because cattle driven north from Texas and other southern states would infect cows from other parts of the country. At one time it was the most serious animal disease in America, from the standpoint of losses. Today, thanks to cattle dipping, quarantines, and other rigid measures, the disease is extensively controlled.

However, even non-infective ticks can be dangerous. A heavy concentration of ticks (which often occurs) can cause considerable blood loss and possibly death. A doctor once removed 300 ticks from a patient. The patient recovered. On the other hand, a jackrabbit found dead in Montana had been attacked by 152 ticks; a post-mortem examination revealed that there was almost no blood in its body.

A more realistic danger is tick paralysis, which occurs in both animals and human beings. The victim may become completely paralyzed and, if the tick is not removed, is likely to die. It is believed that this paralysis is caused by the saliva injected by the tick while feeding.

Cases of tick paralysis have been reported from many parts of the world. One of the most recent to come to my attention was that of a five-year-old girl in Miami, Florida. Both of her legs were paralyzed when she was first seen by a physician. He had her admitted to a hospital. Within twenty-four hours both arms were also paralyzed. By this time several physicians were puzzling over the case, at a loss to find the cause. While they were consulting, a nurse who was combing the little girl's hair discovered a tick attached to the scalp. The tick was removed and the patient made a dramatic recovery. Shortly afterwards she was able to go home.

There have been many cases of death where the tick was not discovered until too late. A careful examination of the hair of the head should be made in all sudden cases of paralysis, especially in young children.

Should Attached Ticks Be Unscrewed?

Once, at the end of a lecture on ticks, two young physicians came to the desk to ask me a question. They wanted to know if right-handed and left-handed ticks existed, and if so, was it necessary to unscrew attached ticks in opposite directions. Most people who live in regions where ticks are common know the answer to this, but in areas where ticks are rare many believe as did the young doctors.

The most common kinds of ticks bury their front end, including the mouthparts into the flesh of their hosts, and if they are not removed, they may remain attached for days or even weeks. The mouthparts have backward projecting spines that hold the tick firmly in place until the parasite becomes engorged with blood. Under these circumstances, it would be idiotic to try to unscrew an attached tick, since this procedure would certainly break the mouthparts and leave them in the wound. There are thus no right-hand and left-handed ticks that should be unscrewed in opposite directions.

There have been a large number of weird methods recommended for successfully removing attached ticks, but according to Dr. C. B. Philip, director of the Rocky Mountain Laboratory, the only sure method is to grasp the tick and pull it off, gently but firmly. The application of irritating materials such as turpentine, lighter fluid, or iodine to the tick's body will sometimes facilitate removal. Do not jerk the parasite, because this is likely to break the mouthparts, thus subjecting the wound to infection. An antiseptic should be applied to the spot immediately, but even with the most careful attention, the chances are that it will itch for several days.

The bites of ticks are irritating, but once the tick is removed, the bite of most species is not likely to cause much difficulty unless infection occurs. However, the bite of a few species may result in nausea or other systemic disturbances, and the site of the bite may cause trouble for days or even weeks. Perhaps the most notorious of these ticks is the so called *tlalaja* or *pajaroella* of parts of California and Mexico. These ticks are greatly feared by many of the local inhabitants who believe that the loss of an arm or leg, or even death, can result from their bite. These beliefs are considerably exaggerated, but the experience of a biologist who was bitten on the leg shows that the bite of this species may be considerably worse than the bite of most ticks. Within a few hours after the tick was removed, the leg swelled greatly, and became numb and irritated; throughout the night the biologist felt very "disagreeable." The leg gradually returned to normal, but it was several weeks before the site of the bite was completely healed.

I have seen some people amuse themselves by pulling ticks off their dogs and then attempting to crush the parasite between their fingernails. This should never be done, despite the satisfactory pop that results if one is successful. Tick-borne diseases can be transmitted in the body fluids, and if a tick is handled, the hands should be washed immediately with soap and water.

A person going into areas where ticks are common should take all precautions to prevent the parasites from attaching to his body. This includes the use of repellents—following the directions on the labels—wearing full-length clothing and high-top boots with trousers tucked into the boot tops. Despite all precautions, an occasional tick sometimes crosses all barriers and manages to get on the body. Thus after returning from a tick-infected region, individuals should work in pairs, examining each other for attached ticks. This is no time for modesty, and the examination should be made "in the raw." Certain tick-borne diseases are more likely to be transmitted after the parasites have been attached for several hours; consequently, the creatures should be removed as soon as possible.

CENTIPEDES

Centipedes are flattened arthropods that have many legs on each side of their bodies. They are able to move rapidly and are found under rocks, among debris, and sometimes even in houses. Centipedes feed on insects and similar small animals. Under the head they have a pair of sharp claws connected to poison glands which help them to overcome stubborn victims. Most centipedes are not over a couple of inches in length and consequently they do not attract special attention. Perhaps the largest centipede in the United States is a rather nicely colored yellow with an orange head, yellow legs, and a blue body. This centipede gets to be about 7 inches long. Some species in the tropics attain a length of over a foot.

Large centipedes are greatly feared by most people, and they are capable of administering a painful bite. American troops, and doubtless others, had some trouble with certain species during World War II. A physician told me that while he was on New Guinea and Bougainville islands in the Pacific, his unit had some two dozen soldiers hospitalized for a day or so from the bite of a centipede about 10 inches in length. No deaths occurred, however, and after the men learned to shake out their shoes and clothing —places where the centipedes liked to hide—no more bites occurred.

English biologist Dr. J. L. Cloudsley-Thompson states that a child in the Philippines died from the bite of a centipede on the head, but death in human beings is certainly a very unusual occurrence. The relative unimportance of centipede bite with respect to human life is emphasized by the subject matter discussed at the First International Conference on Venoms a few years ago. All important venomous animals, from jellyfish to venomous snakes were considered, but centipedes were completely disregarded.

Occasionally, people are startled to see a many-legged creature an inch or so in length scampering across the floor; one is sometimes trapped in the bathtub. These are house centipedes, which feed primarily on such pests are cockroaches and flies. House centipedes are not especially attractive by most human standards, but since they eat large numbers of harmful insects, they should be encouraged rather than stepped on.

CRUSTACEANS

Almost everyone is familiar with the larger crustaceans, such as lobsters, crawfish, crabs, and shrimp. Few people realize, however, that both fresh and salt water literally teem with enormous numbers of minute crustaceans, some so small that they are barely visible to the unaided eye. In some instances so many of these little creatures occur that the water is literally crustacean soup. By using a very fine mesh net, people have actually collected enough within a relatively short time to furnish a meal for several men.

The small crustaceans are of incalculable value to human beings indirectly in that they are important items in the food of many fish. It has been claimed that it would be impossible for fish to survive if it were not for these tiny animals. Unfortunately, as we shall see, some of the crustaceans are also unwittingly harmful; certain human parasites live in their bodies during a stage in their life cycles.

Crustaceans breathe by means of gills and most of them live in water all of their lives. Some crabs, pillbugs, and a few other species, however, are essentially land inhabiting. The so-called land crabs, which are primarily tropical and subtropical, live in burrows in forest regions and ramble around mostly at night in search of food. But their eggs must be laid in water and during the mating season vast numbers descend upon the ocean in incredible numbers for mating and egg deposition.

Many crustaceans employ a spectacular method of escaping from their enemies. A lobster, for instance, if seized by the leg may deliberately break off the limb, leaving it in the clutches of the enemy while the remainder of the body makes good its escape. This does not disconcert the lobster, since it can grow a new limb within a relatively short time.

The group name, crustacean, comes from a Latin word meaning "a crust." As is true for other arthropods, the hard outer covering of the body is dead material which will not stretch, and as a consequence it must be shed from time to time so that the crustacean can grow. While the new covering is still soft, the creature can grow for a time, but it is relatively unprotected. The crustaceans seem to realize this fact and, as a consequence, they will often remain in hiding for two or three days until the new shell has become hard.

The females of many crustaceans, such as crabs, lobsters, and crawfish, often carry their eggs attached to their bodies until they hatch and this may be for many months. The eggs are usually attached to small projections on the undersurface of the tail region.

Eggs of fresh-water crawfish are comparatively large and somewhat resemble bunches of small grapes. When the eggs hatch the infant crawfish do not immediately leave the female as do the young of crabs and lobsters. They may remain attached for several days to the undersurface of the female's tail so that for a time the mother is literally crawling with youngsters.

What Crustacean Is the Most Important Source of Human Food?

In the United States, and probably on a world-wide basis, shrimp constitute the most important food crustaceans. Even as early as 1945 the annual shrimp catch in the United States and Alaska was valued at more than $20 million. This places shrimping in the number four position of value in American fisheries. Salmon, tuna, and oysters are the only fishery products that exceed shrimp in value.

In 1950 the shrimping industry was given a shot in the arm by the discovery of vast new shrimp beds off the coast of Dry Tortugas at the tip of the Florida Keys. Most of these crustaceans are large and because of their golden-pink color, are called pink shrimp. They can be caught in quantity only at night. Previously, shrimping was a daytime operation, and this is doubtless the reason that these valuable beds were undiscovered for so long.

One of the interesting things about these new shrimp beds is that, according to popular account, they would probably never have been discovered except for sharks. Many sharks that were caught off the Florida Keys had their stomachs stuffed with giant shrimp. This area had been tried repeatedly by shrimpers with no luck, but two men decided to try again. They seined all day unsuccessfully; then cast their net once again just after nightfall. This time the men hit the jackpot, and ever since the area has crawled with shrimp boats, some from as far away as New Jersey.

The shrimp's tail, which snugly encloses the intestine, is the only part of the crustacean that is regularly eaten by people. The remainder of the body is not wasted, however, but is dried and sold as shrimp bran or meal. Within recent years there has been considerable demand for shrimp bran as an ingredient of poultry and stock foods.

Are Crawfish Harmful?

Crawfish, or crayfish, live in or near ponds and streams and they are occasionally caught on fish hooks. Some crawfish make burrows, which may be several feet deep, on the banks of ponds or streams or in swampy areas. The lower end of the burrow contains water, but the outside opening is often above the water level and it is usually surrounded by a chimney-like pile of mud. Crawfish generally hide in their holes or in other protected spots during the day and do most of their prowling at night.

In parts of the Mississippi delta region they are so numerous that cotton and corn cannot profitably be raised unless the culprits are reduced in numbers. It has been estimated that farmers are prevented from using as much as a thousand square miles of good farming land because of these pests. The crawfish chew up the young plants just after sprouting and they may destroy a large field within a single night.

There may be as many as 10,000 to 12,000 holes per acre and one ambitious plantation owner collected barrels of the crustaceans from his farm within a single season.

On a world-wide basis, rice probably suffers more than any other single crop from the attentions of crawfish and other crustaceans. In some cases the plants themselves are eaten; in others the burrowing activities destroy the rice directly, or allow the flooded fields to drain, thereby exposing the young plants to too much direct sunlight. In India and Puerto Rico, crabs are the crustacean villains; in Spain and the Federated Malay States, shrimp-like little fellows are involved.

Yet various crustaceans have their useful side. Crawfish have been used for food in parts of the United States and Europe, and they have been so popular that people have even reared them on crawfish farms. The crustaceans also make excellent bait for certain fish, and when mixed with meal, have been used for chicken feed. They are excellent scavengers, quickly consuming material that might otherwise pollute the lakes and streams. The crawfish is probably also used more than any other one arthropod as an animal for dissection in elementary biology and zoology courses.

Where Do Barnacles Fit in the Animal Kingdom?

For many years even biologists were content to regard barnacles as a kind of mollusk. Then some individual decided to find out something about the habits and home life of the creatures. Much to everyone's amazement it was discovered that the growth and development of barnacles were totally unlike those of mollusks. Rather it was found that these processes were similar to those of many crustaceans. Further study revealed other similarities to crustaceans, and since that time barnacles have been accepted as true but somewhat odd crustaceans.

When the usual barnacle hatches it is a small free-swimming form, not much different from that of many other crustaceans. As it grows, it passes through a number of stages, but eventually it must attach itself to a surface where it will remain for the rest of its life. After attachment, the barnacle ultimately transforms into the adult. This transformation includes the development of shells that may surround most of the body. Barnacles attach themselves by their front end—so they spend their adult lives standing on their heads. They feed upon minute organisms in the water which enter their mouths with the currents created by the waving of the modified legs.

The barnacles may select many types of surfaces, including rocks, piers, living creatures—such as turtles and whales—and the bottoms of ships.

On a large ship, sometimes as much as one hundred to three hundred tons of barnacles can accumulate. This much foreign material obviously reduces the speed and efficiency of a ship, and as a consequence, it must be placed in drydock regularly, scraped, and repainted. Many years ago it was estimated that ship fouling cost the United States shipping industry more than $100 million per year.

It would be difficult to convince ship owners that any good could ever come from a barnacle, but man has actually found some use for them. In parts of South America a common barnacle attains a length of 8 or 9 inches and a width of 3 or 4 inches. These are sought for food and are considered more of a delicacy than many other shellfish. On the other side of the world in the Orient certain species are regularly cultured and used for fertilizer.

Seven MOLLUSKS

The name mollusk means "soft." All the mollusks have relatively soft bodies as compared with those of lobsters, crabs, shrimp, and crawfish. Mollusks include snails, clams, oysters, squids, octopuses, and similar species. The soft bodies of many of them are protected by one or two shells. The shells are secreted by the animals themselves, and are usually permanently attached to their bodies. These shells are sometimes called valves, and mollusks with two shells, such as oysters, clams, mussels, and scallops, are known as bivalves. Edible mollusks of this group are often called shellfish.

Some mollusks have no shell at all, or only the remnants of one. Shellless mollusks include the octopuses and slugs, the latter being creatures similar to snails except for the absence of a shell. A squid does not have an obvious shell because it is surrounded by tissue and is not visible externally.

The range in size among mollusks is amazing. Some snails can barely span the head of a pin, whereas giant squids may attain a length of more than 50 feet and a weight of several tons. There is also considerable variation in the environment in which mollusks live. Octopuses and squids are found only in salt water, but bivalves occur in both fresh and salt water. Some snails are the only truly land-dwelling mollusks.

The mollusks are the second largest animal group, exceeded in numbers only by the arthropods. More than 41,500 species are known. As might be expected in such a large group, a great variety of food and reproductive habits are represented.

OCTOPUSES AND SQUIDS

An octopus has a bulbous body with eight arms or tentacles, that are all about the same length. A squid's body is much more elongated; the end opposite the arms has a couple of flattened fins and it is often somewhat pointed. In addition, a squid has ten arms or tentacles, two of which are much longer than the other eight. Squids and octopuses are found only in salt water.

Both animals have sucking discs on their arms which are used to capture food. Some of these discs may be as big as saucers on the larger squids, and even small discs have tremendous holding power. Squids and octopuses normally eat living sea animals, such as crabs and fish, which they tear to bits with their horny, parrot-like beaks. When hungry, however, they are not especially choosy. Almost any kind of animal, including their own species, will be eaten if it can be overpowered.

These mollusks were traveling by jet propulsion and using "smoke screens" long before people thought of such devices. The jet propulsion is

accomplished by water and a special cavity or chamber which can be opened or closed. When the creatures are not in a hurry, the cavity is open so that water enters freely. If they become excited, however, the cavity is closed except for a small opening in a short connecting tube. Sudden contraction of the walls of the chamber forces water out under pressure through the small opening. As a result, the octopus or squid is propelled in the opposite direction. A frightened squid can zip through the water with surprising speed, and if near the top of the water may even shoot above the surface and sail through the air for some distance.

Within the bodies of squids and octopuses is a structure called the ink sac which contains a black or brownish liquid. When one of these mollusks is attacked, the ink is thrown into the water forming an effective "smoke screen" behind which the squid or octopus often makes its escape. According to Dr. G. A. MacInitic, of the California Institute of Technology, the ink of an octopus actually paralyzes the olfactory nerves of its enemies so that they cannot smell. Off the coast of California, moray eels—long fish with many sharp teeth—are reported to prefer octopuses to any other article of diet. These fish are supposed to locate their food, at least partly, by their sense of smell. A moray eel which had octopus ink discharged in its face was seen to touch the octopus with its nose and not try to eat it. Later, after the effects of the ink had apparently worn off, the fish had no difficulty locating the octopus and trying to add the mollusk to its menu.

Female octopuses guard and clean their eggs and will fight off intruders that might want to make a meal of them. So far as known, squids do not guard their eggs; the females apparently forget all about the matter after the eggs are laid. The eggs are usually deposited in masses which are covered by a jelly-like material. This jelly protects the eggs from fungus growths and is presumably distasteful to other animals that might be tempted to have a batch of squid eggs for breakfast.

Thanks to several poets, most people have heard of nautiluses, of which the chambered and paper species are the best known. These mollusks, related to squids and octopuses, are not known to be of particular significance to people except that they are occasionally used for food, but one idea about the paper nautilus should be mentioned.

The belief that the paper nautilus squats in its shell, spreads its somewhat flattened arms as sails, and goes scudding over the ocean may have originated with Aristotle more than two thousand years ago. Since Aristotle's time, poets have written of this supposed habit and many biologists as well as laymen have thought it to be true. In fact the scientific name of the creature, which is *Argonauta,* is doubtless based upon this belief.

Unfortunately for poets, this reported practice has now been discredited. The natural home of the nautilus is in deep water, many fathoms beneath the surface. So far as is known, it does not come to the surface unless thrown up by storms or other unusual circumstances. A few specimens, obviously sick or injured, have been found at the surface, but these were not in any mood to spread their arms and go sailing.

How Dangerous Are Octopuses?

There are few stories and movies dealing with pearl diving or hunts for sunken treasure that do not have at least one episode in which the hero tangles with an octopus, sometimes called a devilfish. The octopus usually rues the day he became embroiled because he ends up with much of his anatomy scattered over the ocean floor. Dangers from octopuses have been considerably exaggerated, but there is evidence that attacks occasionally do occur.

One of these incidents occurred off the coast of Australia in October 1949. The story appeared in the *North Queensland* (Australia) *Register*. Australian biologist Maynard E. MacDougal sent me a clipping of the story. Members of the crew of a small boat were engaged in diving for trochus or topshells, a kind of marine snail, the shells of which are used for making buttons and ornamental work. Suddenly one of the divers felt his arm seized by the tentacles of an octopus. Fortunately, one arm was free, and the man at once grasped his knife, which is standard equipment for divers in these waters. After a considerable struggle, during which deep wounds were inflicted on the octopus, the man managed to rise gasping to the surface.

Octopuses vary in size from an inch in length to the enormous Pacific octopus that has been reported to have a tentacle span of 40 feet. The largest octopus I know of, whose measurement has been verified, had a tentacle span of 28 feet. It may be, however, that 40-foot individuals do exist. I have not seen any weights given for large specimens, but a 10-foot octopus was found to weigh 110 pounds.

Even relatively small octopuses can cause injury, and may even be dangerous in a way most of us would not imagine—they have a poisonous bite. Octopuses have two hard, beak-like jaws, resembling the beak of a parrot. Large specimens can inflict painful wounds, and even small ones must be regarded with respect because of the venom which may be injected when biting. This venom is useful to the octopus, since it has rapid effect upon the crabs which octopuses often eat.

Most cases of octopus bite are likely to be quite painful, but would usually not endanger human life. However, Dr. Bruce W. Halstead, of Loma Linda University, cites a case of death in an Australian diver following the bite of an octopus. According to the account, the bite occurred on the back of the diver's neck. Within a short time the man became nauseated

and had difficulty in breathing. He was taken to a hospital where he died about two hours after being bitten.

Where Do the Kraken Swim?

The folklore and mythology of Scandinavian countries have many references to an enormous squid-like creature called a krake or kraken. According to legend, this sea monster ambushed passing ships, which it seized and dragged beneath the surface. When not especially hungry, the kraken was content to eat only a few of the crew whom it plucked from the rigging.

No one knows for sure just how large squids may become, but so far none has been found that approaches the noble proportions ascribed to the kraken. Giant squids do exist, however, although they live in deep water and are rarely seen. One has occasionally been washed ashore, and it is from these specimens that we have obtained the most accurate information. The largest one I know of that was examined by a biologist had an over-all length of 55 feet including the longest tentacles. The body was 20 feet long, over 3 feet in diameter, and had a circumference of 12 feet. This squid probably weighed a ton or so.

Despite legends and folklore, danger to human beings from squids is slight. The only reasonably verified attack on human beings that has come to my attention occurred off the coast of Newfoundland some years ago. According to the story, fishermen saw a large object floating at the surface and rowed over to examine it. One of the men struck the mass, which, much to their horror, immediately came alive with resentment. Up reared an enormous head with glaring eyes and a large parrot-like beak. Two tentacles were wrapped around the boat, and the creature struck the boat a tremendous blow with its beak. One of the men seized an axe and chopped off the tentacles. The squid immediately beat a hasty retreat, emitting large quantities of black inky fluid into the water. One of the severed tentacles eventually fell into the hands of a minister who preserved it and reported the story. Even in this case, it must be noted that the squid did not attack unprovoked.

There are many different kinds and sizes of squids, and even some of the smaller ones are of some importance to human beings. A rich brown pigment called sepia can be made from the ink of certain squids and, in the past at least, this material has been in considerable demand by artists. Squids, as has been mentioned, do not have shells outside their bodies like many mollusks, but they do have a kind of shell inside. Some squids are called cuttlefish, and from the shells of these comes the cuttle bone commonly used in bird cages.

Many small squids are used for fish bait, but perhaps the most interesting use for them is for human food. Large numbers are consumed even in the United States, and in some years more than a million pounds of squids are captured for food off the west coast of this country.

Even the less attractive octopus is used today for making soup; in ancient times the Romans and Greeks considered it to be the finest sea food obtainable. In fact, a well-known Greek nobleman is reported to have died as a result of eating octopus. People today, however, need not avoid a dish of octopus because of this story unless they attempt to compete with the nobleman. He is supposed to have consumed entirely a three-foot octopus, and to have died from overeating.

SNAILS

There are more different kinds of snails and their relatives than any other kind of mollusk. The coiled shell is one of the most characteristic features of snails with which many of us are familiar.

The person who first connected Cupid and his arrows with love-making must have known the courting habits of certain land snails. Two snails approach each other, apparently with mating as the main objective. Suddenly each snail shoots a hard sliver of material at the other one. These love darts, as they are called, penetrate the tissues of the snails and presumably get them into the right frame of mind to complete the mating process. At any rate, mating does occur shortly after "Cupid's arrows" find their marks.

Many a tidy housewife has been made unhappy by the sudden appearance of narrow glistening lines that crisscross over walls, sidewalks, porch, or basement floors. These ribbons or lines are tracks made by snails and slugs. The creatures crawl on their stomachs and a gland near the head continuously secretes a slimy mucus. This spreads into a moist smooth surface over which the creature crawls in comfort.

Many snails will eat dead plant and animal material. They are useful scavengers, therefore, in aquaria, ponds, and streams.

Snails Can Kill People

Snails are usually thought of as harmless creatures. This is true of most of them, but there are a few exceptions. Several kinds of snails living in the ocean have a poisonous bite, and in several established instances death has resulted from the bite.

In 1943, Dr. William J. Clench, of Harvard, and Yoshito Konodo, of the

Bishop Museum, Hawaii, published an interesting account of these snails. They gave specific cases of death and summarized the information then available. One instance is of special interest since it was the first death from snail bite ever reported from Australia. The young man involved was on a pleasure cruise through the Whitsunday Group of islands off the eastern coast of Queensland, Australia. While on one of the islands he collected a prettily marked snail shell and was examining it when the occupant of the shell stuck out its head and bit him on the hand. Alarming symptoms developed, and although the victim was hurried to the mainland for medical care, he died before reaching the hospital—according to one report, within four and a half hours after being bitten.

The several kinds of poisonous snails are called cone shells, because their shells are shaped like a cone. They are all marine forms and may be found in waters about the Hawaiian Islands, New Guinea, Samoa, Australia, and adjacent areas.

Abalones or ear shells are reported to be dangerous in a way entirely different from the cone shells. Although the shell of the abalone resembles that of a clam, the creature is actually a kind of snail. Each abalone has only a single shell, rather than two as in clams. If you look closely, you can see that one part of the shell is slightly spiraled, a characteristic of snail shells. Along one edge of the shell is a series of holes through which water flows in the living animal.

Abalones occur on the west coast of the United States and in some areas they are quite popular as food. They are found in shallow water; and in regions where there is considerable tide fluctuation, some of them are above water during low tide. Here they remain attached to rocks or similar places until the water returns. The undersurface of an abalone is well fitted to attach firmly to flat surfaces, and once attached, it is difficult to loosen. There are few men with sufficient strength to remove these mollusks with their hands. More than one enterprising abalone collector has made the mistake of sticking his fingers under the edge of the shell and trying to yank the mollusk from its attachment in this way. Under these circumstances, the irate abalone immediately clamps its shell even more firmly to the rock, thereby catching the fingers of the careless person. According to some authorities, people have actually been held in this way despite their struggles until the returning tide has put an end to their misery. In all fairness it must be stated that some biologists do not believe these reports, but one writer states that a friend of his helped to recover the body of a Chinese who had been drowned in this way.

At any rate, there are better and safer ways to collect abalone steaks. The mollusk can be pried loose with a strong knife blade or it may be detached if it is suddenly pushed to one side before it has had a chance to attach itself firmly.

Some Snails Eat Oysters

Some snails that live in the ocean actually eat oysters on the "whole shell." The snail perches itself atop an oyster and starts boring through the shell to get inside. When a hole is completely through the shell the snail proceeds to suck out the soft parts of the victim's body.

There are several different kinds of marine snails that attack clams and oysters in this way. Some are appropriately called oyster drills, although some whelks and other snails do likewise. Many oyster drills are relatively small, only an inch or so in length, but they can successfully attack an oyster several times their own size. These oyster drills are common along the Atlantic coast of the United States, and they sometimes cause considerable damage to commercial oyster beds. The annual loss has been estimated at several million dollars, but much of the damage can be prevented if the seed oysters are freed of the snails before they are put in commercial growing beds.

Are Any Land Snails Harmful?

Many land snails have an appetite for flowers and other vegetation, and in some areas they are major pests. The East African snail is one of the most important. This creature, one of the largest of the land snails, may weigh nearly a pound and attain a length of 7 or 8 inches. In many cases it is almost impossible to grow crops successfully because of the depredations of these snails. Some of them were recently imported into California accidentally, but fortunately were discovered before they had a chance to become well established.

These African snails are such pests that people are continuously trying to find natural enemies that will reduce their numbers. One of the latest attempts has been the use of a much smaller snail which attacks and eats its larger cousin. Several hundred of these cannibalistic midgets have been introduced into an island near Guam that teems with the voracious giants. These African snails are well established in the Hawaiian Islands, and for a time the introduction of the carnivorous snail was considered. This idea was abandoned, however, when it was found that the small snail did not show any discrimination in the kinds of snails it attacked. Biologists were afraid that many other harmless snails would be destroyed without affecting the population of the African species.

C L A M S ,   O Y S T E R S ,   A N D   M U S S E L S

The term valve is another word for shell, and these mollusks are some-times called bivalves because they have two valves or shells. The shells often enclose the bivalve's body completely, and they are joined together along one edge at a region called the hinge ligament. When disturbed, the clam or mussel closes the shells completely by powerful muscles; at other times these muscles relax and allow the shells to gape partially open.

Most bivalves move very slowly or, like oysters, do not move at all as adults. Their bodies have a large number of tiny hairlike projections which are kept in motion, and these cause a current of water to flow between the edges of the shells when open. Very small organisms that are brought in with the current are filtered out by the mollusks and used for food.

Some authorities consider the bivalves to be useful scavengers because they consume vast quantities of organisms that might otherwise pollute the water. A member of the United States Bureau of Fisheries has estimated that a single husky oyster can strain approximately 18 gallons of water per day. Thus a single oyster may eat as many as 72 million organisms during each day that its straining apparatus operates for 17 or 18 hours.

Oysters as well as certain other bivalves can compete with most animals in the number of eggs they produce. It has been shown that a female oyster may lay as many as 500 million eggs in a single summer. When the eggs are fertilized they develop into little free-swimming youngsters called spat. In time the young oyster settles down, attaches itself to some object and develops into an adult. Once attached, the oyster is doomed to remain in the same location for the remainder of its life.

Clams That Grow in Fish

Unlike adult oysters, clams or mussels are able to move slowly from place to place. When a clam is at rest, it often lies on its side with the two shells partly agape, and if you examine one of these clams, you may see a wedge-shaped part of the body sticking between the shells. This is called the foot, and it is used by the clam to plow through the mud in moving from place to place. The mussel or clam protrudes the foot and sticks it into the mud as far as it will go. The buried end of the foot then expands to get a good grip, muscles attached to the base of the foot contract, and the clam is pulled slowly forward. In time mussels will crisscross the bottom of a pond or sluggish stream with grooves several feet in length. If you are collecting clams, look at the end of the freshest part of the groove and you will usually find the clam buried in the mud.

The eggs of these mollusks develop for a time within the bodies of the females. After the youngsters have developed a pair of shells they are shot from the body with a stream of water. The young clam now needs a fish to continue to develop. Any stirring of the water causes the young clam to open and close the shells rapidly. It is eventually rewarded when the closing shell happens to catch on a part of a passing fish. The youngsters hang on tightly and the skin of the fish grows over them forming the black spots called blackheads or worms. After further development the clams drop from the fish and take up an independent existence.

A small perch-like fish found in the rivers and streams of central Europe has developed a practice that compensates for playing nursemaid to a batch of infant clams. During the breeding season, the male and female fish, swimming in pairs, search for clams with shells partially agape. The female then extends her egg-laying duct into an astonishingly long tube and lays eggs between the shells of the clam. At the same time the male fish deposits male cells or sperm in the water and they fertilize the eggs. The eggs become attached to the clam's body and remain in this protected spot until they hatch. During all these maneuvers, the clam, if it is a female, often discharges its young and some attach themselves to the fish.

An interesting sidelight on this fish-clam association is the amorous reactions of the male fish. He is stimulated to discharge the sperm or male cells for fertilizing the eggs not by the presence of the female fish, but by sight of the clam.

Man-eating Clams

Man-eating, man-trap, and giant clams are all names for enormous shellfish that are found along the Great Barrier Reef of Australia and in other parts of the Pacific Ocean. They have two shells, as do other clams, but in these mollusks the edges of the shells have wavy margins. In the American Museum of Natural History a pair of these shells, approximately 3 feet across, weighs 579½ pounds. Others have been reported up to 1,000 pounds, but so far as I know this weight has not been confirmed.

These large clams have an unusual way of obtaining food. They eat the small creatures that come in with the water current, as do other clams, but in addition they get food from a "garden" that is actually grown in their tissues. Small one-celled plants settle on a part of the clam's body, called the mantle, and here they grow. The plants use substances for their growth which are secreted by the clam, and from time to time the clam takes some of the "vegetables" into its body and digests them.

Australian biologist Maynard E. Macdougal has studied the life of the Great Barrier Reef for years and has collected many of these giant clams. He states that the shells close as quickly as a rat trap and that the edges

fit so tightly together that they could hold a thin wire. He was once preparing a specimen for a shell collector and had placed the clam in hot water
to kill it. When the shells gaped he thought the mollusk was dead and
started to cut the animal loose from the shell with a long-handled knife.
The shells closed so quickly that the knife was held firmly and there was
so much power in the movement that pieces were broken from the edges
of the shells.

Dr. Roy Chapman Andrews, of the American Museum of Natural
History, also reported an interesting experience with one of these clams.
While in a small boat in the Dutch East Indies (now Indonesia), he saw
one of the mollusks with its shells partly open. He jabbed a paddle between
the shells; the irate clam immediately retaliated by snapping shut on the
offending paddle. Dr. Andrews was unable to withdraw the paddle and
ended by breaking it.

Despite their sinister name, there is no evidence that these clams actually eat people. But reports occasionally tell of a pearl diver getting an arm
or leg caught in this way, and being held under water until he drowns.
Speaking of pearls reminds me that the largest known pearl is of doubtful
value except as a curiosity. It is a misshapen mass known as the Pearl of
Allah that weighs fourteen pounds—rather large for the usual ring or
necklace. This pearl was recovered from a giant clam off the Philippine
Islands, and, according to Dr. R. Tucker Abbott of the Philadelphia
Academy of Natural Sciences, the first native diver's attempt to collect
the pearl ended in tragedy; the clam snapped shut on the man's arm and
drowned him.

Some biologists believe that these giant clams live longer than any other
invertebrate animal (animals without backbones), but no specific information is available on this subject. The reasons for this idea are the enormous
size of these creatures, and reasonably well-established great ages for some
of the smaller shellfish. It is generally agreed that the approximate age of
some species of clams can be estimated by studying the annual or growth
rings on the shell.

By a study of growth rings experts have estimated that certain individuals of American fresh-water clams have lived from 54 to 60 years, and
by the same methods, have reported some European fresh-water clams to
be over 100 years of age. Unfortunately, even reasonably accurate estimates of the ages of these giant clams cannot as yet be made.

What Mollusks Are Most Important for Food?

There is an old saying that the first man to eat a raw oyster was extraor-
dinarily brave; yet today oysters are the most important food mollusks in

the United States and probably in the world. In the United States alone it has been estimated that the yearly catch of oysters amounts to more than 75 million pounds. Several kinds of fishery products exceed oysters in the amount that is caught, but only the salmon catch has a greater monetary value.

Most of the oysters caught in the United States are the so-called eastern oyster from the Atlantic coast, but there is also a fair-sized oyster industry on the Pacific coast. Two kinds of oysters are gathered in the latter region, one being native and the other a species that has been introduced from Japan.

Many years ago it was believed that the wild crop of oysters was inexhaustible, and each year millions of bushels were taken from beds in the Chesapeake Bay and adjacent area. Gradually even these enormous natural oyster beds disappeared and the oyster seemed doomed to be eaten out of existence. Then someone thought of coming to the oysters' rescue by cultivating the shellfish. Actually, oyster cultivation was practiced in China hundreds of years ago, but it is a recent innovation in the United States. Thanks to this development, the oyster crop is relatively stable from year to year.

Oysters are most valuable as food, but within recent years even the shells have been greatly in demand. They are used in building roads, and for the lime they contain; they are also ground to various sizes as so-called poultry grit.

Should Oysters Be Eaten Only During the R Months?

Firmly ingrained is the idea that oysters are poisonous during part of the year. In most cases it is thought that oysters are safe only during those months the names of which contain the letter R. Oysters are no more poisonous at one time of the year than another. There is, however, justification for not eating oysters during the R-less or summer months. This is the breeding or spawning period of many oysters, and if left alone the shellfish have a chance to rebuild the population. Also, after they have spawned, oysters are often stringy and watery, with a poor flavor.

The European oyster, unlike the American species, keeps the young in its body until they have reached a certain stage of development. During this period, the masses of developing young give the parent European oyster an unappetizing appearance which has probably created the prejudice against eating the mollusks during the summer season.

It is true that oysters may become polluted by disease germs, and in the past many cases of typhoid fever and other illnesses were probably caused by contaminated oysters. Fortunately, today in the United States the oyster industry is so rigidly controlled by state and government health officers that you are not likely to get contaminated produce if you trade with a legitimate dealer.

Some Shellfish Can Kill a Bird

While hardly to be classified as major enemies of birds, some shellfish occasionally manage to give a good account of themselves in such combat. Oystercatchers or mussel catchers, shore birds with black and white plumage, have long beaks and legs that are usually red. They jab their sharp beaks into the opened shells of clams and oysters so accurately that the shellfish is usually paralyzed and eaten before it can close its shells. Occasionally, however, the bird misses its mark, or makes the mistake of selecting an overly husky individual. If the shell closes on the offending beak, despite its struggles the bird may be held under water until it drowns. Sometimes birds that have managed to struggle to shore have been found and released, but the occasional discovery of dead birds with the shellfish still attached shows that these little dramas of nature may result in death for both actors.

The toes and feet of birds are exposed to the "attacks" of irate shellfish even more often than are their beaks. Not infrequently a wading bird will step into the gaping shells of a clam or mussel; the shellfish retaliates by closing on the toe or foot. Sometimes the bird will escape by sacrificing its toe, but often the victim will be held until it drowns or has starved to death. Along the Pamunkey River in eastern Virginia, according to reports, residents have given up raising ducks because mussels cause such a high mortality among the ducklings.

What Animal Causes Piers and Wharves to Collapse?

Certain kinds of clams that have forsaken the mud-grubbing habits of their relatives are responsible for much of this damage. Sometimes called shipworms, these creatures have a worm-like body but they are true clams. When full grown they may be from 6 inches to over 4 feet in length, depending upon the species.

Shipworms are attracted to all types of wooden structures in the water and start burrowing soon after they are hatched. The burrowing is accomplished by the shells which have been modified into efficient boring structures. The shells occur only at the front end of the body and they are relatively small. They have rows of teeth, and when they are rotated the wood is rasped away. The resulting sawdust passes through the digestive tract of the shipworm so that the creature more or less literally eats its way along.

Millions of dollars worth of piers and similar structures are destroyed each year. One of the most spectacular results of the clams' work occurred in San Francisco in 1919 and 1920. During this period wharves and docks collapsed, causing damage estimated at $20 million.

Although shipworms probably do more harm than good, they also serve a useful purpose. They destroy sunken wooden ships and other debris which might otherwise accumulate and become a menace to navigation. In Thailand shipworms have been put to another practical use. Pieces of wood are placed in water where these clams abound and allowed to remain here for several months. The wood is then recovered and the succulent shipworms found in it are used for food.

Eight WORMS

Many years ago when biologists started a system of classification of animals, all "worm-like" creatures without a backbone were classified into one group called Vermes. This group included the tapeworms, the flukes, the fishing worms, the leeches, the various worms found in fresh and salt water, and many creatures that are not worms at all. The original classification has since been radically changed. We now have flatworms, roundworms or nematodes, and segmented worms, each group of which is given a different name. The word Vermes is no longer used in classification, but vermifuge is still a recognized general term for a worm medicine.

There are so many different kinds of these animals that it is almost impossible to make statements that will apply to all of them. Some, such as the earthworms, live in the soil; many occur in ponds, streams, and in the ocean; and a large number are important parasites of animals and human beings.

The number of worms in existence is almost incredible. It has been estimated that in some regions several billion earth-inhabiting roundworms or nematodes occur per acre in the top five inches of soil. In fact, one enthusiastic student of roundworms maintains that, if all matter in the universe were destroyed except nematodes, the outlines of the earth, including hills and valleys, would still be recognizable because of the tremendous numbers of worms.

R O U N D W O R M S

Are Any Worms Destructive to Agriculture?

Until relatively recently, little attention was given to the possible effects upon plants of the soil-inhabiting nematodes, or roundworms, but as information on these worms accumulates, there is increasing evidence that some of them are among the most important plant pests in existence. In late 1955 one writer estimated that these worms destroy one-tenth of the total crop production in the United States.

The most harmful species of nematodes attack the roots of plants; the resulting wilting or stunting was often thought to be caused by inferior soil, but it is now believed that the boring of the worms into the roots makes openings which allow fungi, bacteria, and other harmful organisms to gain access to the plant tissues.

Roundworms are widely distributed over the world, and one kind or another will attack hundreds of different plants, including some of our most important crops such as cotton, citrus fruits, potatoes, sugar beets, and many others.

Much land here and abroad which has been abandoned as supposedly worn out or exhausted may simply have had an oversupply of nematodes. There is also a possibility that the pests were an important factor in the fall of the Mayan civilization of Mexico.

Are Any Nematodes Beneficial?

In view of the large number of nematode worms in existence, it is fortunate that some species are definite assets to man. Many nematodes help to reduce dead plants and animals to a state in which the materials can be used by living plants; but the worms are perhaps most valuable in keeping harmful species in check. Some kinds eat other nematodes, and many are parasites of harmful insects.

Several years ago a biologist listed 759 different kinds of insects known to be attacked by nematodes, and a recent estimate states that the known number is perhaps twice that today. Important insects parasitized by nematodes include the codling moth, corn earworm, boll weevil, grasshoppers, and the Japanese beetle.

Man has probably exploited the nematode parasite of the Japanese beetle more than any other species. The parasites have been cultured in the laboratory and distributed over a large area in New Jersey in an attempt to control this important pest. Later examinations here showed that in some regions as much as 80 per cent of the Japanese beetle grubs was attacked. The beetle population declined, and the nematodes were probably a major factor in this reduction.

What Was the Fiery Serpent of Biblical Times?

Many centuries ago when the Israelites were wandering in the wilderness, some of them were attacked by creatures called fiery serpents. The Bible does not tell much about the nature of these creatures, but many biologists believe that they were a kind of parasitic worm called the guinea worm.

The adult of this animal is only a fraction of an inch in thickness, but it may be 3 or 4 feet long. It lives in the tissues of a human being and, when ready to reproduce, it comes close to the surface of the skin, where a blister is formed. The young worms must get into the water in order to live, and the adult worm usually moves to the surface of the body on an arm or a leg. If the person with the worm in his body wades in the water, or washes his arm with the blister on it, many little worms come from the blister and slide into the water. They then get into a small crustacean called a waterflea and continue their development. A person may pick up a guinea worm if he accidentally swallows an infected waterflea in drinking water. The young worm bores out of the stomach, gets into the tissues, and gradually grows as it burrows about beneath the skin.

This burrowing fiery serpent may cause considerable damage and occasionally death. The parasite is hard to remove because it is so slender that it breaks easily. If part of the worm is left in the body it may decay and cause the surrounding tissue to become infected. Native doctors used to pull the worm from a patient. Recently physicians have developed injections to dissolve the worm.

Guinea worms are common in parts of Africa and Asia and the same or similar worm has been found in the United States. The American worm, however, has been found only in animals including raccoons, mink, and foxes, and probably will not attack people.

LEECHES, EARTHWORMS, AND PALOLOS

The Medicinal Worm

Nearly all ponds or streams have their quota of bloodsuckers that attach themselves to the bare skin of any human being who comes within their

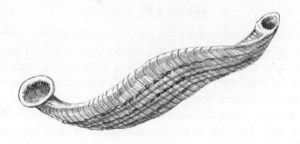

reach. These creatures are really leeches, a kind of worm related to the more familiar and considerably less obnoxious earthworms. Those that live in water feed upon small aquatic organisms or upon blood by attaching to man or an animal. They are usually black or brown, and those that most frequently tackle human beings are up to an inch or so in length.

The worms have two suckers with which they firmly attach themselves to surfaces, and removing one of them from the skin is difficult. The bite of a leech is relatively painless. If uninterrupted, the animal will fill its body with blood and then drop off its victim. The blood is very slowly digested and the creature does not need another meal for weeks or even months.

A firmly attached leech should be removed carefully because the jaws are buried in the wound, and if they are broken infection may result. The best way to get a leech off is to put a little salt or vinegar on it or hold a lighted cigarette near its body. This will often cause the worm to turn loose of its own accord. When a leech feeds, it secretes a material that keeps the blood from clotting, and the wound is likely to bleed for some time after the parasite is removed. Bleeding may be stopped by pressure. Some tropical aquatic leeches get in the mouth when very small, usually in unsterilized drinking water, and attach themselves to the inside of the mouth or nasal passages. Such an attached leech should be removed by a physician.

For many years, letting blood from the body of a person was considered standard medical practice, and leeches have often been employed for this purpose. They were especially used for conditions such as localized inflammations which were treated by the removal of a relatively small amount of blood. Leeches are not employed in modern medical practice, but even today some amateurs use them for the treatment of bruises such as black eyes.

Earthworms Are Big Business

In one issue of an American outdoor magazine were twenty advertisements dealing with earthworms. These advertisements stemmed from thirteen states, from New Jersey to Georgia and west to California. In many cases instructions for raising worms were available; all kinds, from tremendous African earthworms to brown-nosed angle hybrids, were described. The prices ranged from approximately one-half cent to one cent each. One dealer maintained that he had a shipping capacity of 500,000 daily, and if he sold only a small part of his capacity the volume of the business must have been tremendous.

A majority of the animals raised on these worm farms, as they are called, are probably sold for fish bait; but earthworms are also in demand for other reasons. A few years ago, after the well-remembered Netherlands floods, several million earthworms were sent to that country from farms in the United States. The burrowing activities of the worms are credited with contributing greatly to the speedy return to cultivation of many flooded areas.

Charles Darwin was one of the first to point out the value of earthworms. The creatures literally eat their way through the soil, and this helps to keep the soil loose and porous, allowing air and water to enter. At night the worms often come to the surface and deposit mounds of dirt pellets. Darwin estimated that the earthworm pellets on an average acre were sufficient to provide ⅕ inch of new soil per year to the surface.

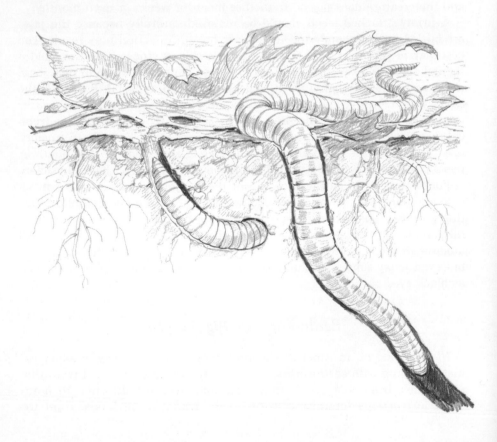

It has recently been reported that certain hybrid earthworms, known as soilution worms, are of tremendous value to fruit and berry growers. The animals are said to cause young trees to grow twice as fast as normally, and if they are added to strawberry beds the yield will be doubled.

Earthworms are also of considerable value in other ways. They are useful for study in biology and zoology classes. The soft nutritious bodies furnish food for many useful animals including birds and small mammals. Even human beings eat worms in some countries. Australia boasts of the largest earthworms in the world, where they are known to attain a length of 11 feet. These worms are highly prized as food.

Worms That Make Love by Moonlight

To the palolo or balola worms of the Pacific Ocean, moonlight is of prime importance to the survival of the race. These worms breed for only four days each year, two in October and two in November. The actual dates vary somewhat from year to year, but since the time is apparently dependent upon the phases of the moon, it can be predicted to the day. These breeding sprees occur at dawn on the day before, and on the day of, the last quarter of the moon in October and in November. This is approximately a week after the full moon. The adult worms live in coral reefs near the islands of Fiji, Samoa, and other Polynesian islands. They grow to be 15 or 16 inches long and they have two distinct parts to their bodies; the rear end is more slender than the front end.

When the day of the big event arrives, the worms come to the entrance of their burrows and stick the rear ends of their bodies into the water. This part of the body, which contains the reproductive cells, is broken off and floats to the surface. Within a short time, the water over a large area looks like worm soup. Countless millions of worm rear ends float from the reefs below to take part in the ceremony. The wriggling pieces soon shed the reproductive cells in such large numbers that the water becomes milky in appearance. Meanwhile, the front parts of the worms, which have remained below the surface, set about growing a new rear end, and a year later the whole breeding process is repeated.

The natives of the islands know well the breeding time and place of the palolo. Worm dishes of various types are considered a delicacy. The South Sea islanders troop to the scene for miles around; the worms are scooped up by the bucketful and great feasts are held. Scientists who have participated in these feasts say that the dishes prepared from the worms look like spinach and taste something like fish eggs.

FLUKES

What Causes Snail Fever?

In Japan, the Philippines, and adjacent areas, a disease called snail fever was one of the most serious diseases with which American soldiers had to contend during World War II; consequently, methods of preventing the disease were widely publicized. Snail fever is definitely misnamed since the expression implies that the disease is caused by snails. The only connection snails have with the disease is that the parasite which is responsible passes part of its life cycle in the body of a fresh-water snail.

The technical name for the disease, which is caused by a worm known as a blood fluke, is schistosomiasis; it is easy to see why it is spoken of as snail fever. The adult worms live in the human body in the blood vessels, the bladder, and the intestine. If the eggs that pass from the human body land in water they hatch, and the resulting little larvae bore into the bodies of fresh-water snails. When the worms leave the snails the worms are infectious for man.

People become infected with schistosomiasis by wading or swimming in water containing the worms. The parasites bore through the skin, get in the blood vessels, and are eventually carried to the intestine and bladder. Here the cycle starts over again. The disease can be quite serious since the worms can cause the development of ulcers in the intestine and bladder.

Human blood flukes do not occur in the United States, but certain other animal blood flukes sometimes attack human swimmers. These animal flukes do not cause schistosomiasis in man, but if a person happens to be sensitive to the parasites he may develop a rash that is called swimmers itch. The parasites causing swimmers itch are widely distributed in the United States, but are more common in some of the midwestern states.

There are no other flukes in the United States that routinely attack man, but a fluke that causes "liver rot" in sheep occurs here. This parasite has occasionally been reported as occurring in human beings in the West Indies and other parts of the world, but I have not heard of any human cases in this country. The infective stages of the sheep liver fluke occur on grass and water plants, and it is believed that human beings become infected by eating water plants such as watercress.

Human lung, liver, and intestinal flukes occur in parts of the Orient. Cooking food properly is the best way to avoid these parasites, since they are usually picked up from insufficiently cooked fresh-water crabs, fish, and a water plant called water chestnut.

HOOKWORMS AND TAPEWORMS

What Causes Ground Itch?

As a child living in the southern United States, I can well remember being warned of the seriousness of ground or dew itch. According to the description, ground itch was a rash that occurred on the feet during the summer when most children and many adults went barefooted. Many years later I discovered that one type of rash called ground itch was the result of a human parasite called the hookworm.

Hookworms live in the human intestine, where they attach themselves to the intestinal wall, bite through the skin, and feed on blood. If many parasites are present, the patient loses a large amount of blood. In cases of long standing the patients are in such a weakened condition that they are subject to other diseases. They may also be dull, listless, and without ambition. In the past, the southeastern part of the United States gained the reputation of having a high percentage of lazy inhabitants. At that time a large proportion of the people in many localities were suffering from hookworm infection, and this may well have been a primary cause of the reputation.

A person infected with hookworms passes the eggs from his body, and if they are deposited on the ground they hatch into very small hookworms or larvae. The larvae develop into stages that are infectious for other people. If the bare skin of a person, such as hands or feet, comes in contact with the larvae, the parasites bore into the skin. The penetration of the parasites often causes the development of ground itch. They enter small blood vessels and ultimately reach the intestine where they develop into adult hookworms. Complete elimination of hookworm disease could be accomplished within a relatively short time if all human beings could be taught proper sanitary habits.

Hookworms that normally occur in the intestines of cats and dogs sometimes attack people, but the results are different from those produced by human hookworms. The larvae burrow about just beneath the outer skin, causing irritation and the development of crooked inflamed burrows. The inflamed areas are gradually enlarged as the parasite creeps along, and this condition has been called creeping eruption.

Individual protective measures against creeping eruption and human hookworm are the same: Avoid contact of the bare skin with the ground in areas where the diseases occur. Children's sand boxes, which are especially attractive to cats, should be made cat- and dog-proof in localities where cat and dog hookworms are prevalent.

How Large Are Human Tapeworms?

There are three kinds of large human tapeworms. These parasites are found in various parts of the world, including the United States. They are the pork tapeworm, the beef tapeworm, and the fish tapeworm. A person gets the parasites by eating insufficiently cooked pork, beef, and fish, respectively. In each case, after the infectious stage is taken into the mouth it passes to the intestine, attaches to the intestinal wall, and grows into an adult.

The beef tapeworm is usually considered to attain the greatest length, up to 100 feet in length, but I have not been able to confirm this figure. The fish tapeworm is the widest, and it too attains a respectable length. The late Dr. Asa Chandler, of Rice University, cites a case of a Russian woman in whom six fish tapeworms were snugly reposing. The patient was given medication, and when the tapeworms passed from her body, the six stretched the tape to a total of 290 feet. Under the circumstances, each of these tapeworms should have been long enough to satisfy anyone, even though individual beef tapeworms may occasionally get somewhat longer.

Nine CNIDARIANS AND ECHINODERMS

There is no simple common name for the group of animals that includes the jellyfish, corals, sea anemones, and a little creature called hydra that is often studied in biology classes. They are usually spoken of as cnidarians, a term derived from the scientific name of the group. The "c", incidentally, is not pronounced. These animals are all aquatic. Most live in the ocean, although a few, such as hydra, occur in fresh water. Until recently the scientific name for this group of animals was Coelenterata.

In structure cnidarians are among the simplest of animals, but some of them have considerable influence upon the life of people and other animals. Many of these creatures have arms or tentacles covered with tiny stinging cells. The stinging cells are used for defense and for obtaining food. Most cnidarians move very slowly, but when a fish or other animal accidentally bumps into the tentacles, the stinging cells go into action. If the fish is not too large it will be stunned and eaten.

JELLYFISH, CORALS, SEA ANEMONES, AND HYDRAS

One of the cnidarians, a jellyfish-like creature called the Portuguese man-of-war, has been known to kill and eat a full-grown mackerel. Despite their stinging cells, however, jellyfish themselves do not go unscathed. Various cnidarians are used for food by other marine animals; according to Dr. G. A. MacInitie, of the California Institute of Technology, the ocean sunfish, mentioned on page 269, subsists almost entirely upon jellyfish and other cnidarians. These the sunfish consumes with greedy slurping noises that can be heard for some distance.

How Dangerous Are Jellyfish?

The stings of the small jellyfish, uncomfortable as they are, are not likely to endanger human life. But larger specimens are quite different. According to Dr. Ralph Buchsbaum, of the University of Pittsburgh, one large jellyfish has been recorded with a disc of over 12 feet and tentacles more than 100 feet long. Professor Louis Agassiz, one of the most famous early workers in American biology, is stated to have measured one with tentacles over 120 feet long. Indeed, jellyfish have longer "arms" than any other animal in the world. Anyone embraced in the arms of such a large jellyfish suffers intense pain, develops difficulty in breathing, and may become partially paralyzed.

Some authorities consider the so-called sea wasp that occurs in the Indian Ocean and off the coasts of Australia and the Philippine Islands to be the most dangerous of these large jellyfish. Over the years there have been several cases of death from the stings of jellyfish, probably this species, from these areas. In extreme cases, death may result in from three to ten minutes following contact with one of these sea wasps.

The Portuguese man-of-war is also a dangerous species. These creatures are widely distributed, and they are often found near the coasts of the United States. The Portuguese man-of-war has a gas-filled bag or float, often beautifully colored with blue or orange tints, that extends several inches above the water. Death-dealing tentacles, however, trail beneath the water, and all sensible swimmers will head elsewhere when a Portuguese man-of-war makes its appearance.

The injection of a material known as calcium gluconate is sometimes of considerable assistance in treating jellyfish sting. This is the same substance often used in the treatment of black widow spider bite.

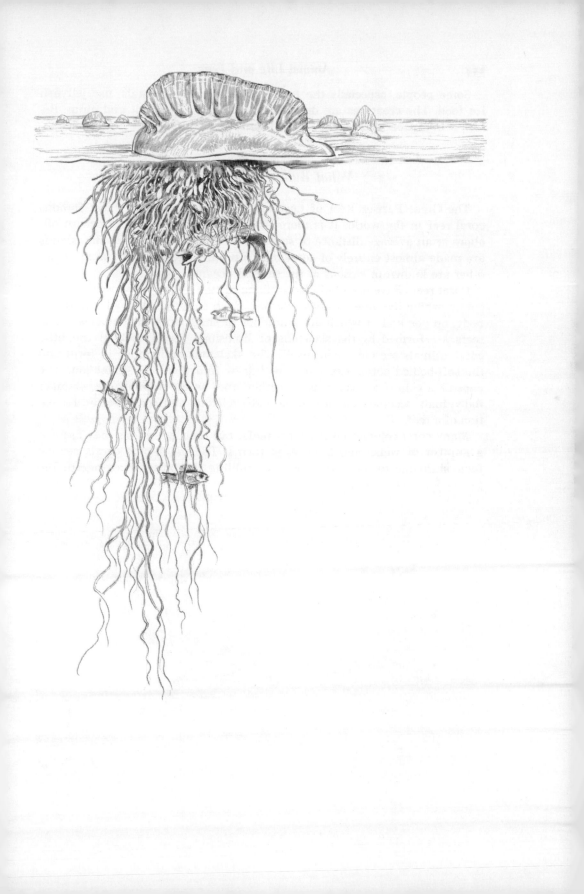

Some people, especially the Japanese and other Orientals, use jellyfish for food. The creatures are dried and are treated with salt and alum. Before being eaten, the concoction is usually soaked, flavored, and cooked.

What Builds Coral Reefs?

The Great Barrier Reef of northeastern Australia is the most famous coral reef in the world. It is more than 1,200 miles long and occurs offshore at an average distance of some 20 to 30 miles. Many Pacific islands are made almost entirely of coral rock, and great reefs of one kind or another are known in various of the several oceans.

Coral reefs have been built by millions of tiny animals, the reef-building corals, which live in enormous colonies. Each coral has a small cylindrical body, on one end of which are a number of small arms or tentacles. Coral reefs are formed by the skeletons of limestone which each of the little coral animals secretes about itself. The skeletons are cuplike in form and the soft-bodied corals can partly withdraw into them for protection. The cups of a colony are cemented together and, as the animals die, younger individuals become attached to the old skeletons and continue the formation of a reef.

Many coral colonies do not form reefs, but their secretions may assume a number of weird and interesting forms. The organ-pipe corals secrete their skeletons to form an object resembling the pipes of an organ; the

staghorn coral resembles a deer's antlers; and the skeletons of brain corals take shape like the human brain. The skeletons of some coral are valuable for making trinkets and jewelry; this is especially true of the precious coral of commerce. These corals form upright branched colonies somewhat similar to small trees and shrubs. The central axis of the branches is a hard bright red core, and it is from this that beads and other jewelry are made. Precious corals occur only in parts of the Mediterranean Sea and in the Sea of Japan.

Of What Use Are Sea Flowers?

Sea flowers, also called sea anemones, are among the most attractive creatures in the ocean, and they are often responsible for the beauty of many underwater seascapes. Aside from their beauty, certain sea anemones are of considerable practical value to certain other animals found in the ocean.

Crabs are usually not considered to be outstandingly brilliant, but a species in the Indian Ocean has developed an association with sea anemones which should certainly cause it to be rated above the morons of the animal kingdom. Sea anemones, like other cnidarians, have stinging cells on their tentacles, and these crabs take full advantage of these potentialities. One of these crabs is seldom seen without at least one anemone, and they are often seen stalking about with two, one in each of its largest claws. If the crab is molested by a fish or other denizen of the deep, it thrusts the anemone full in the face of its astonished attacker. The aggressor is thus more than likely encouraged to seek an easier meal elsewhere.

Off the coast of Australia enormous sea anemones that may attain a diameter of 2 feet occur. Here a weird association has developed between these monster sea flowers and some small brilliantly colored fish, known as clown fish. These fish are almost constant companions of the anemones. They deposit their eggs at the base or "feet" of the sea flowers; they retreat among the tentacles if danger threatens, and may even dash into the open mouths of their protectors. The small fish reciprocate by occasionally placing bits of food within reach of the anemones, and they have even been reported to entice larger fish into the lethal embrace of the tentacles.

One of the most amazing things about this association is that the clown fish are not injured by the tentacles which are so deadly to other kinds of life in the area. It is believed that the clown fish are immune to the venom of the stinging cells, and that they probably gain this immunity by occasionally nibbling on the tentacles.

Some species of sea anemones that occur in the Black Sea, the Mediterranean, and off the coast of Africa, are thought to be dangerous to human life and are considered to be an occupational hazard of sponge fishermen.

In structure sea anemones are among the simplest of animals, but despite this simplicity (or possibly because of it) some of these creatures have established astonishingly great age records. Authorities on animal ages have accepted as authentic ages of from 65 to at least 85 years for some of these sea flowers. Sea anemones have been kept for many years in at least two different laboratories, and their presence for the numbers of years mentioned above is supported by reputable scientists. With the possible exception of certain clams, for which evidence of great age is somewhat questionable, sea anemones are considered to be the champion Methuselahs of invertebrate animals. And, it might very well be that they could compete with any species in the entire animal kingdom.

ECHINODERMS

Few animals are more appropriately named than the echinoderms, a name meaning spiny-skin. This group includes starfish, sea urchins, sea cucumbers and sand dollars. All of these creatures are marine, and can be seen "at home" only in the ocean.

Aside from the spines which may be long or short, one outstanding feature of echinoderms is a water vascular system that includes structures known as tubefeet. The system is composed of a series of tubes filled with water; each tubefoot, of which there are a larger number, is shaped something like a medicine dropper or pipette, and each is connected to a small branch of the water vascular system. The functioning of the tubefeet depends upon the regulation of water pressure within them. The feet can be extended or shortened, and the ends, which work like a suction cup, will grasp or relax as the echinoderm regulates the water pressure. The tubefeet are used for locomotion, for obtaining food, as sense organs, and even for breathing.

A majority of echinoderms are small or medium in size, but there are a few of large size. Some of the sea cucumbers, for instance, may get to be 3 feet in length. A few echinoderms are brilliantly colored and make up a conspicuous part of underwater seascapes.

What Animal Can Open an Oyster?

Although many animals can "open" a clam or oyster by breaking its shell, few will attempt to do so by pulling the shells apart. Such a creature is the starfish.

The animal wraps its arms about an oyster, attaches its tubefeet to the shells, and starts pulling. The starfish has hundreds of tubefeet and it can keep up a steady pull; it uses the feet in groups, thus allowing some to rest while others are pulling. At last the oyster or clam is worn down and the shells fall apart. The echinoderm then performs one of the most amazing acts in nature: It pushes its stomach through its mouth, turning it wrong side out, and wraps it about the soft body of the shellfish that is now exposed. The starfish remains in this incongruous state until digestion is partially complete, then retrieves its stomach before moving on to the next victim.

It has recently been suggested that the starfish does not depend entirely on strength to open the shells of a stubborn clam or oyster. There is some evidence that the echinoderm secretes a substance that partially paralyzes the shellfish, thereby causing the opening of the shell to be much easier. Whatever the truth of the matter, there is no question that in some areas starfish are among the most serious pests of commercial oyster beds. Oyster fishermen learned many years ago that starfish could be caught in large numbers by scraping mops over the sea bottom and over the oyster beds; the starfish catch the strands of the mop and are hauled out of the water. At one time fishermen supposedly killed the offending starfish by cutting them in pieces and throwing them back in the ocean. It was soon found that the joke was on the men rather than on the starfish; each piece of starfish can regenerate the missing parts and ultimately become a complete animal again.

For those of us who visualize a starfish as a relatively small creature with only 5 arms or rays, it may be a surprise to learn of the size of a species that occurs in the north Pacific in the vicinity of Alaska and British Columbia. This largest species of starfish has 20 to 24 arms, may attain a diameter of 4 feet, and weigh as much as 10 pounds. The starfish is called the sunflower star or 20-rayed star. In addition to its large size, which in itself is astonishing, this starfish must also have a cast-iron stomach. It is said to be capable of swallowing whole, and digesting with perfect impunity, a long-spined sea urchin. A day or so later, the shell and spines of the sea urchin, perfectly cleaned, will be ejected, and the sunflower star goes about its business as though nothing had happened.

Cucumbers That Grow in the Ocean

Certain echinoderms called sea cucumbers greatly resemble the vegetable in the shape of their body, but on one end they have a number of arm-like structures that look very much like sea weeds. Small sea animals, probably mistaking the arms for sea weed, settle here in large numbers. When an arm is sufficiently loaded with these creatures, the sea cucumber sticks the end of the arm into its mouth and closes it. The arm is then withdrawn and the food remains.

Sea cucumbers are popular for food in some parts of the world. In the Philippine Islands and parts of the Orient, sea cucumber fishing has been a large industry. The creatures are caught, cleaned, and dried; then sold as *bêche-de-mer* (worm of the sea) or *trepang*, which is used primarily in the making of soup.

These creatures appear to be quite helpless, but many a lobster has received the surprise of his life when it attacked one of them. Attached to the intestine of a sea cucumber are branched structures which help the creature

in breathing. When a sea cucumber is attacked these branched structures and parts of the intestines are thrown from the body into path of the attacker. The material often swells upon contact with the water and the enemy may become hopelessly entangled. This drastic action does not cause any permanent embarrassment to the sea cucumber; it crawls to safety and sets about growing a new set of organs.

Ten PROTOZOANS AND SPONGES

The minute animals called Protozoa, a name meaning "first animals," are the simplest forms within the animal kingdom. The bodies of most of them are made up of only a single cell. Even with one cell, however, protozoans carry on all important life functions such as reproduction, respiration, movement, and the digestion of food. And though we do not ordinarily see them, they are of major importance in the natural world.

Protozoans are not invisible in the true sense of the word, but most of them cannot be seen with the unaided eye. If we examine one under a microscope, however, we find that it is surprisingly complex. Some have definite structures that are used as weapons or for collecting food. Some have long whip-like projections that are used in locomotion, and others secrete shells which for beauty and intricacy are unsurpassed in the entire animal world.

Since protozoans have only a single cell in their bodies, one would hardly expect them to compete in size with most of the other groups of animals. However, there are also giants among the Protozoa. The largest protozoans are parasites of fish. One kind (*Myxobolus*) causes what is called boil disease in certain European fishes, and specimens may approach 3 inches in length. One of the smallest protozoans causes a human disease known as kala azar or leishmaniasis; these tiny mites are about 1/25,000 of an inch long. Dr. Theodore Jahn, of the University of California, states

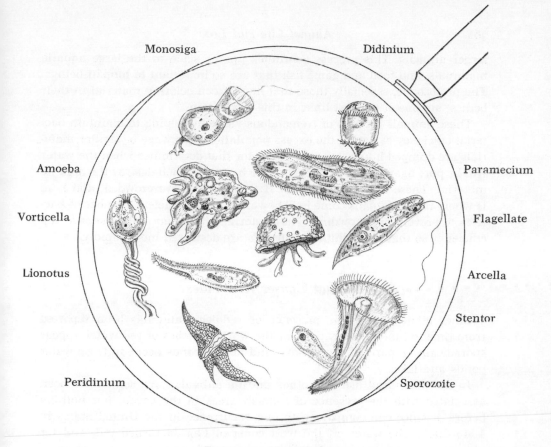

Monosiga Didinium

Amoeba Paramecium

Vorticella Flagellate

Lionotus Arcella

Stentor

Peridinium Sporozoite

Protozoans Magnified

that there is a greater size range among the Protozoa than in any other animal group. He has estimated that the largest protozoan has approximately two quintillion times the volume of the smallest one.

The Value of Protozoans in the Economy of Nature

It is unfortunately true that scientists often know more about harmful members of animal groups than about their beneficial brethren. Their knowledge with respect to Protozoa is no exception. Detailed information on the role of beneficial protozoans in the general scheme of things is sadly lacking, but we do have sufficient knowledge to make a few general statements.

Beneficial protozoans are probably of most importance in the so-called food chain that occurs in the oceans, lakes, and streams. Here the small animals eat smaller plants and animals, and they in turn are eaten by larger animals. This process continues up the scale to the large aquatic mammals, and food and game fish that are so important to human beings. The protozoans, especially those that have green coloring material in their bodies, are one of the first links in this food chain.

These animals are also of tremendous value in helping to maintain bacterial efficiency by eating the excess population. If sewage or similar materials are dumped into water, one big factor that determines when the water will be pure again is the efficiency of the bacteria which destroy the organic material. These bacteria work best if they are not overcrowded, and here is where the protozoans come in. They often eat a sufficient number of bacteria to prevent overcrowding. The bacterial population is thus kept at top efficiency so that the polluting materials are destroyed more rapidly.

What Causes Red Tides?

Since biblical times the presence of reddish water has been reported from time to time in many parts of the world. Patches of red water appear sporadically in parts of the oceans; and at times they occur in fresh-water ponds and lakes.

In the past, dead fish and other marine animals have sometimes been associated with the presence of reddish areas in the ocean, but nothing before or since can compare with one occurrence in the United States in 1946–1947. The water off the west coast of Florida turned red, and for nine months the residents battled to bury or destroy a growing mass of dead fish that piled up on shore. Some 200 million pounds were killed during this period—approximately one-tenth of the annual production of the entire United States fishing industry.

Experts swarmed into the area and after extensive experiments and peerings through microscopes, the riddle of the dead fish was solved: They were being killed by tiny reddish protozoans. Now these same little animals normally occur in sea water, but they do not injure fish and other sea animals as long as their numbers remain small. Sometimes, however, for a reason unknown, this protozoan, *Gymnodinium brevis*, suddenly goes on a rampage of reproduction. The little animals increase to such an enormous extent that the ocean water actually becomes syrupy. It was thought at one time that the fish were suffocated because they could not get enough oxygen from the water. It is now known, however, that their death was caused by a powerful poison or toxin produced by the protozoans. Human swimmers in the red tide have not shown any serious ill effects, although some have developed a temporary rash on the skin.

To date no satisfactory methods for fighting the red tide have been developed. In limited areas a copper sulphate solution will kill the creatures, but it is doubtful if the use of this chemical would be practical on a large scale.

Another protozoan, appropriately called *Haematococcus,* a name meaning blood berry, increases in numbers so rapidly that it can turn a rain barrel into buckets of "blood" within a relatively short time. The protozoan can also reproduce in snow and as a result change the landscape from a white to a bright red color. Such red snow has been reported from various parts of the world including the Rocky Mountains of the United States and the Alps of Switzerland.

What Made the Cliffs of Dover White?

Few people realize that the famous chalk cliffs of the coast of Dover, England, are composed of untold millions of skeletons of very small protozoans. Today enormous numbers of these little creatures live in the ocean, and each one has a tiny skeleton about its body. When the animals die, the skeletons sink to the bottom.

These protozoans have been living and dying for millions of years, and it is estimated that the accumulated skeletons are responsible for approximately one-third of the mud on the ocean bottoms. This material is so easy to distinguish and it covers such a large part of the ocean floor that it has been given the name of globegerina ooze, *Globegerina* being the name of the protozoans that produce most of the skeletons. As this ooze slowly accumulates it becomes packed into harder formations by the weight of the

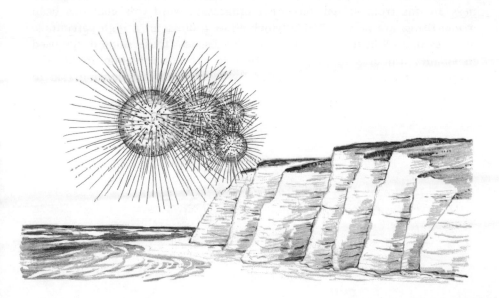

water and the skeletons on top. The resulting chalk beds, may be as much as a thousand feet thick. The skeletons of Protozoa are also found in various kinds of limestone including that used in the pyramids of Egypt and many buildings in Paris. The white cliffs of Dover and the chalk and limestone beds were at one time part of the ocean floor, but they were raised above the sea in past geologic times.

Certain protozoans with skeletons are also of considerable importance in oil drilling operations, being associated with definite kinds of rock formations. By examining samples of borings from proposed oil wells, scientists can often predict the chances of striking oil.

The Animal That Causes Sleeping Sickness

Several diseases have been called sleeping sickness at one time or another, but the name should be limited to one that is found only in Africa. In untreated cases, the patient almost invariably passes into a coma and eventual death.

African sleeping sickness, also designated by the jawbreaking name African trypanosomiasis, is caused by a protozoan which is transmitted through the bite of the tsetse fly. This fly occurs in a broad belt across central Africa.

Sleeping sickness has been one of the obstacles to the development of more than 4 million square miles of tropical Africa. Near the turn of the century approximately half a million natives died of the disease within a period of ten years.

Even today all the problems connected with the control of sleeping sickness are far from solved, but great progress toward this goal has been made. Drugs are now available which show promise of a high percentage of cures if used in the early stages of the disease; these same drugs used in smaller amounts are reported often to prevent infection in healthy people. Last but not least, the tsetse fly itself has been exterminated in

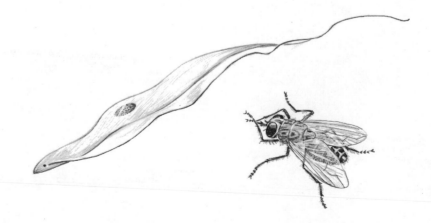

some areas, and with modern methods and insecticides fly-free regions may be greatly extended in the near future.

One of the principal problems in controlling African sleeping sickness is that no one yet knows what connection this malady may have with a disease of game and domestic animals known as nagana. The protozoans causing the two diseases look much alike, and some authorities think they are one and the same. If they are identical, tsetse flies could of course bite animals with nagana and then transmit it to man as sleeping sickness.

Whatever its connection with sleeping sickness, nagana is of major significance in its own right; it is regarded as the most important protozoan disease of livestock in the world. Game animals, such an antelope, may have the protozoans in their blood, but they seem to be relatively immune. Not so domestic animals; it is highly fatal to horses, cattle, pigs, goats, and sheep. Whole herds and flocks may be wiped out in a relatively short time, and a recent check of cattle deaths in Nigeria, a country in east central Africa, showed that 30 per cent was due to nagana.

SPONGES

The Plant That Was an Animal

True sponges are the skeletons of animals that live in the oceans. Although imitations have replaced sponges for many uses, the real article is still in sufficient demand to support a thriving industry.

Sponges are not highly developed animals. As adults they are attached to a rock or other base, and since they do not move about, they were for a long time thought to be plants. Young larval sponges, however, swim about for a time before they attach themselves and grow into an adult sponge.

There are a few sponges that live in fresh water, but all with commercial value are found in salt water. The living sponges, which somewhat resemble pieces of raw liver, are collected on fishing boats and prepared for market. Methods of treatment vary, but the objective in all cases is to remove all the living material from the sponge, leaving the marketable spongy skeleton. Most sponges come from the Mediterranean Sea, the western Atlantic, and the Gulf of Mexico around the coasts of Florida.

Even animals find uses for sponges. Many species, including small fish, secrete themselves among the channels and pores of living sponges, and certain crabs attach small pieces of living sponges to their backs. These pieces grow and within a short time the crab is covered. This camouflages the crustacean so that he can hide from his enemies and sneak up on his potential food.

The sponge industry furnishes an excellent example of the important interrelationships of living organisms. In 1938 the Bahama Island area produced more commercial sponges than any other one region. By 1947 the production was less than one-fifteenth of the 1938 figure. The reason: A fungus disease had struck the sponge beds which almost wiped out the industry. Though the disease is being attacked, it is estimated that full recovery will take at least twenty more years.

Selected References

In the preparation of this book, reference has been made to a large number of books, magazine articles, and original scientific publications. Although it is impractical to include all the publications that have been used, the selected books should be of aid to readers who are interested in learning more about animals. Many of these should be available from local libraries.

GENERAL

BRENEMAN, W. R. *Animal Form and Function*, 2nd ed. Ginn & Company, Boston, 1959.

BUCHSBAUM, RALPH. *Animals Without Backbones*, rev. ed. University of Chicago Press, Chicago, 1948.

COMFORT, ALEX. *The Biology of Senescence*. Routledge & Kegan Paul, London, 1956.

DRIMMER, FREDERICK (ed.). *The Animal Kingdom*, 3 vols. Doubleday & Company, Inc., New York, 1954.

EADIE, W. ROBERT. *Animal Control in Field, Farm and Forest*. The Macmillan Co., New York, 1954.

ELLIOTT, ALFRED M. *Zoology*, rev. ed. Appleton-Century-Crofts, Inc., New York, 1957.

GRAY, PETER (ed.). *The Encyclopedia of the Biological Sciences*. Reinhold Publishing Corp., New York, 1961.

HALSTEAD, BRUCE W. *Dangerous Marine Animals.* Cornell Maritime Press, Cambridge, Md., 1959.

HULL, THOMAS G. *Diseases Transmitted from Animals to Man.* Charles C Thomas, Springfield, Ill., 1947.

HUNTER, GEORGE W. III, FRYE, WILLIAM W., and SWARTZWELDER, J. CLYDE. *A Manual of Tropical Medicine,* 3rd ed. W. B. Saunders Company, Philadelphia, 1960.

MANTER, H. W., and MILLER, D. D. *Introduction to Zoology.* Harper & Row, Publishers, New York, 1959.

SCHMIDT-NIELSEN, KNUT. *Animal Physiology.* Prentice-Hall, Inc., Englewood Cliffs, N.J., 1960.

WENDT, HERBERT. *Out of Noah's Ark.* Houghton Mifflin Co., Boston, 1959.

WHALEY, W. GORDON, BRELAND, OSMOND P., HEIMSCH, CHARLES, PHELPS, AUSTIN, RABIDEAU, GLENN. *Principles of Biology,* rev. ed. Harper & Row, Publishers, New York, 1957.

WILLIAMS, J. *The Fall of the Sparrow.* Oxford University Press, New York, 1951.

MAMMALS

BOURLIER, FRANÇOIS. *The Natural History of Mammals.* Alfred A. Knopf, New York, 1954.

COLE, H. H. and CUPPS, P. T. *Reproduction in Domestic Animals,* 2 vols. Academic Press, New York, 1959.

GRIFFIN, DONALD R. *Echoes of Bats and Men.* Doubleday & Company, Inc., New York, 1959.

HVASS, HANS. *Mammals of the World.* Methuen & Co., Ltd., London, 1961.

INGLES, LLOYD GLEN. *Mammals of California and Its Coastal Waters.* Stanford University Press, Stanford, 1954.

MOORE, CLIFFORD B. *Ways of Mammals.* The Ronald Press, New York, 1953.

SIMPSON, GEORGE GAYLORD. *Horses.* Oxford University Press, New York, 1951.

TROUGHTON, ELLIS. *Furred Animals of Australia.* Charles Scribner's Sons, New York, 1947.

WENDER, LEO. *Animal Encyclopedia.* George Allen & Unwin, London, 1947.

BIRDS

ALEXANDER, W. B. *Birds of the Ocean,* 2nd ed. G. P. Putnam's Sons, New York, 1954.

CRAIGHEAD, JOHN J., and CRAIGHEAD, FRANK C. JR. *Hawks, Owls, and Wildlife,* The Stackpole Co., Harrisburg, Pa., 1956.

DELACOUR, JEAN. *The Waterfowl of the World,* 3 vols. Country Life Ltd., London, 1954.

FISHER, JAMES, and LOCKLEY, R. M. *Seabirds.* Houghton Mifflin Co., Boston, 1954.

FITTER, R. S. R. *The Pocket Guide to British Birds.* Collins, London, 1952.

GILLIARD, THOMAS. *Living Birds of the World*. Doubleday & Company, Inc., New York, 1958.

HEINROTH, OSKAR, and HEINROTH, KATHARINE. *The Birds*. The University of Michigan Press, Ann Arbor, 1958.

MARSHALL, A. J. *Biology and Comparative Physiology of Birds*, 2 vols. Academic Press, New York, 1960–1961.

MURPHY, ROBERT C., and AMADON, DEAN. *Land Birds of America*. McGraw-Hill Book Co., New York, 1953.

PALMER, RALPH S. (ed.). *Handbook of North American Birds*, vol. 1. Yale University Press, New Haven, 1962.

WALLACE, GEORGE J. *An Introduction to Ornithology*. The Macmillan Co., New York, 1955.

WING, LEONARD W. *Natural History of Birds*. The Ronald Press, New York, 1956.

REPTILES AND AMPHIBIANS

BELLAIRE, ANGUS D'A. *Reptiles*. Harper & Row, Publishers, New York, 1957.

CARR, ARCHIE. *Handbook of Turtles*. Comstock Publishing Associates, Ithaca, N. Y., 1952.

COCHRAN, DORIS M. *Living Amphibians of the World*. Doubleday & Company, Inc., New York, 1961.

COLBERT, EDWIN H. *Dinosaurs*. E. P. Dutton & Co., New York, 1961.

DITMARS, RAYMOND L. *Reptiles of the World*, rev. ed. The Macmillan Co., New York, 1937.

————. *Snakes of the World*. The Macmillan Co., New York, 1943.

INGER, ROBERT F., and SCHMIDT, KARL P. *Living Reptiles of the World*. Hanover House, New York, 1957.

OLIVER, JAMES A. *The Natural History of North American Amphibians and Reptiles*. D. Van Nostrand Co., Inc., New York, 1955.

POPE, CLIFFORD H. *The Reptile World*. Alfred A. Knopf, New York, 1956.

SCHMIDT, KARL P., and DAVIS, D. DWIGHT. *Field Book of Snakes*. G. P. Putnam's Sons, New York, 1941.

STEBBINS, ROBERT C. *Amphibians of Western North America*. University of California Press, Berkeley, 1951.

WRIGHT, ALBERT HAZEN, and WRIGHT, ANNA ALLEN. *Handbook of Frogs and Toads of the United States and Canada*, 3rd ed. Comstock Publishing Co., Ithaca, New York, 1949.

————. *Handbook of Snakes*, 2 vols. Comstock Publishing Associates, Ithaca, N. Y., 1957.

FISHES

BROWN, MARGARET E. *The Physiology of Fishes*, 2 vols. Academic Press, New York, 1957.

HERALD, EARL S. *Living Fishes of the World*. Doubleday & Co., Inc., New York, 1961.

HUBBS, CARL L., and LAGLER, KARL F. *Fishes of the Great Lakes Region*, rev. ed. Cranbrook Institute of Sciences, Bloomfield Hills, Mich., 1958.

LA MONTE, FRANCESCA. *North American Game Fishes*. Doubleday & Co., Inc., New York, 1958.

NORMAN, J. R. *A History of Fishes*, 5th Ed. Hill and Wang, New York, 1960.

PERLMUTTER, ALFRED. *Guide to Marine Fishes*. New York University Press, New York, 1961.

ROUNSEFELL, GEORGE A., and EVERHART, W. HARRY. *Fishery Science*. John Wiley & Sons, New York, 1953.

A R T H R O P O D S

BAKER, EDWARD W., and WHARTON, G. W. *An Introduction to Acarology*. The Macmillan Co., New York, 1952.

BATES, MARSTON. *The Natural History of Mosquitoes*. The Macmillan Co., New York, 1949.

BORRADAILE, L. A., and POTTS, F. A. Rev. by G. A. Kerkut. *The Invertebrata*, 3rd ed. Cambridge University Press, Cambridge, 1958.

BORROR, DONALD J., and DELONG, DWIGHT M. *An Introduction to the Study of Insects*. Holt, Rinehart and Winston, New York, 1954.

CARPENTER, STANLEY J., and LaCASSE, WALTER. *Mosquitoes of North America*. University of California Press, Berkeley, 1955.

CHANDLER, ASA C., and READ, CLARK P. *Introduction to Parasitology*, 10th ed. John Wiley & Sons, Inc., New York, 1961.

CLOUDSLEY-THOMPSON, J. L. *Spiders, Scorpions, Centipedes and Mites*. Pergamon Press, New York, 1958.

HERMS, WILLIAM B. Rev. by Maurice T. James. *Medical Entomology*, 5th ed. The Macmillan Co., New York, 1961.

HUNTER, GEORGE W. III, FRYE, WILLIAM W., and SWARTZWELDER, J. CLYDE. *A Manual of Tropical Medicine*, 3rd ed. W. B. Saunders Co., Philadelphia, 1960.

KLOTS, ALEXANDER B., and KLOTS, ELSIE B. *Living World of Insects*. Doubleday & Company, Inc., New York, 1959.

METCALF, C. L., and FLINT, W. P. Rev. by R. L. Metcalf. *Destructive and Useful Insects*, 4th ed. McGraw-Hill Book Co., Inc., New York, 1962.

PESSON, PAUL. *The World of Insects*. McGraw-Hill Book Co., Inc., New York, 1959.

STEFFURUD, ALFRED (ed.). *Insects, the Yearbook of Agriculture*. U. S. Government Printing Office, Washington, D. C., 1952.

WIGGLESWORTH, V. B. *The Principles of Insect Physiology*, 4th ed. Methuen & Co., Ltd., London, 1950.

Index

About the Author

OSMOND P. BRELAND has traveled widely during the last thirty years, researching the habits of animals and answering the special questions of students. Currently professor of zoology at the University of Texas, Dr. Breland has taught also at universities in Indiana, New York, and the Dakotas.

His interest in separating animal fact from fiction began during childhood in Mississippi. Since then, as scientist and teacher, he has found that many people have delightfully fanciful, though inaccurate, ideas about the ways of animals. In keeping track of common questions asked about animals, Dr. Breland has developed source materials for his nontechnical books of animal information.

His first book on the subject, *Animal Facts and Fallacies,* published in 1948, found a wide reception among general readers and was followed in 1957 by *Animal Friends and Foes.* Drawing upon these two books and on recent research and experimentation, Dr. Breland here offers a single volume on the behavior of both vertebrate and invertebrate animals.

In addition to his popular writing, he is a regular contributor to several scientific journals and has authored college biology texts.